Introduction to
Chemical Process Control

Introduction to
Chemical Process Control

DANIEL D. PERLMUTTER
School of Chemical Engineering
University of Pennsylvania

John Wiley & Sons, Inc.,
New York • London • Sydney

Library of Congress Catalog Card Number 65-24925
Printed in the United States of America

To my mother and to the memory of my father.

Preface

The coming of the second industrial revolution has been heralded in numerous professional and lay publications, and there seems little need to convince the reader that automatic control is a subject worthy of some attention. Taking this for granted, we may expect that engineering students (in or out of school) will want to understand some of the technical aspects of automation.

This is a book intended for chemical engineers. The examples, the emphasis, and even the terminology were chosen with this in mind, but the subject matter development does not in any way follow a unit-operations pattern. Rather, the logic is dictated by the process dynamics and control viewpoint. Thus, for example, chemical reactors come up for discussion in Chapters 1, 5, 8, and 10; heat transfer problems are considered in Chapters 1, 6, and 9; and in each case some point is being made which has wider implications than the unit operation at hand. In short, a unified treatment of the control area uses the chemical engineering background as a vehicle.

The specific needs of chemical engineers are taken into account by choice of particular topics, and several subjects are treated at lengths that are justifiable only by the requirements of our profession. Because of the nonlinearities that appear to chemical engineers at every turn, an entire chapter is devoted to the matter of linearization and the related problems of initial conditions and regulator action, and another chapter treats nonlinear systems by phase-plane analysis. In Chapters 6, 7, and 8, the focus is on experimental data, sometimes the only practical way to describe the dynamics of the complex systems of chemical engineering interest. In Chapter 9, the sensitivity function is used to explain the very common occurrence of cascade control in distillation columns.

By the same token, several topics which are often emphasized in servomechanism texts are de-emphasized here. Root locus design techniques, and the study of compensation on the Nyquist plot are both mentioned, but it seems to the author that other matters are more pressing for chemical engineers, who have occasion to design control loops by choosing from among commercially available hardware, but who do not ordinarily design the controller functions. Since open-loop instabilities are very rare indeed in chemical engineering apparatus, and are obviously not present when systems are characterized by experimental data, the most general form of the Nyquist stability condition is not developed. Instead, the widely applicable, more restrictive form is proved rigorously.

Regarding prerequisites, a background in differential equations is assumed, as is also the familiarity with the highlights of heat transfer, distillation, and kinetics that is ordinarily expected of an undergraduate senior. The Laplace transform is introduced as an operational tool in the course of developing the subject matter, each subsequent theorem entering as needed (The time-shift theorem, for example, does not appear until Chapter 8, where it serves to introduce the work on dead time). The various arguments involving the complex domain are put in terms of complex numbers, rather than as theorems of mapping and integration for the complex variable.

An effort was made to present only those arguments with which the reader could agree in good conscience. Thus, the Routh-Hurwitz criterion for stability was omitted entirely, rather than ask the student to accept it on faith. In its place, we have offered the Mikhailov condition. This treatment retains the advantage of being able to handle higher order systems without polynomial factoring, and in addition provides a smooth transition to the Nyquist criterion without requiring either conformal mapping on the one hand or an appeal to intuition on the other.

The subject matter organization used in this book grew in large measure out of lecture notes developed over several years at the University of Illinois. For the receptive atmosphere they provided, I am indebted to my colleagues in the Chemical Engineering Division, especially to Max S. Peters for his earliest encouragement. Review comments by Professors R. J. Adler and C. B. Brosilow of the Case Institute of Technology were most helpful.

Thanks are also due the John Simon Guggenheim Memorial Foundation for fellowship support, the School of Chemical Engineering at the University of Pennsylvania for a necessary leave of absence, and Professor A. E. Bryson for his hospitality at Harvard University, where the manuscript was completed. The secretarial and typing efforts of Mrs. Patsy McArthur, Miss Marjorie Honn, and Mrs. Becky Weiss certainly deserve my appreciation.

Throughout, my wife and children contributed most importantly by being there.

DANIEL D. PERLMUTTER

Cambridge, Mass.
September, 1965

Contents

Introduction to
Chemical Process Control

1 *Preliminary Consideration*

1-1. INTRODUCTION

A great variety of important problems that are solved by steady-state analysis is well known to every chemical engineer. Examples may be found in any of the unit operations or in a number of other areas, but the study of automatic control is a notable exception. To speak of control is to speak of time-dependent changes. The problems of interest can in fact hardly be formulated without a dynamic framework, since even simple specifications call for recovery of a variable (in time) according to some pattern. To make any progress in this field then, we must seek not merely relationships between static variables, x and y, but rather dynamic relationships between $x(t)$ and $y(t)$.

In orienting himself to a new subject one needs to know above all what questions to ask. The central themes of development of this book will deal with questions in two broad classes. The first arises from the necessity of treating in detail unsteady-state behavior. Basically, we are asking here: How should a dynamic problem be formulated, quantitatively? What analytic tools are available for solution? The answers call initially for the formulation of differential equations to describe particular process characteristics. If the emphasis is on the equations, the procedure is called **modeling,** if on the process, the subject is commonly referred to as **process dynamics**. For engineering uses these differential equations are systematically transformed to simpler forms that can be treated by convenient algebraic and graphical methods.

The second large class of questions of interest pertains to the role of control devices. In essence: How can controller behavior be incorporated into the dynamic analysis? What can reasonably be expected from automatic control, and how are the associated limitations taken into account? It is through these questions, for example, that we will be led to the subject of feedback in Chapter 2, but only after we have developed an approach and some analytic tools in this chapter. For some the preliminary matters that follow will be a review, for others a brief introduction to operator notation. In either case it will establish a common ground for the subsequent chapters.

1–2. A FAMOUS EXAMPLE: THE WELL-STIRRED VESSEL

To outline a procedure by which simple process equipment may be described by differential equations, we first consider in some detail the well-stirred vessel, shown in Fig. 1–1. By well stirred we mean to say

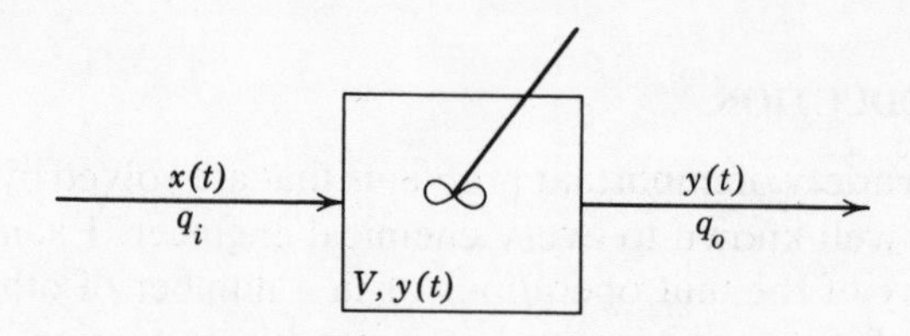

Fig. 1–1. A well-stirred vessel with continuous flow.

that the contents of the vessel is uniform in composition and temperature. Whatever the purpose of this part of the process, it is evidently of some value to know how the effluent concentration responds when a change is made (or occurs unintentionally) in the feed composition.

Denoting the input and output concentrations of a component of interest by x and y, an unsteady-state material balance equates the accumulation rate to the difference between component inflow and outflow:

$$\frac{d}{dt}(Vy) = q_i x - q_0 y \tag{1–1}$$

The well-stirred model is essential here, for otherwise the effluent concentration y would not be identical with the concentration of the fluid *inside* the vessel. For convenience we also assume that the vessel volume V is constant, and that the two flowrates q are constant and equal. This reduces the differential equation to

$$V\frac{dy}{dt} = qx - qy \tag{1–2}$$

a first-order, linear equation with constant coefficients. The response $y(t)$ will of course depend on the form of the input $x(t)$. We would not expect the response to a sudden input change to be identical to that for a gradual change or a continuously fluctuating change.

In order to proceed, therefore, we will suppose that the input concentration level changes suddenly (instantaneously) from zero to a. Algebraically, we write this as

$$\begin{aligned} x(t < 0) &= 0 \\ x(t > 0) &= a \end{aligned} \tag{1-3}$$

Graphically, this function appears as Fig. 1–2. Because of its shape it is

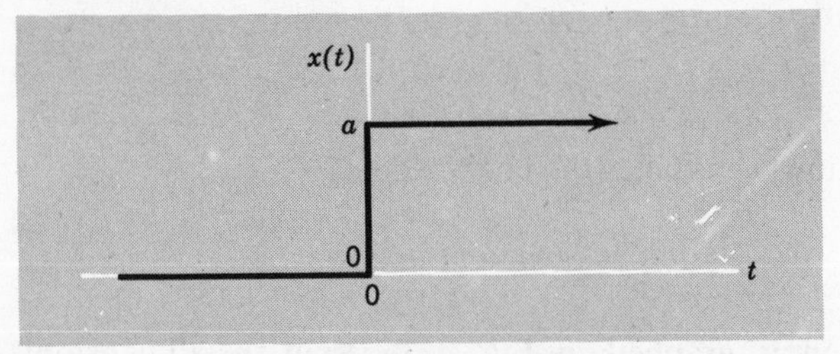

Fig. 1–2. The step function.

usually referred to as a **step function**, or if $a = 1$ it is called the **unit step**. Strictly speaking this $x(t)$ has not been defined at the point $t = 0$. Therefore, if the initial value of x is needed for boundary value purposes, it is often convenient to use the notation

$$\begin{aligned} x(0^-) &= 0 \\ x(0^+) &= a \end{aligned}$$

the plus and minus signs indicating that the respective values of x apply at points very close to, but not at zero.

1–3. THE CLASSICAL SOLUTION

Since we desire to know $y(t)$ for all time *after* the input step change, the value of $x(t > 0)$ can be substituted in equation (1–2):

$$V \frac{dy}{dt} = qa - qy \tag{1-4}$$

The solution for $y(t)$ may be found by separation of variables or any one of the well-known elementary methods for solving differential equations. The result is

$$y(t) = a - be^{-(q/V)t} \tag{1-5}$$

where b is an integration constant which may be found from a boundary condition on y. Consider the case where the vessel is initially free of solute. Then $y(0) = 0$, and from equation (1–5): $y(0) = 0 = a - b$. Thus, $b = a$ and

$$y(t) = a[1 - e^{-(q/V)t}] \qquad (1\text{–}6)$$

It should be noted that the two constants that characterize the system appear in the final result only in the form of a ratio. As we will see in later chapters, it is useful to speak of this ratio as the time constant, $\tau = V/q$. Had this abbreviation been included at an earlier stage, equation (1–2) would rearrange to read

$$\tau \frac{dy}{dt} + y = x(t) \qquad (1\text{–}7)$$

Then equation (1–6) takes the final form

$$y(t) = a(1 - e^{-t/\tau}) \qquad (1\text{–}8)$$

This relation is graphed in Fig. 1-3, using the dimensionless time scale, t/τ.

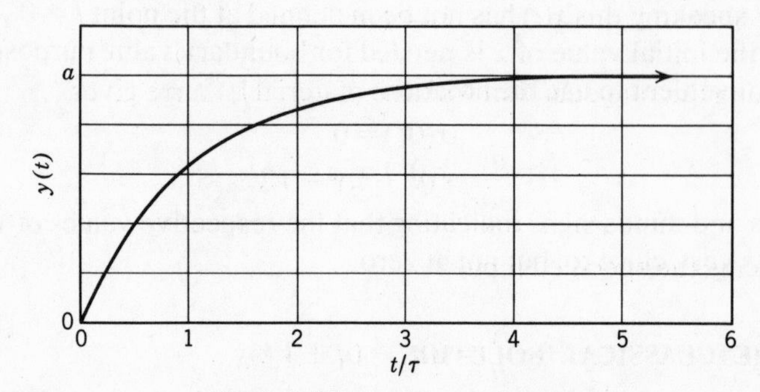

Fig. 1–3. First-order step response.

By this time, the reader may be wondering why so much attention has been paid to a single specific case. There are two reasons. First, we have reviewed in some detail the so-called classical method of solution. This will help us understand (by contrast and analogy) the transform method to be developed in Section 1–8. Secondly, although it was derived for a single case, equation (1–8) is, of course, the solution to *any* differential equation of the *form* of equation (1–7) for the same input and initial condition. This equation is in fact descriptive of a number of important chemical engineering systems and devices. The following two examples illustrate this point.

1-4. A CHEMICAL REACTOR

To extend the discussion to a system decidedly chemical in nature, consider that a reaction occurs in the well-stirred vessel. The previous assumptions regarding $V, q, x(t)$, and $y(0)$ apply, but the input step is of size a_0. The solute material balance is similar to equation (1–2), but includes an additional term to allow for the disappearance of the component of interest by the reaction rate r:

$$V\frac{dy}{dt} = qx - qy - Vr \tag{1–9}$$

Suppose that the reaction is known to be first-order and isothermal; that is, the rate is proportional to the solute concentration: $r = ky$, where k is the reaction-rate constant. It is important to observe in passing that the word "order" as used in kinetics has no relation to the order of a differential equation. In kinetics, an n-th order reaction obeys the rate equation

$$r = ky^n \tag{1–10}$$

Combining the rate equation with the material balance gives

$$V\frac{dy}{dt} = qx - qy - Vky$$

Introducing the specified input:

$$V\frac{dy}{dt} = qa_o - (q + Vk)y$$

Defining the time constant for the system as

$$\tau = \frac{V}{(q + Vk)} \tag{1–11}$$

gives

$$\tau\frac{dy}{dt} + y = \frac{qa_0}{q + Vk}$$

an equation which is identical to (1–7) if the right-hand terms are the same. Since the equation solution is in no way dependent on the particular symbols used, the solution to this problem is also equation (1–8), provided that in interpreting the result we take

$$a = \frac{qa_0}{(q + Vk)}$$

and τ from equation (1–11).

1-5. A HEAT-TRANSFER PROBLEM

As a final example, consider an unsteady-state heat-transfer problem. Water is to be heated batchwise in a well-stirred vessel by an electric immersion resistance heater. Initially, the entire system is at room temperature, v_A. When the heater switch is closed, thermal energy enters the water at a constant rate of Q Btu/hr. As the water temperature increases, the convection losses to the surroundings become appreciable. We seek a relation that will predict the rise in water temperature v with time.

Unlike the previous problems of this chapter, this analysis requires an energy balance. Letting

C_p = heat capacity of water
ρ = density
V = volume
U = over-all heat-transfer coefficient between the water and the room temperature surroundings
A = the area for heat transfer to the surroundings

an energy balance is

$$\frac{d}{dt}(\rho V C_p v) = Q - UA(v - v_A)$$

As before, the left side is an accumulation term, and the right-hand terms represent input and output respectively. Implicit is the understanding that the heater itself has negligible thermal capacity. Treating all the parameters as constants, the system time constant is

$$\tau = \frac{\rho V C_p}{UA} \qquad (1\text{–}12)$$

and

$$a = \frac{Q}{UA} \tag{1-13}$$

Then:

$$\tau \frac{dv}{dt} + v - v_A = a$$

Finally to arrive at equation (1–7), we redefine the temperature scale relative to the reference value, v_A:

$$y = v - v_A$$

$$\frac{dy}{dt} = \frac{dv}{dt}$$

$$y(0) = v(0) - v_A = v_A - v_A = 0$$

Again, it should be clear that if $\tau, a,$ and y are properly interpreted, the answer to this problem is to be found in equation (1–8) and Fig. 1–3.

1–6. EXPERIMENTAL DATA

On occasion it is necessary to use experimental data to answer two related questions. First: can a particular system be satisfactorily represented by a first order differential equation such as (1–7), and second: if so, what is the time constant, τ? Note that it may be established easily from equation (1–8) that $y = 0.632a$ at $t = \tau$, and that the initial slope at $t = 0$ is a/τ. For a fast (rough) answer to the question regarding first-order behavior, these two items may be checked against each other.

A more careful analysis should take into account all the experimental data. This may be done graphically, if equation (1–8) is rearranged to the logarithmic form

$$ln\left(\frac{a - y}{a}\right) = -\frac{t}{\tau}$$

Precise first-order behavior should evidently produce a straight line on semilog coordinates with slope $= -1/\tau$, as in Fig. 1–4. The degree

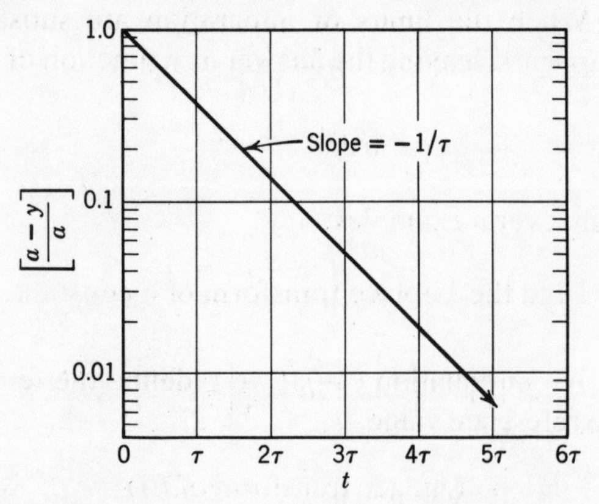

Fig. 1–4. First-order behavior on semilog coordinates.

of departure from such a line is a qualitative measure of behavior not to be classed as first-order.

1–7. THE LAPLACE TRANSFORM

In Section 1–3 it was suggested that there exists an alternative to the classical method of differential equation solution. This method uses an operator notation to transform a differential equation such as 1–2 into an algebraic equivalent. Eventually, after the algebraic problem is solved, the desired answer is found by an inverse transformation. The entire process has quite reasonably been compared to the use of logarithms to transform multiplication to addition and exponentiation to multiplication. After the simpler computation is completed, the inverse transformation (that of finding the antilog) produces the answer to the original problem. However, on occasion, it is advantageous to stay in the realm of logarithms in order to establish some particular relationship. In the last section, for example, the first-order time constant was more accurately evaluated from a semilogarithmic plot than from arithmetic coordinates. Similarly, we will find that some system characteristics are more conveniently studied in the Laplace transform domain than in the differential equation time domain.

The transform derivations can be developed from a single definition. The Laplace transform of the function $f(t)$ is defined by the operation

$$\mathscr{L}[f(t)] = \int_0^\infty f(t)e^{-st}dt \tag{1–14}$$

in which s is a parameter which is constant with respect to the integration process. When the limits of integration are substituted for the variable, t disappears, leaving the answer as a function of s. Thus:

$$\mathscr{L}[f(t)] = F(s) \tag{1–15}$$

Let us consider several examples:

Example 1. Find the Laplace transform of a constant, a. SOLUTION:

$$\mathscr{L}[a] = \int_0^\infty ae^{-st}dt = \frac{a}{s}\Big[-e^{-st}\Big]_0^\infty = \frac{a}{s} \tag{1–16}$$

Example 2. Find the Laplace transform of $f(t) = e^{-at}$. SOLUTION:

$$\mathscr{L}[e^{-at}] = \int_0^\infty e^{-at}e^{-st}dt = \int_0^\infty e^{-(s+a)t}\,dt$$

$$= \frac{1}{s+a}\Big[-e^{-(s+a)t}\Big]_0^\infty = \frac{1}{s+a} \tag{1–17}$$

As expected, the transforms are indeed functions of s.

Example 3. Find the Laplace transform of $f(t) = a(1 - e^{-t/\tau})$. SOLUTION:

$$\mathscr{L}[a(1 - e^{-t/\tau})] = \int_0^\infty a\,(1 - e^{-t/\tau})\,e^{-st}\,dt$$

$$= \int_0^\infty a\,e^{-st}\,dt - \int_0^\infty a\,e^{-t/\tau}\,e^{-st}\,dt$$

$$= \frac{a}{s} - \frac{a}{s + 1/\tau}$$

$$= \frac{a}{s(\tau s + 1)} \tag{1–18}$$

It is apparent that one can proceed in this manner to build a table of transforms of most of the elementary functions. On occasion, it is necessary to resort to a secondary calculus procedure such as integration by parts, as in the next example.

Example 4. Find the Laplace transform of $f'(t)$, the first derivative of $f(t)$. SOLUTION:

$$\mathscr{L}[f'] = \int_0^\infty f' e^{-st} dt$$

Integrating by parts

$$\mathscr{L}[f'] = \left[fe^{-st}\right]_0^\infty + \int_0^\infty fse^{-st}\, dt$$

The first term on the right gives zero at the upper limit and $f(0)$ at the lower limit. If there is any ambiguity concerning a discontinuity at $t = 0$, it is resolved simply by using $f(0^+)$, since the integration limit really has this meaning. The second term on the right is s multiplied by the defining operation for the Laplace transform. Hence:

$$\begin{aligned}\mathscr{L}[f'] &= 0 - f(0^+) + s\,\mathscr{L}[f] \\ &= s\,\mathscr{L}[f] - f(0^+) \\ &= sF(s) - f(0^+) \end{aligned} \qquad (1\text{–}19)$$

1–8. THE TRANSFORM SOLUTION

We are now ready to return to the well-stirred vessel problem to show how the transform method can be applied. Begin with equation (1–7) and transform the equation term-by-term, using the definitions:

$$\mathscr{L}[y(t)] = Y(s)$$
$$\mathscr{L}[x(t)] = X(s)$$

where by convention a capital letter function of s is used to denote the Laplace transform of the corresponding small letter function of t. From Example 4 (equation 1–19) we can write

$$\mathscr{L}\left[\tau \frac{dy}{dt}\right] = \tau[sY(s) - y(0)] = \tau s Y(s)$$

since the initial condition on y is zero in this case. Then equation (1–7) transformed will read

$$\tau s Y(s) + Y(s) = X(s)$$

and by factoring and rearranging algebraically

$$Y(s) = \left(\frac{1}{\tau s + 1}\right)X(s) \tag{1–20}$$

or

$$Y(s) = G(s)X(s) \tag{1–21}$$

The bracketed term of equation (1–20) which defines $G(s)$ is called the **transfer function** of the system. Note that it is not dependent on any particular input function, for as a matter of fact we have not yet introduced one. Nevertheless, as was the case with the classical solution, an explicit answer for $Y(s)$ or $y(t)$ will require that we specify $X(s)$, or its equivalent $x(t)$. Let us continue the parallel derivation by using the step function input of magnitude a, as before.
For:

$$x(t < 0) = 0$$
$$x(t > 0) = a$$

the transform of $x(t)$ is

$$X(s) = \int_0^{\infty} ae^{-st}\,dt = \mathscr{L}[a]$$

because the value of x to the left of $t = 0$ has no bearing on the integral in question. As was found in Example 1, $\mathscr{L}[a] = a/s$. Substitution in equation (1–20) gives

$$Y(s) = \left(\frac{1}{\tau s + 1}\right)\frac{a}{s}$$

The last remaining step is to return from the s-domain to the time domain; i.e.,

$$y(t) = \mathscr{L}^{-1}[Y(s)]$$

the symbol $\mathscr{L}^{-1}[\;\;]$ indicating inverse transformation. This is most easily accomplished in this case by inspection of Example 3 (equation 1–18):

$$y(t) = \mathscr{L}^{-1}\left[\frac{a}{s(\tau s + 1)}\right] = a(1 - e^{-t/\tau}) \tag{1–22}$$

A more systematic procedure for inverse transformation will be developed in Chapter 4.

In summary then we find that the Laplace transform method for solving differential equations gives the same result as the classical method. The detailed technique was of comparable length *in this case*. The transform method gives a specific solution in that it requires a boundary condition in order to transform the derivative of a variable. The classical method can be solved in general terms with arbitrary integration constants. On the other hand, the transform analysis can proceed to the point of finding the transfer function for a system without being tied down to a specific input function as is needed for integration by the classical method. This last point makes possible the simplified analysis in the s-domain that was mentioned earlier. In the next chapter, we will explore some of the benefits of this technique.

EXERCISES

1–1. What orders of reaction besides first-order allow the input-output relations for a stirred chemical reactor to be represented by a first-order differential equation? If the chemical kinetics were second-order, would a second-order system result? Would a linear system result? For what kinetic orders is the equation soluble by standard forms?

1–2. In textbooks on differential equations, the solution to a linear, first-order equation of the general form

$$\frac{dy}{dt} + \alpha(t)y = x(t)$$

is sometimes given as

$$y(t) = y(0)\exp\left[-\int_0^t \alpha(t)\,dt\right] + \exp\left[-\int_0^t \alpha(t)\,dt\right]\left[\int_0^t x(\sigma)\exp\left[\int_0 \alpha(\sigma)\,d\sigma\right]d\sigma\right]$$

Show that this reduces to the expected answer for the case of the stirred-vessel system with a step input.

1–3. Compare $\mathscr{L}[a]$ with $\mathscr{L}[ae^{-\lambda t}]$. How do the transforms differ? Compare $\mathscr{L}[e^{-\mu t}]$ with $\mathscr{L}[e^{-\lambda t}e^{-\mu t}]$. How do these transforms differ? These are examples of a more general property of transform pairs. Can you formulate this as a theorem?

1–4. The following experimental data were obtained from a cylindrical (3-ft ID $\times$ 6 ft) well-stirred water heater, after a step change in power supplied to the immersion heater.

Time, min	Temperature, °F
0	70
4	80
8	89
12	96
16	103
20	110
24	115
32	126
40	133
48	140
56	146
64	150
72	153
80	156
88	159
240	170

Find the system time constant by each of three methods. Do they agree? Find the overall heat transfer coefficient U, and the change in the heat input Q. The ambient temperature is 70°F.

1–5. The following data are taken from a graph presented by Bartok, Heath, and Weiss.[1] They were obtained from a study of mixing in a 161 cc jet-stirred

$y/y(0)$, Effluent Concentration Divided by Initial Concentration	t, Time, sec
1.00	0.0
0.99	1.8
0.90	3.0
0.83	3.7
0.80	4.5
0.72	6.0
0.66	8.0
0.57	10.5
0.44	13.0
0.35	15.0
0.32	17.0
0.28	18.3
0.20	23.0
0.15	26.2
0.10	31.0
0.075	35.0
0.052	39.0
0.03	46.0

[1]Bartok, W., C. E. Heath, and M. A. Weiss, *A. I. Ch. E. Journal,* **6**, 685 (1960).

reactor as follows: A radioactive krypton tracer was added to a steady nitrogen flow of 10.4 cc/sec. After a steady state was established, the krypton flow was reduced to zero (step change in inflow) and the response (exit krypton concentration) was followed with time. Do the measurements support the assumption of a well-mixed reactor? Use a graphical comparison with the well-mixed case for your analysis.

1–6. Compare the response of a mixed vessel (no chemical reaction) to that of a mixed reactor (first order kinetics), assuming each to be disturbed by a step in feed concentration from zero to a. In both cases, the initial concentration within the vessel is zero. Sketch the responses on the same coordinates. Which responds faster? Which goes further in its response? Would your answers be any different if the input step were downward from the concentration level $x(0^-) = b$ to $x(0^+) = a$?

1–7. Use integration by parts to prove that

$$\mathcal{L}[at] = \frac{a}{s^2}$$

Can the same approach be used to find $\mathcal{L}[t^2]$? Generalize this to find

$$\mathcal{L}[t^n] = \frac{n!}{s^{n+1}}$$

Can this formula be applied to solve equation (1–9) for the case of n-th order kinetics? Explain.

1–8. Extend the analysis of Section 1–5 to include an input stream at constant flow rate q and constant temperature v_i, and an effluent stream at flow rate q. What are τ and a if the solution is put in the form of equation (1–8)? How are the variables v and y related? What is the steady-state value of v if $Q = 0$?

1–9. Use the result (1–19) to find $\mathcal{L}[f'']$ and then generalize the formula for the n-th derivative.

2 *Block-Diagram Notation*

Engineers are fond of diagrams and tend to think in these terms. One of the advantages of the transfer function defined by equation (1–21) is that it suggests a very useful diagrammatic representation. This notation is versatile in that the general designation $G(s)$ can be used (Fig. 2–1*a*), or if it is known, the specific transfer function can be put in the block. For the well-stirred vessel, for example, one has Fig. 2–1*b*.

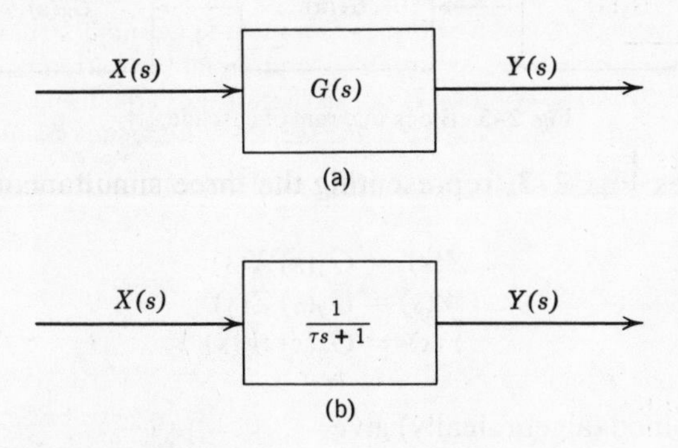

Fig. 2–1. Block diagrams. (a) General. (b) Specific function.

The block diagram is really a mathematical statement in the same sense as the equation: $Y(s) = G(s)\ X(s)$. We can think of this relationship in either of two ways. On one hand, recalling that $G(s)$ is the transform of a differential operator, we would say that $Y(s)$ is the result of $G(s)$ *operating* on $X(s)$. On the other hand, because the Laplace transformation has reduced the differential equation to an algebraic one, we can say simply that $Y(s)$ is the product of $G(s)$ and $X(s)$. Each of these descriptions is correct – the second is more fruitful, because it permits us to begin to formulate our ideas in the relatively simpler (algebraic) s-domain.

2-1. A CASCADE

To illustrate the block-diagram approach, consider a situation (as in Fig. 2-2) in which three well-stirred vessels are arranged in series. As

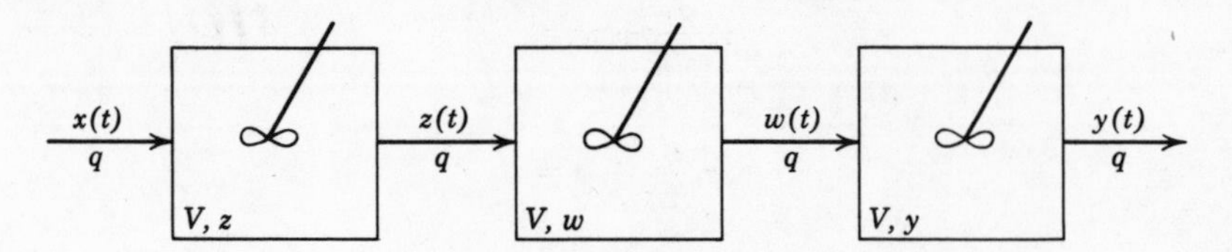

Fig. 2-2. A three-vessel cascade.

in our previous study we are concerned with a concentration disturbance $x(t)$, and wish to know how this will effect a final effluent $y(t)$, assuming all initial conditions are zero. In our block-diagram notation

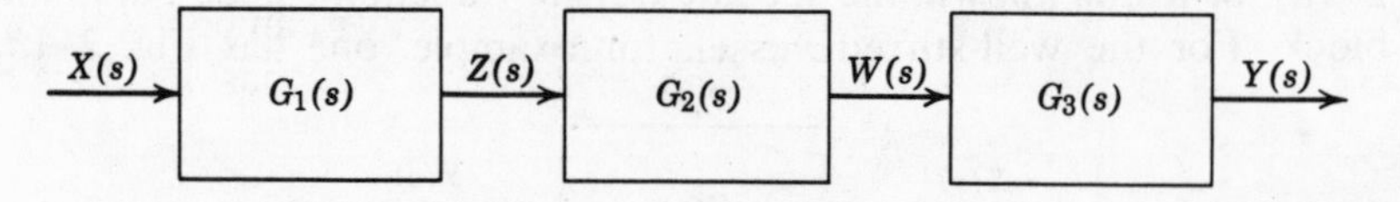

Fig. 2-3. Block diagram of cascade.

this becomes Fig. 2-3, representing the three simultaneous relations:

$$\begin{aligned} Z(s) &= G_1(s)\,X(s) \\ W(s) &= G_2(s)\,Z(s) \\ Y(s) &= G_3(s)\,W(s) \end{aligned} \tag{2-1}$$

which combined (algebraically) give

$$Y(s) = G_3W = G_3G_2Z = G_3G_2G_1X(s) \tag{2-2}$$

If now the three transfer functions are each of the simple first-order kind:

$$Y(s) = \left(\frac{1}{\tau_1 s + 1}\right)\left(\frac{1}{\tau_2 s + 1}\right)\left(\frac{1}{\tau_3 s + 1}\right)X(s) \tag{2-3}$$

and the over-all relation between $X(s)$ and $Y(s)$ is the transfer function

$$G(s) = \frac{1}{(\tau_1 s + 1)(\tau_2 s + 1)(\tau_3 s + 1)} \tag{2-4}$$

For comparison, let us examine the classical differential equation approach. The three simultaneous relations are:

$$\tau_1 \frac{dz}{dt} + z = x$$

$$\tau_2 \frac{dw}{dt} + w = z \tag{2-5}$$

$$\tau_3 \frac{dy}{dt} + y = w$$

To solve these simultaneously for the relationship between y and x, we first differentiate to obtain the auxiliary relations:

$$\tau_2 \frac{d^2w}{dt^2} + \frac{dw}{dt} = \frac{dz}{dt}$$

$$\tau_3 \frac{d^2y}{dt^2} + \frac{dy}{dt} = \frac{dw}{dt} \tag{2-6}$$

$$\tau_3 \frac{d^3y}{dt^3} + \frac{d^2y}{dt^2} = \frac{d^2w}{dt^2}$$

Repeated substitution and algebraic rearrangement yields the differential equation form

$$\tau_1\tau_2\tau_3 \frac{d^3y}{dt^3} + (\tau_1\tau_2 + \tau_2\tau_3 + \tau_1\tau_3) \frac{d^2y}{dt^2}$$

$$+ (\tau_1 + \tau_2 + \tau_3)\frac{dy}{dt} + y = x(t) \tag{2-7}$$

which is the time-domain equivalent of equation (2–3). Although it must be admitted that the advantage of the transform method is rather small in this case, it should be clear that for systems of equations of greater complexity the potential for simplification is considerable. Toward the end of this chapter, for example, we consider an automatic control problem to show the ease of application of block algebra. It must be emphasized that block algebra may be used only if initial conditions are all zero. This matter is discussed in detail in Section 2–4.

2–2. OTHER TRANSFER FUNCTIONS

To this point, the only transfer function considered in detail has been that relating the concentrations in and out of a well-stirred vessel. As the reader probably suspects, there are other relations of importance that lead to different $G(s)$. Let us examine a process vessel once again, focusing attention this time on its storage capacity. We choose the flowrate as the input variable $x(t)$, and the liquid level as the response variable $y(t)$. This time no concentration variables are involved, and a single fluid (say water) will do nicely. Pictorially, the problem is shown in Fig. 2–4. The block notation of Fig. 2–1*a* is applicable, but once

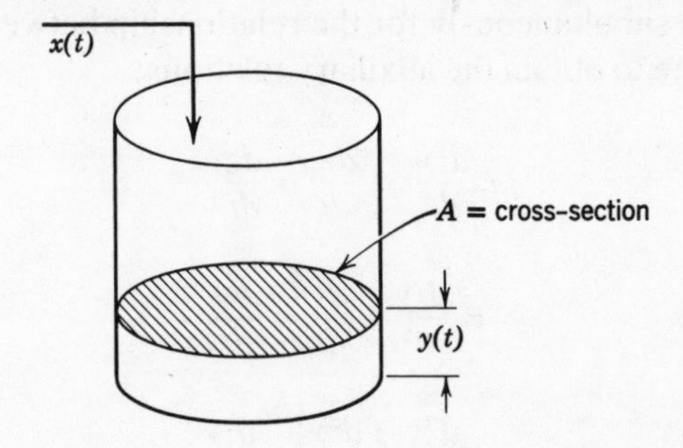

Fig. 2–4. A cylindrical process vessel.

more a material balance is needed to identify $G(s)$ explicitly. Since the vessel is filled without a drain line:

$$\frac{dV}{dt} = A\frac{dy}{dt} = x(t) \tag{2–8}$$

Letting $y(0)$ be zero, transformation gives:

$$AsY(s) = X(s)$$

$$Y(s) = \frac{1}{As}X(s)$$

$$G(s) = \frac{1}{As} \tag{2–9}$$

and the block may be so labeled.

This simple result is especially valuable, for it emphasizes that a block diagram is *not* an ordinary flowsheet. The reader should note that the arrow labeled $Y(s)$ does not represent a material flow, and in fact as pointed out above, the vessel does not have a drain line. It is nonsense, of course, to speak of the liquid level as "flowing out" of the vessel, but it makes perfectly good sense to think of information flow. It is on occasion very helpful to consider a block diagram as an information flowsheet. When it is especially necessary to maintain the important distinction between material flow and information flow, we will use the terms **forcing** variable and **response** variable, instead of input and output.

Another important observation: a transfer function can have units. In the liquid level example:

$$G(s) = \frac{Y(s)}{X(s)} = \frac{1}{As} \text{ min/ft}^2$$

If, on the other hand, the forcing and response variables have the same units, the transfer function will be dimensionless. This was the case in the concentration study of the last chapter. Another point from equation (2–8):

$$y = \frac{1}{A}\int_0^t x\,dt$$

that is, the vessel acts as an analog integrator, summing the infinitesimally small volumes that come in over a time interval. From equation (2–9) we see that the s-domain operation of dividing by s is the equivalent of t-domain integration. Similarly from equation (1–19) we observe the inverse: that multiplication by s is the equivalent of t-domain differentiation (provided again that initial conditions are zero).

2–3. A SYSTEM WITH TWO FORCING VARIABLES

To make the liquid storage vessel part of a continuous operation, a drain line and variable-speed pump may be added, as in Fig. 2–5. Consider the pump to be of the positive displacement type, so that the pumping rate u is dependent only on the pump speed. For this flow system the response variable is affected by two forcing variables, x and u. We may call them information inputs, but in fact, the information

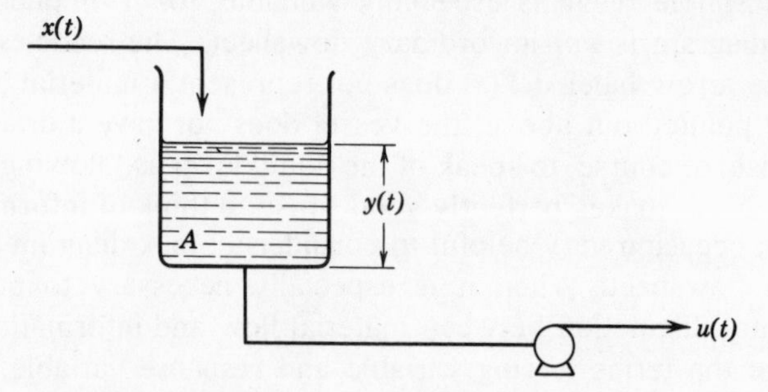

Fig. 2-5. A process vessel with drain line.

input u is actually a flow output. This time, the material balance includes an effluent term:

$$A\frac{dy}{dt} = x - u$$

$$AsY(s) = X(s) - U(s)$$

$$Y(s) = \frac{1}{As}X(s) - \frac{1}{As}U(s) \qquad (2\text{-}10)$$

We now need a diagram (Fig. 2-6*a*) with two blocks, and a notation to

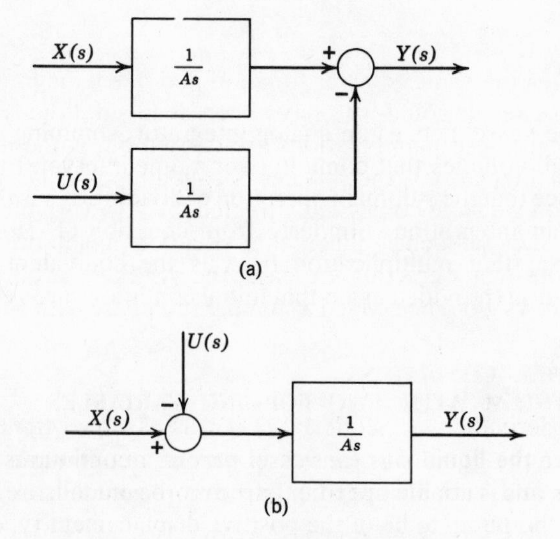

Fig. 2-6. Alternative block diagrams for dual input system. (a) From equation (2-10). (b) From equation (2-11).

show the subtraction. The symbolic subtraction operator (the circle with signed arrows) is called a **comparator.** Alternatively we could have factored equation (2–10):

$$Y(s) = \frac{1}{As}\left[X(s) - U(s)\right] \tag{2–11}$$

This equation gives the block diagram of Fig. 2–6*b*. Thus we see that a block diagram is not a unique representation, but rather that a number of diagrams can represent the same relationship. For a given problem, one particular form may be easier to handle than another. The last block diagram, for example, is frequently used in automatic control applications. Then if $u(t)$ is the **disturbance**, y is called the **controlled** variable, and x, the **manipulating** variable.

Sometimes, however, it is advantageous to combine x and u into a single forcing variable, the net flow into the vessel z.

$$z(t) = x(t) - u(t)$$

$$Z(s) = X(s) - U(s) \tag{2–12}$$

then:

$$Y(s) = \frac{1}{As} Z(s) \tag{2–13}$$

which gives the same transfer function and block diagram as equation (2–9). This result could also have been deduced directly from Figure 2–6*b*. When these manipulations are carried out without reference to the original equations, the process is called block-diagram algebra. In this section we have consistently treated the flow variable u as having a negative sign (effluent). Since this situation might be reversed, we should note that were this the case, the symbolic circle with positive signed arrows would be called a **summer** (compare with Fig. 2–17).

2–4. INITIAL CONDITIONS

In the derivation of Section 2–2 it was assumed that the tank was initially empty. This was most convenient, but of course in practical situations this is not always true. In the more general case

$$AsY(s) - Ay(0) = X(s)$$

$$Y(s) = \frac{1}{As} X(s) + \frac{1}{s} y(0) \tag{2–14}$$

This form is perfectly manageable if a solution is sought for $y(t)$: proper substitutions are then made for $X(s)$ and the boundary condition, and the resulting $Y(s)$ is put through the operation of inverse transformation. However, if our interest is in transfer functions and block notation, the last term in equation (2–14) *is* a stumbling block. To avoid this initial condition difficulty, it is useful to take a hint from the dual-input problem just examined. The similarity in form between equations (2–10) and (2–14) suggests that the problem can be simplified by a substitution.

We define $\hat{y}$ (read "y-hat") as the deviation of y from its initial condition $y(0)$, or: $\hat{y}(t) = y(t) - y(0)$. Using this definition, we observe that

$$\frac{d\hat{y}}{dt} = \frac{dy}{dt}$$

$$\hat{y}(0) = y(0) - y(0) = 0$$

$$\mathscr{L}\left[\frac{d\hat{y}}{dt}\right] = s\mathscr{L}[\hat{y}] - \hat{y}(0) = s\mathscr{L}[\hat{y}]$$

To this point we have dealt only with systems where initial conditions were zero. Since for these cases $\hat{y}(t) = y(t)$, the notation $\mathscr{L}[y] = Y(s)$ was entirely unambiguous. But now to generalize to cases where $\hat{y}(t) \neq y(t)$ and $\mathscr{L}[\hat{y}] \neq \mathscr{L}[y]$, we are forced to decide which of these time variables to associate with the notation $Y(s)$. For convenience in what follows, we will henceforth reserve the capital letter function of s for the transform of a hat-variable:

$$Y(s) = \mathscr{L}[\hat{y}(t)]$$

Of course, for zero initial condition this will happen also to represent $\mathscr{L}[y(t)]$.

Returning to the problem at hand it may be written as

$$A\frac{d\hat{y}}{dt} = \hat{x}$$

where for consistancy our new notation is also applied to the input x, assuming that $x(0) = 0$. Then:

$$Y(s) = \frac{1}{As}X(s)$$

We have recovered the desirable form, and draw the following conclusion: The transfer function only has meaning if all initial conditions are zero; however, the presence of a non-zero initial condition can be accounted for quite simply by measuring the variable of interest as a deviation from the known value at $t = 0$. In effect, we use a variable which does have the zero initial condition that we want. Henceforth, we will use the hat designation on a time function to show that this has been done.

2–5. LINEARITY AND CONSTANT COEFFICIENTS

The transfer function is of course the convenient algebraic form that was alluded to in the Introduction. As shown above it has great utility in developing the block-diagram manipulations. Accordingly, it is of primary importance to establish precisely what class of differential equations can be transformed.

We have seen that common functions of time, and time derivatives of all orders $d^n y/dt^n$ can be transformed (Problem 1–9). The procedure fails however, if a term exists of greater *degree* than one in the dependent variable such as: y^2, $(dy/dt)^2$, $y(dy/dt)$, etc. The first of these, for example, cannot be transformed because it demands the integration

$$\int_0^\infty y^2 e^{-st}\, dt$$

Thus only *linear* differential equations, those of first degree are acceptable. This class must be further restricted however, to disqualify terms with time-varying coefficients, since such terms cannot be transformed even though linear.

The well-stirred vessel can provide a simple example of a linear equation that is not transformable, if we examine equation (1–1) for the case of constant feed concentration $x = a$, but time-dependent flowrate $q(t)$. Then, provided that the fluid volume does not change:

$$V\frac{dy}{dt} = aq(t) - q(t)y$$

It is the last term in this equation that is linear in the variable y, but has a time-dependent coefficient. In short, the block-diagram advantages are only available for systems that can be represented by linear differential equations with constant coefficients.

2-6. ADDITIONAL COMPONENTS

On many occasions components are intentionally added to a given system for certain purposes. As a preliminary to automatic control of the liquid level in our process vessel, we would probably add a control valve to the feed line. Specifically, with an eye to the future, let us choose one whose opening is responsive to an air-pressure signal. A typical device of this sort is illustrated in Fig. 2–7. It is termed a

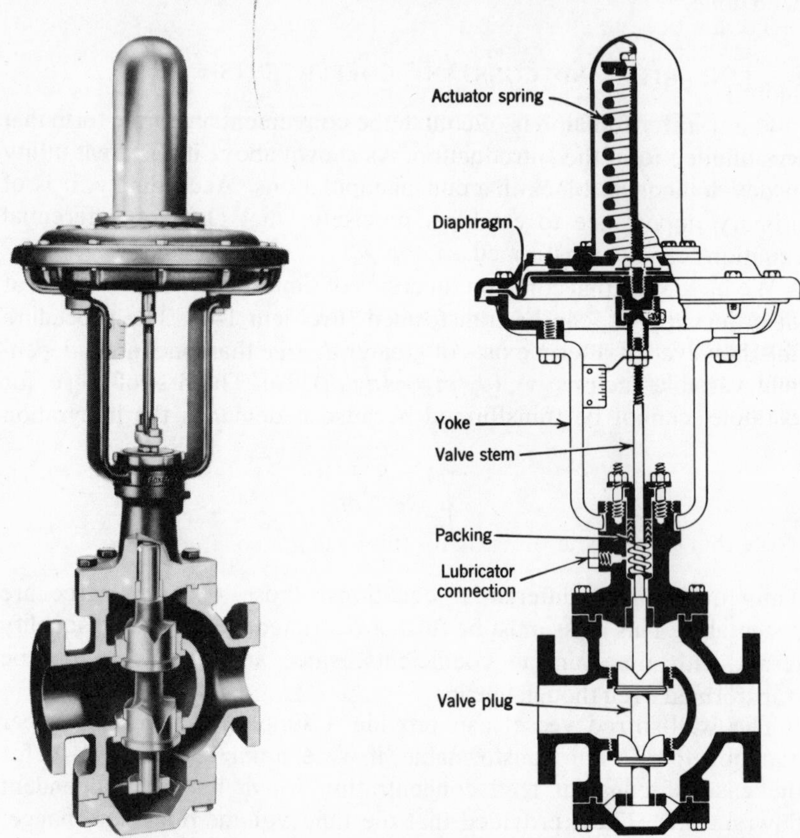

Fig. 2–7. Pneumatic motor valve (Courtesy The Foxboro Co.).

pneumatic motor valve to emphasize that the valve stem is driven by a pressure-sensitive diaphragm. But the details of hardware are not our concern here. In block-diagram terminology the valve is a black box which produces a flow output x for a given pressure input p. This is shown by the left block in Fig. 2–8, and the rest of the figure indicates how the valve and vessel are functionally related.

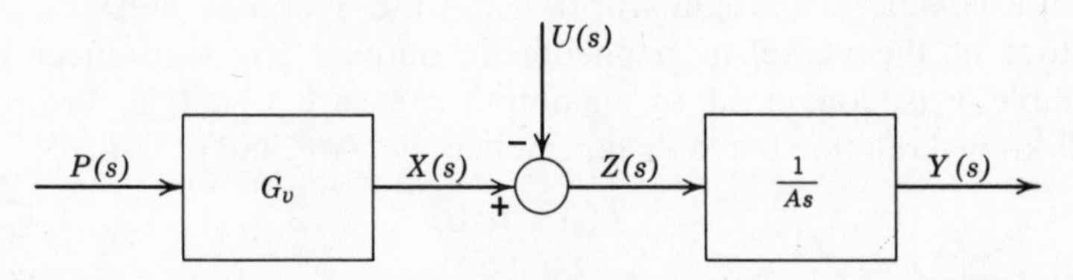

Fig. 2–8. Block diagram for vessel and control valve.

To identify the valve transfer function more specifically, details are needed on its static and dynamic characteristics. We will reserve a more complete discussion of these points for a later chapter, since for our present purpose it is adequate to assume very simple behavior. Assuming that the valve is linear and very fast in its action, we can describe it completely by the equation:

$$\hat{x} = K_v \hat{p} \tag{2–15}$$

i.e., the flowrate deviation is proportional to the deviation of the input pressure from its initial value. The relationships between these variables and x and p can be seen from Fig. 2–9. Transforming equation (2–15) gives

$$X(s) = K_v P(s) \tag{2–16}$$

Note that the transfer function for this case is a constant.

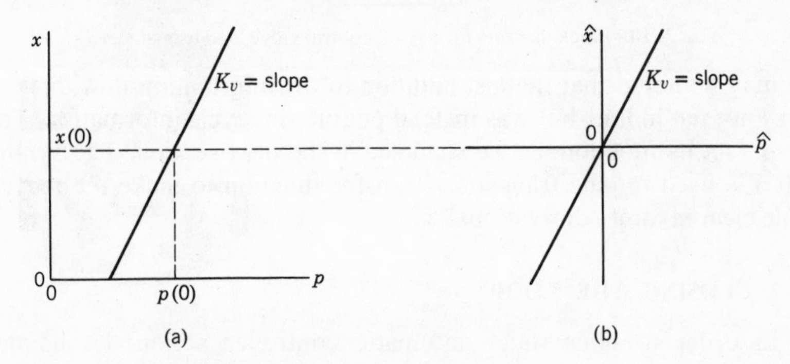

Fig. 2–9. Characteristics of linear, fast-acting valve. (a) Original variables. (b) Deviation variables.

Since the level variable y is not ordinarily measured directly, we will also add a device downstream in order to convert the information into more usable form. Such a device is called a **transducer**. For this simple case, a flexible diaphragm will transmit the hydraulic pressure at the bottom of the vessel as a pneumatic output. The transducer input variable y is converted to an output pressure signal, b. Using the well-known relation between fluid height, density, and pressure:

$$b(t) = \rho y(t) \qquad (2\text{–}17)$$

This relation also applies at any initial condition $b(0) = \rho y(0)$. Therefore, by subtraction:

$$\hat{b}(t) = \rho \hat{y}(t)$$

$$B(s) = \rho Y(s)$$

and the transfer function for this transducer is

$$H(s) = \frac{B(s)}{Y(s)} = \rho \qquad (2\text{–}18)$$

again, a constant. The block diagram has grown to become Fig. 2–10.

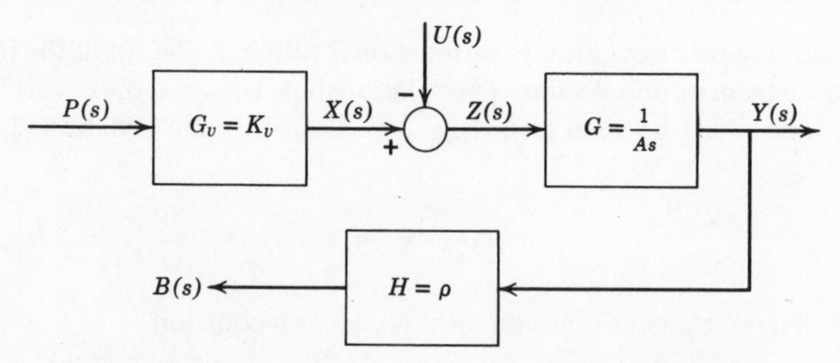

Fig. 2–10. Block diagram for vessel, control valve, and transducer.

It may be noted that the last addition to the information-flow diagram was not put in line, but was instead put off as recycle information. This is in fact its function, as we shall see in the next section. The symbol $H(s)$ is used for the transducer transfer function to make the recycle role clear in future derivations.

2–7. CLOSING THE LOOP

In order to understand automatic controller action, let us first consider how the level-control system described above would be operated manually. Whenever the operator detected a deviation of the control variable y from the desired value, he would regulate the pressure p until by so doing he returned y to its desired level. Essentially then he would perform two functions: (1) error detection, and (2) corrective regulation. It is clear that an automatic controller must also function in these ways. However, since a good substitute for human eyes is hard to find our automatic device will detect the pressure b instead of the visual variable y. It was in anticipation of this adaptation that the transducer was introduced in the first place.

As with the human operator the automatic error detector also compares a variable with its desired value. Denoting the **set-point** or **reference** value by r, the error is:

$$e = r - b \tag{2-19}$$

Since this definition is applicable at all times

$$e(0) = r(0) - b(0)$$

$$\hat{e} = \hat{r} - \hat{b}$$

$$E(s) = R(s) - B(s) \tag{2-20}$$

In block notation, equation (2–20) is shown by a comparator.

The second task of the controller is that of corrective regulation. The human operator will attempt to correct rapidly, but with sufficient anticipatory action to prevent excessive overshoot. His response to a particular disturbance might depend on the error, its rate of change, the operator's experience, or all these together. The more significant factors that the operator is able to take into account, the better will be the control. To be sure, we cannot expect a piece of hardware to show human memory or judgment. On the other hand we might reasonably expect faster action than from a human, and less deterioration due to fatigue. We will use the symbol $G_c(s)$ to represent some (as yet undetermined) controller transfer function.

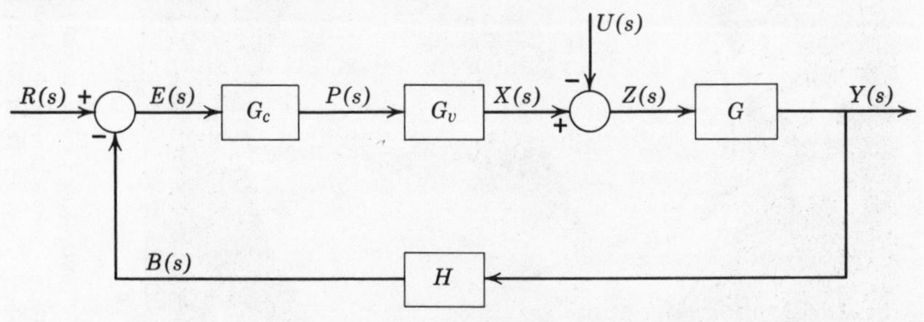

Fig. 2–11. Block diagram for closed-loop control.

Referring to the block notation again, we observe that the control action, whether manual or automatic, acts to return information from the system output to its input and thereby "closes the loop." This is shown by Fig. 2–11. This control scheme is called **closed-loop, feed-back,** or **negative feedback** control, the last because of the sign at the

Fig. 2–12. Pneumatic controllers. Left: external appearance of a proportional controller. Right: cut-away view of a three-mode controller, showing: (1) proportional gain adjustment, (2) integral control adjustment, (3) derivative control adjustment, (4) set point adjustment, (5) chart drive, (6) relay. (Courtesy The Taylor Instrument Co.)

comparator. For ease of construction and maintenance, the comparator and corrective device are usually sold in a single package, such as that illustrated by Fig. 2–12. The entire control loop can also be shown in a more pictorial diagram by using the symbols of Fig. 2–13. In this

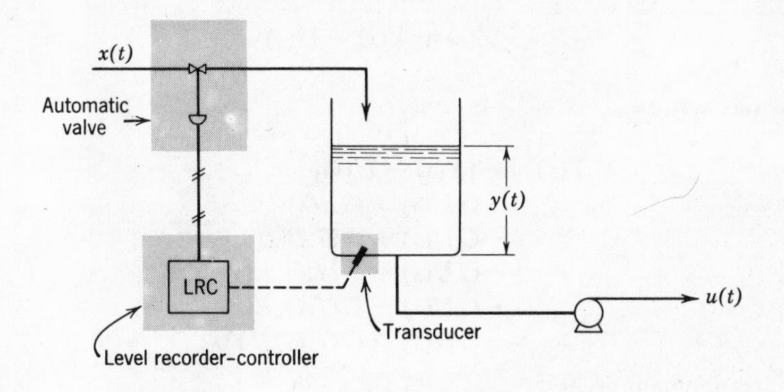

Fig. 2–13. A closed-loop level control.

and subsequent diagrams of this sort the dashed line represents information feedback from the transducer, the double-marked line shows the controller output signal.

2–8. CLOSED-LOOP TRANSFER FUNCTION

We are now in a position to reap one of the benefits of our compact block notation. We apply the method to Fig. 2–11 to derive the relationships between each of the inputs, $R(s)$ and $U(s)$, and the system control variable $Y(s)$. From these results we will be able (by inverse transformation) to predict how the liquid level y responds to a change in either the reference value r or the disturbance u when feedback control is used. The problem we have been working on is general in that the system output $Y(s)$ is affected by two kinds of inputs: (1) the intentional reference $R(s)$, and (2) the unwanted disturbance $U(s)$. Let us consider these individually.

A typical chemical engineering control problem is one of continuous regulation. The reference value is held constant and the closed loop operates to hold $y(t)$ as close as possible to the desired value, in spite of unwanted fluctuations in $u(t)$. This is called **regulator** operation. With $r(t)$ constant at $r(0)$, $\hat{r}(t) = 0$, and $R(s) = 0$. On the block diagram, the arrow marked $R(s)$ disappears, and $E(s) = -B(s)$. The following block algebra may be performed (see Fig. 2–11):

$$Y(s) = GZ(s)$$

Since the net flow variable

$$Z(s) = X(s) - U(s)$$

we may write

$$\begin{aligned} Y(s) &= G[X(s) - U(s)] \\ &= -GU(s) + GX(s) \\ &= -GU(s) + GG_vP(s) \\ &= -GU(s) + GG_vG_cE(s) \\ &= -GU(s) - GG_vG_cB(s) \\ &= -GU(s) - GG_vG_cHY(s) \end{aligned}$$

Rearrangement gives

$$Y(s) = -\left(\frac{G}{1 + G_cG_vGH}\right)U(s) \tag{2–21}$$

On occasion, especially in startup problems, the disturbance is constant with time and it is desired that the control variable follow a prearranged reference change. This type of control, called **servo** operation, is also very common in machine operation, communications, and many other (nonchemical) engineering applications. For this case, $\hat{u} = 0$, $U(s) = 0$ and the block-algebra derivation for the closed loop follows:

$$Y(s) = GZ(s)$$

But now $Z(s) = X(s)$. Therefore:

$$\begin{aligned} Y(s) &= GX(s) \\ &= GG_vP(s) \\ &= GG_vG_cE(s) \end{aligned}$$

Since $E = R - B$

$$\begin{aligned} Y(s) &= GG_vG_cR(s) - GG_vG_cB(s) \\ &= GG_vG_cR(s) - GG_vG_cHY(s) \end{aligned}$$

Rearrangement of this last equation gives:

$$Y(s) = \frac{GG_vG_c}{1 + GG_vG_cH}R(s) \tag{2–22}$$

It is important to note that either equation (2–21) or (2–22) could have been written by inspection from the block diagrams. The closed-loop transfer function between any two variables in a loop can be written as a ratio: The numerator is the forward-cascade transfer function (the product of all the G's) between the variables. The denominator is *one* plus the product of all the G's in the loop. The reader should convince himself that this rule applies to the previous cases.

If the two inputs are considered to act simultaneously, an algebraic analysis similar to the foregoing yields

$$Y(s) = \frac{G_c G_v G}{1 + G_c G_v G H} R(s) - \frac{G}{1 + G_c G_v G H} U(s) \qquad (2\text{–}23)$$

demonstrating that it is permissible to add the individual responses to arrive at the combined response. This result is characteristic of linear systems and is sometimes offered as a definition of linearity. It is also called the **principle of superposition**. In equation (2–23) or in either of the two equations from which it was composed we have an explicit statement of the effect of feedback. To make a comparison with the no-control case, we may reconsider Fig. 2–11 with the feedback path broken. The resulting cascade yields

$$Y(s) = G_c G_v G R(s) - G U(s)$$

which differs from equation (2–23) only in the transfer function denominators.

2–9. PROPORTIONAL CONTROL

In closing the loop in the last section, we were able to leave unspecified the all-important control transfer function G_c. A number of possibilities will in fact be developed in the chapters to come. Here we begin this study with the simplest linear case, in which the corrective action $\hat{p}$ is made proportional to the detected error $\hat{e}$:

$$\hat{p} = K_c \hat{e}$$
$$P(s) = K_c E(s) \qquad (2\text{–}24)$$

and the transfer function is the **proportional gain**, K_c. In process controllers, however, it is not this parameter that is used to describe a dial setting, but rather a dimensionless reciprocal called **proportional band** and expressed as a percentage. By definition this index is

$$\% \text{ P.B.} = 100 \frac{1}{K_c} \frac{\Delta p_{max}}{\Delta e_{max}} \tag{2-25}$$

where Δe_{max} and Δp_{max} are the input and output total possible spans in the appropriate units. These relationships may be expressed graphically as in Fig. 2–14*a*. Sometimes the % P.B. is defined verbally rather than

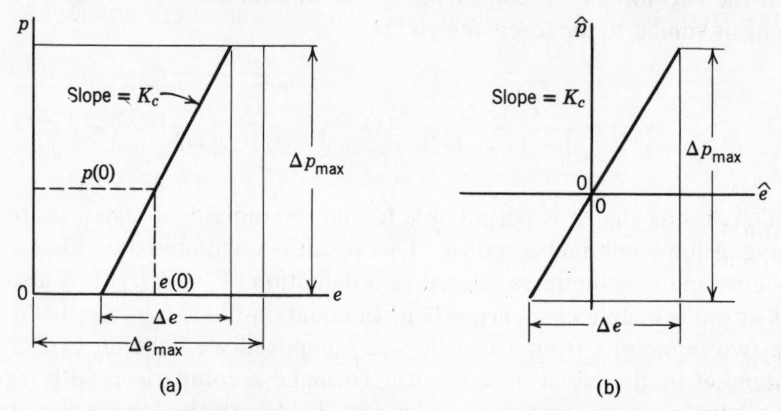

Fig. 2–14. Proportional control. (a) Original variables. (b) Deviation variables.

by equation (2–25): it is the percentage of the input span Δe_{max} that will cause the output variable p to cover its full span. This statement can easily be confirmed by noting from the figure that Δe is the input span that is called for. This parameter may be introduced into equation (2–25) by substitution for

$$\Delta p_{max} = K_c \Delta e$$

Then:

$$\% \text{ P.B.} = 100 \frac{\Delta e}{\Delta e_{max}}$$

which fits the verbal definition.

REMARKS

In this chapter we have begun to answer major questions in both of the classes mentioned in the Introduction. We found it especially convenient to describe dynamic elements and combine information on individual, connected parts, if a problem was first formulated in terms of transfer functions. Furthermore, from the derivations of Section 2–8 we now know how to account for feedback control quantitatively. This result is the most far-reaching of this chapter, since it will provide a basis for virtually all the subsequent developments on the control of linear systems.

EXERCISES

2–1. A cylindrical tank is provided with feed and drain lines. The drain rate is determined by adjustment of a manual valve. Assume that this rate m is proportional to the level in the tank, h; the proportionality constant is the reciprocal of valve resistance:

$$m = \frac{1}{R}h$$

(a) Find the transfer function relating level to input flow if the tank is initially empty. Find the transfer function relating exit flow to input flow. Is there a system time constant?

(b) How would your analysis change if m were proportional to the head differential:

$$m = \frac{1}{R}(h - k)$$

where k is a constant downstream head? For this case the tank must have a finite initial level $h(0) \geq k$ (otherwise there would be backflow). *Hint:* It will be helpful to assume that $(dh/dt) = 0$ at $t = 0^-$. Is this a reasonable assumption?

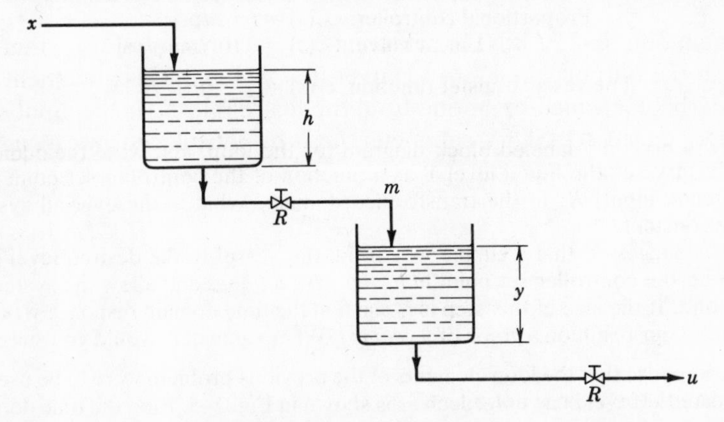

Fig. 2–15. A two-tank flow system.

2–2. The tank of Problem 2–1a is drained into a second tank of identical dimensions. The second tank is emptied through a valve like that of the first. Find transfer functions for *X versus Y*, and *X versus U*, and for the combined system, assuming that the arrangement is as shown in Fig. 2–15. Both tanks are initially empty. What time constants are involved?

2–3. Reconsider the system of the prior problem with the single modification that the first tank drains into the second below the liquid level, as shown in Fig. 2–16. Under these conditions,

$$m = \frac{1}{R}(h - y)$$

Draw a block diagram for this system to show how $X(s)$ effects $Y(s)$ through $H(s)$.

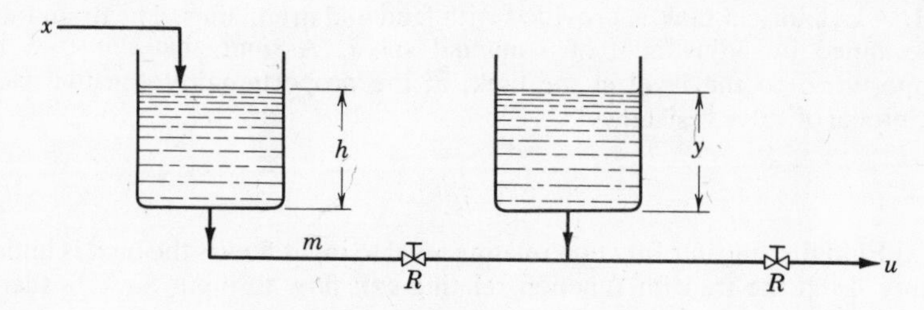

Fig. 2–16. A modified two-tank system.

2–4. Consider the following startup problem: A vessel 10 ft high and 4 ft in diameter is to be filled with liquid to a level of 6 ft. It is initially empty. The filling is to be accomplished automatically, by using a control loop with the following elements:

$$\text{Measuring element: } H(s) = 0.5 \text{ psi/ft}$$
$$\text{Proportional controller: } G_c(s) = 6 \text{ psi/psi}$$
$$\text{Linear valve: } G_v(s) = 3 \text{ (ft}^3\text{/min)/psi}$$
$$\text{The vessel transfer function: } G(s) = \frac{1}{4\pi s} \text{ ft/(ft}^3\text{/min)}$$

Draw a carefully labeled block diagram for the loop, and write the equation that expresses the liquid level Y as a function of the controller set point (the reference input) R, in the transformed domain. What is the over-all system time constant?

It is suggested that a simple way to fill the vessel to the desired level is to turn up the controller set point in a *step-wise manner* and allow the system to respond. If the size of this step is r_o psi, find the time domain response $y(t)$, and sketch your result on a graph of y *versus* t. What value of r_o would you suggest?

2–5. Suppose that the loop elements of the previous problem were to be used to regulate the level in a vessel such as is shown in Fig. 2–5. Find the time domain responses, $\hat{y}(t)$ and $y(t)$, following a step disturbance in effluent rate of size u_0 ft^3/min. Sketch these results. What is the maximum u_0 that the system can handle?

2–6. How would equation (2–21) have differed if the regulator loop described in Section 2–8 had used positive feedback instead of negative? Apply your result to Problem 2–5. Is the result an improvement?

2–7. Consider the three-vessel cascade of Section 2–1, with non-zero initial conditions. Suppose: $x(0^-) = z(0) = w(0) = y(0) \neq 0$, and $x(0^+) = x(0^-) + a$. Is the transfer function equation (2–4) still applicable? If so, what deviation variables need to be defined? How is equation (2–7) affected by this change? What are the initial values of the higher derivatives at $t = 0$?

2–8. With reference to the system shown in Figs. 2–11 and 2–13, suppose that a disturbance in supply pressure affects $P(s)$. Arrange a block diagram to show this, and use the new diagram to write a closed-loop transfer function relating $Y(s)$ to the new disturbance $U_1(s)$.

2–9. A heat exchanger is to be used to heat tube-side water by means of shell-side hot oil. The hot water temperature, $v(t)$, is controlled by automatic manipulation of the pressure to a pneumatic motor valve on the oil line. The temperature of the inlet oil $u(t)$ is the major disturbance to the process. Experimental data indicate that the transfer function relating u and v may be written as

$$G_u = \frac{V(s)}{U(s)} = \frac{2}{100s^2 + 20s + 1} \quad \frac{°\text{F}}{°\text{F}}$$

Sketch a block diagram and a pictorial diagram for a control loop for such an exchanger, including a proportional controller and a fast-acting measuring device. The controller uses air pressure for input and output signals. Label all the variables and transfer functions.

2–10. Derive the closed-loop transfer function between $U(s)$ and $Y(s)$ from the dual-loop block diagram Fig. 2–17. Does your result agree with the rule of thumb given in Section 2–8 for finding closed-loop functions by inspection?

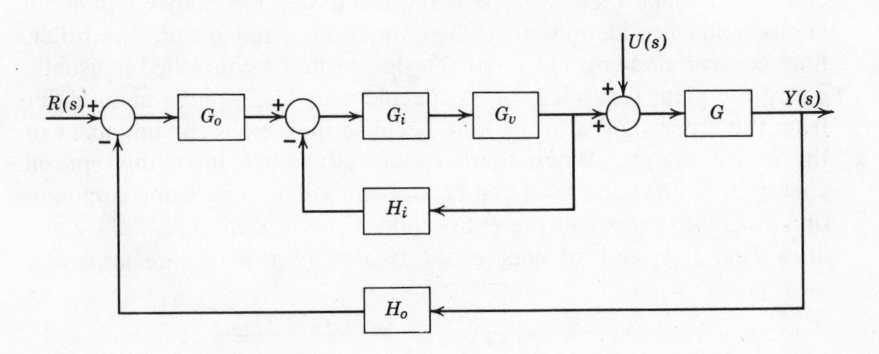

Fig. 2–17. A dual-loop block diagram.

3 *Various Inputs*

In the last chapter we saw that the blocks representing the parts of a larger system could be combined according to fairly simple rules. In doing this the output of a block became the input to a subsequent block modified, where applicable, by the system inputs. The designation input may refer to a signal entering a component, a series of components in cascade, a complete loop, or for that matter a complete factory. The word system may similarly be used in a number of ways, by using the context to make clear what is being discussed. Ordinarily individual components are identified by their functions (transducer, controller, final control element, etc.), but the device being controlled is usually called the **plant** regardless of its specific use. The inputs r and u differ from the other signals in the loop because they cross the boundary of the entire system. When there is any advantage in it, this special character of $R(s)$ and $U(s)$ can be shown explicitly by using combination blocks to represent the entire loop. From equation (2–23) we can draw Fig. 3–1, and, of course, the two system inputs are apparent.

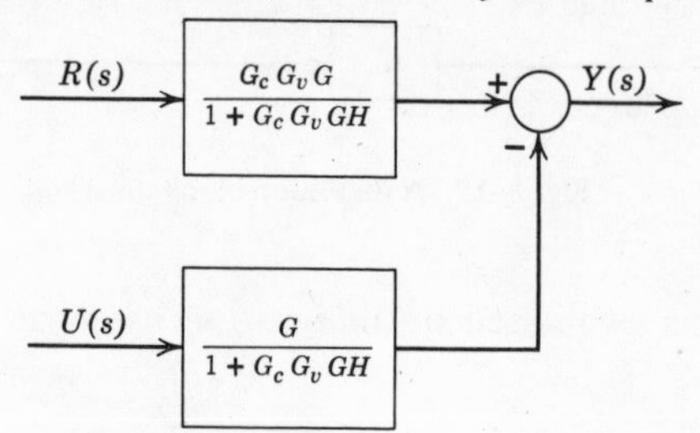

Fig. 3–1. Combination block diagram for a closed loop.

To this point, the input or disturbance signal to a system has generally been left as a nonspecified variable. The input to a particular storage vessel was labeled x, or u, but only in the single case of the introductory, well-stirred vessel was the nature of the input fixed: in that case, a step function of size a. Now it is desirable that we broaden our view to include other functions. It should be understood that while the symbol x will be used for the input in what follows, the discussion would apply equally well to system inputs r or u.

3–1. THE RAMP INPUT

Supposing as before that our well-stirred system is disturbed by a concentration input, but that this time the change occurs at a uniform rate, we can write:

$$x = x(0) + at \qquad t \geqslant 0$$
$$\hat{x} = at \qquad t \geqslant 0 \qquad (3\text{–}1)$$

For our purposes, the value of x for $t < 0$ is irrelevant, but for mathematical formality, we may add as we did for the step function that: $x(t < 0) = 0$. The graphical representation (Fig. 3–2) gives the **ramp** function its name. If $a = 1$, it is called a unit ramp.

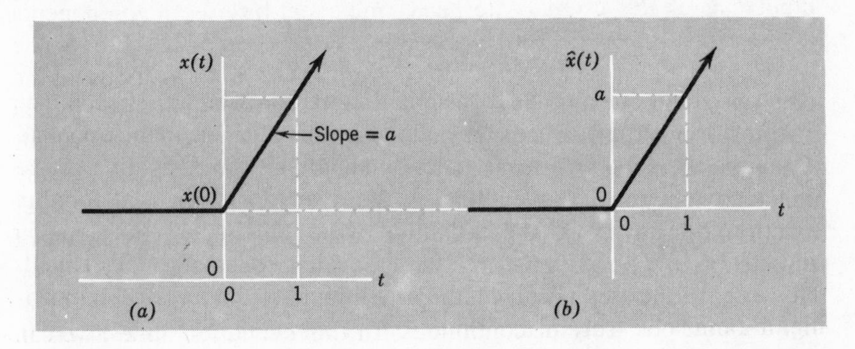

Fig. 3–2. The ramp function. (a) Original variable. (b) Deviation variable.

The Laplace transform of this $\hat{x}(t)$ is

$$X(s) = \mathscr{L}[\hat{x}(t)] = \int_0^\infty ate^{-st}\, dt$$

This integral was evaluated by integration by parts as Problem 1–7. From that result:

$$X(s) = \frac{a}{s^2} \qquad (3\text{–}2)$$

It is interesting to note that the interpretation of $(1/s)$ as an integration operator holds very well for the step and ramp. In the time domain, the ramp is exactly the integral of the step: in the Laplace domain, they differ by the $(1/s)$ factor. Carrying this inductive argument one step further, the transform (a/s^3) should correspond to the time function:

$$\hat{x}(t) = \int_0^t at\,dt = \frac{at^2}{2}$$

and in fact, it does, as can be proved by more formal transformation.

3–2. THE IMPULSE

Tabulating the transforms of the three inputs just considered puts in evidence an interesting pattern:

$x(t > 0)$	$X(s)$
1 (unit step)	$1/s$
t (unit ramp)	$1/s^2$
$\frac{1}{2}t^2$	$1/s^3$

This raises the question as to whether a time function exists such that its transform is the constant, 1. Following the induction in the opposite direction, the sought-for time function should be the derivative of the unit step function. Conventionally, the symbol $\delta(t)$ is used for this function. For any $t \neq 0$, the derivative of the step function (its slope) is zero: $\delta(t \neq 0) = 0$. At $t = 0$ the step is strictly speaking not defined. However, if the step is considered as a limit of a real physical happening, it cannot be truly discontinuous. In this event, its slope at $t = 0$ becomes infinite: $\delta(t = 0) = \infty$. The $\delta(t)$-function (read "delta-function") or **unit impulse** may be schematically represented by Fig. 3–3*a*. For some purposes, it is preferable to consider the impulse to occur at some time t_0, after $t = 0$. Then the unit impulse is written as $\delta(t - t_0)$, and appears graphically as Fig. 3–3*b*.

The emphasis on the impulse as a limit is of great importance here, in order that the infinite magnitude of zero duration (Fig. 3–3) can have physical interpretation. Imagine for example that an input under study is the flowrate to a vessel. There are obviously many ways in which a given quantity of water, say 1 ft^3, could be added to the volume in the vessel. Even if we confine our attention to only step changes in net

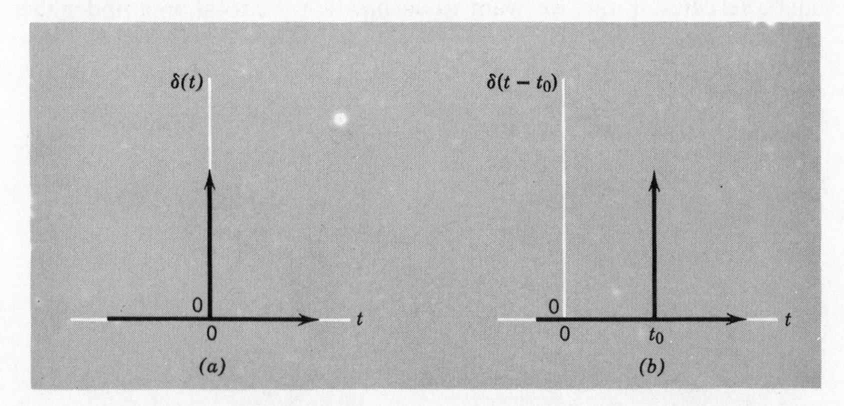

Fig. 3–3. The impulse function. (a) An impulse at $t = 0$. (b) An impulse at $t = t_0$.

flowrate various combinations of flow and duration time present themselves; for example:

Net Inflow Rate, ft^3/min	Duration, min
1	1
2	0.50
4	0.25
10	0.10

We can compute $y(t)$, the response to each of these inputs, from equations (2–13) and (1–16) or from the corresponding differential equation and boundary condition. The results appear in Fig. 3–4. As expected, additional liquid volume raises the level in the vessel to a new constant value. Only the rate of rise is effected by the manner of addition.

We might ask this question: What is the fastest way in which the fixed quantity of water can be added? In the limit, an infinite flow for zero time would be fastest, if these terms are interpreted as limits in Fig. 3–4; that is, if the rectangle in Fig. 3–4*a* is allowed to grow in height and shrink in time with constant area under the curve. The limiting $y(t)$ response to the impulse is found in Fig. 3–4*b* to be a step for this case.

To make use of the delta-function analytically and computationally, this graphical argument needs to be formalized by completing the definition of $\delta(t)$ as a mathematical statement. This last property must be an integral expression in order that $\delta(t)$ will have two important characteristics. First, we want to assure that the total area under the curve is unity:

$$\int_0^{\infty} \delta(t - t_0)\, dt = 1 \tag{3-3}$$

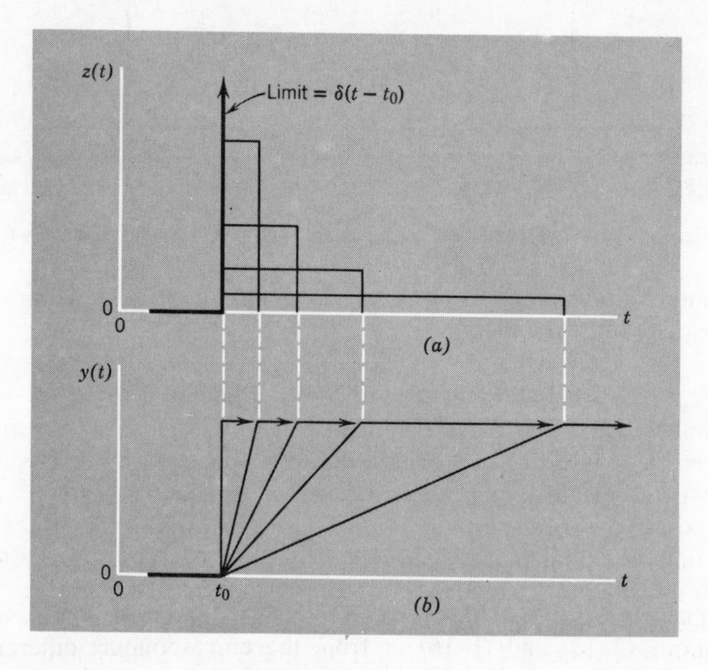

Fig. 3–4. The impulse function as a limit. (a) Input flow. (b) Level response.

Second, it is important to us that

$$\mathscr{L}[\delta(t)] = 1$$

This was the interest that motivated the examination of $\delta(t)$ in the first place. Both requirements will be met if the integral property is defined by

$$\int_0^{\infty} \delta(t - t_0) f(t)\, dt = f(t_0) \tag{3-4}$$

for any arbitrary function f. If $f(t) = 1$, equation (3–4) reduces to (3–3), whereas if $f(t)$ is taken as e^{-st}:

$$\mathscr{L}[\delta(t - t_0)] = \int_0^\infty \delta(t - t_0)e^{-st}\, dt = e^{-st_0}$$

and

$$\lim_{t_0 \to 0} \mathscr{L}[\delta(t - t_0)] = \mathscr{L}[\delta(t)] = \lim_{t_0 \to 0} [e^{-st_0}] = 1$$

To describe an impulse of other than unit size, a constant factor is included. Multiplication by a constant does not change the zero or infinite values of $\delta(t)$, but does show up in the integrals:

$$a\delta(t) = 0 \qquad t \neq 0$$
$$a\delta(t) = \infty \qquad t = 0$$
$$\int_0^\infty a\delta(t - t_0)\, dt = a$$
$$\mathscr{L}[a\delta(t)] = a \tag{3–5}$$

It should be appreciated that the impulse disturbance can never exactly be created physically, nor for that matter can a perfect step or ramp. They are all idealizations; nevertheless, some system behavior can be approximated very well by an impulse or step when variables change over time durations much smaller than the time constants of a system.

One of the more interesting properties of the impulse forcing function is evident if one applies it to the equation which defines the transfer function of a system: $Y(s) = G(s)\, X(s)$. If $\hat{x}(t) = \delta(t)$, the unit impulse, $X(s) = 1$ and $Y(s) = G(s)$; that is, in the s domain the response of a system to a unit impulse is the transfer function. Put another way, the transfer function of a system is the Laplace transform of its response to a unit impulse.

3–3. SINUSOIDS

Another input function of great importance to theory and for certain experimental studies is the sine wave:

$$x(t) = x(0) + a \sin \omega t \qquad t \geqslant 0$$
$$\hat{x}(t) = a \sin \omega t \qquad t \geqslant 0 \tag{3–6}$$

As before $\hat{x}(t < 0)$ may be set equal to zero, although this point is not important if as is usually the case only positive times have physical interest. The parameters a and ω are illustrated in Fig. 3–5. When transformed (using integral tables):

$$X(s) = a\int_0^\infty (\sin \omega t)e^{-st}\, dt = \frac{a\omega}{s^2 + \omega^2}$$

Similarly, a wave displaced in time by a quarter-cycle gives:

$$\hat{x}(t \geqslant 0) = a \sin(\omega t + \frac{\pi}{2}) = a \cos \omega t$$

$$X(s) = \frac{as}{s^2 + \omega^2}$$

If the wave has a different amplitude and is displaced in time, but not by a multiple of $\pi/2$, it can be written as

$$\hat{x}(t) = K \sin (\omega t + \phi) \tag{3-7}$$

This function cannot be described by a cosine alone, but can be written as the sum of a sine wave and a cosine wave of different amplitude.

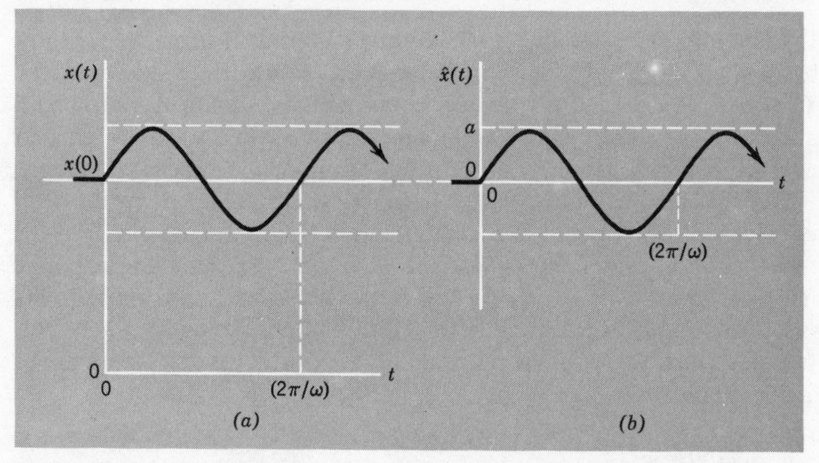

Fig. 3–5. The sine function: (a) Original variable. (b) Deviation variable.

Such an identity can be demonstrated from the summation formula of elementary trigonometry.

$$K \sin(\omega t + \phi) = K(\sin \omega t \cos \phi + \cos \omega t \sin \phi) = K_1 \sin \omega t + K_2 \cos \omega t \tag{3-8}$$

where

$$K_1 = K \cos \phi$$
$$K_2 = K \sin \phi$$

The reverse computation of K and ϕ from available values of K_1 and K_2 may be based on the observations that

$$\frac{K_2}{K_1} = \frac{\sin\phi}{\cos\phi} = \tan\phi$$

and

$$K_1^2 + K_2^2 = K^2(\cos^2\phi + sin^2\phi) = K^2$$

from which

$$K = \sqrt{K_1^2 + K_2^2}$$

$$\phi = \text{arc}\tan(K_2/K_1) \tag{3–9}$$

From equation (3–8):

$$\mathscr{L}[K\sin(\omega t + \phi)] = \mathscr{L}[K_1 \sin\omega t] + \mathscr{L}[K_2\cos\omega t]$$

$$= \frac{K_1\omega}{s^2+\omega^2} + \frac{K_2 s}{s^2+\omega^2}$$

$$= \frac{K_1\omega + K_2 s}{s^2+\omega^2} \tag{3–10}$$

3–4. GENERALIZED INPUTS

There is an important distinction that can be made between the loop inputs $R(s)$ and $U(s)$. The reference signal $R(s)$ is man-made. It is either constant for a regulator, or else it varies in a predetermined manner for servo operation. The various inputs discussed above are of this sort: once $r(t)$ is established, the entire future is fixed, mathematically speaking. Such functions are called **deterministic**. Frequently, important process disturbances are also deterministic, arising say from step changes in upstream parts of a plant, but $u(t)$ does not always have such character. On occasion it is largely unpredictable except in a probabilistic sense. If the value of a variable can only be predicted in such a sense, the function is called **random** or **stochastic** or simply **noise**. The details of such analysis are beyond the scope of this book.

In many cases of practical interest an input signal, whether reference or disturbance, is deterministic; yet not the simple step, ramp, impulse, or sinusoid. Any such input[1] can be expressed as a Fourier series over an interval of interest ($0 < t < T$) by

$$\hat{x}(t) = \frac{a_0}{2} + \sum_{n=1}^{\infty}\left(a_n \cos\frac{2\pi n}{T}t + b_n \sin\frac{2\pi n}{T}t\right) \tag{3-11}$$

where:

$$a_n = \frac{2}{T}\int_0^T \hat{x}(t)\cos\frac{2\pi n}{T}t\,dt$$

$$b_n = \frac{2}{T}\int_0^T \hat{x}(t)\sin\frac{2\pi n}{T}t\,dt$$

If the function is periodic with period T, then the series will represent $\hat{x}(t)$ at all times, but since the value of T may be chosen arbitrarily for a nonperiodic function, this is not a practical limitation. In the latter case, the series expansion will reproduce $\hat{x}(t)$ in the chosen interval, but not outside that span. In this manner an arbitrary function can be decomposed into a sum of sine and cosine waves of different frequency and amplitude. If this function is the input to a particular system, it can be considered to be composed of a set of sine waves superimposed on each other. One question of great importance may be formulated as follows: Can the output of such a system be found by superimposing the individual effects of each wave in the input? For linear systems, by the principle of superposition, the answer is *yes*.

In the chapters that follow, considerable emphasis will be placed on sinusoidal analysis and sinusoidal inputs. Unless the reader recalls occasionally the points of this section, he is likely to find himself asking repeatedly why this particular input should receive so much attention above all others. The answer lies in the fact that the sine wave is a convenient prototype. As we have noted, any deterministic input may be decomposed into sinusoids. These in turn may be studied one at a time and then their respective effects simply added for a linear system.

[1]The function must satisfy the Dirichlet conditions: no more than a finite number of discontinuities, maxima, and minima, and a finite integral $\int_0^T |x|\,dt$. This is not a significant restriction for the ordinary functions of engineering interest.

3–5. A BRIEF TABLE OF TRANSFORMS

For future reference, we collect here in tabular form the various transforms that have been derived in the text, examples, and problems.

$\hat{f}(t)$		$F(s)$
$a\,\delta(t)$	(impulse)	a
a	(step)	a/s
at	(ramp)	a/s^2
t^n		$n!/s^{n+1}$
e^{-at}		$1/(s+a)$
$a \sin \omega t$		$a\omega/(s^2+\omega^2)$
$a \cos \omega t$		$as/(s^2+\omega^2)$
$K \sin(\omega t + \phi)$		$(K\omega \cos\phi + Ks \sin\phi)/(s^2+\omega^2)$
$a(1 - e^{-t/\tau})$		$\dfrac{a}{s(\tau s+1)}$
$\dfrac{d\hat{y}}{dt}$		$s\hat{Y}(s)$
$\dfrac{d^n\hat{y}}{dt^n}$		$s^n\hat{Y}(s)$

3–6. THE WELL-STIRRED VESSEL REVISITED

Much of what has been developed in the earlier chapters can be summarized and connected with the ideas of this chapter by recalling the preliminaries that led to equation (1–20) as a representation of concentration changes in the well-stirred vessel. This result was general in that the input was left unspecified. In Section 1–8 the step input was studied in detail. We may now consider three specific inputs other than the step. For the impulse:

$$Y(s) = \frac{a}{\tau s + 1}$$

For the ramp:

$$Y(s) = \frac{a}{s^2(\tau s + 1)} \tag{3–12}$$

For the sinusoid:

$$Y(s) = \frac{a\omega}{(s^2+\omega^2)(\tau s + 1)} \tag{3–13}$$

In order to return to the time domain, it is of course necessary to invert the transform. However, as may be seen from the examples above, even a number of fairly simple transforms cannot be inverted by inspection (some can—the impulse, for example). If we are to avoid a transform table of extraordinary length, it will be necessary to find a systematic procedure for handling polynomial functions of this sort. This is the subject matter of the next chapter. We will find that our analysis leads also to some unexpected benefits regarding criteria on system behavior.

EXERCISES

3–1. A process vessel of 10 ft^2 cross-section (see Fig. 2–5) is disturbed by a change in feed rate. Sketch response curves to show $y(t)$ and $\hat{y}(t)$ for:

(a) An input step from zero to 20 ft^3/min; from 10 to 20 ft^3/min.
(b) An input impulse of 10 ft^3.
(c) An input cosine wave: $\hat{x} = 5 + 5 \cos 2t$.

In all cases, assume that $u(t) = x(0^-)$ and that $y = 5$ ft at $t = t_0$, the time of flowrate change. Are you able to extend the curves to $t < t_0$?

3–2. The Euler equation relates complex algebra to the sinusoids by

$$e^{jx} = \cos x + j \sin x$$

where $j = \sqrt{-1}$. Use this relation to show that

$$\sin \omega t = \frac{1}{2j} e^{+j\omega t} - \frac{1}{2j} e^{-j\omega t}$$

$$\cos \omega t = \frac{1}{2} e^{+j\omega t} + \frac{1}{2} e^{-j\omega t}$$

and from these expressions find the Laplace transforms of cos ωt and sin ωt.

3–3. Use equation (3–10) and the result of Problem 1–3 to find $\hat{y}(t)$, given that

$$Y(s) = \frac{3s + 2}{s^2 + 4s + 5}$$

Generalize this result to find

$$\mathcal{L}^{-1}\left[\frac{K_1\omega + K_2(s + \mu)}{(s + \mu)^2 + \omega^2}\right]$$

3–4. Graph the function

$$\hat{y}(t) = 2\sin\left(\omega t - \frac{\pi}{3}\right)$$

Show that it can be written in the form:

$$\hat{y}(t) = K_1 \sin\omega t + K_2 \cos\omega t$$

by evaluating K_1 and K_2. Graph this last equation from its parts. Are the results equivalent?

3–5. Find the Fourier Series that represents the repeated step function of Fig. 3–6. Graph the sum of the first three terms in this series.

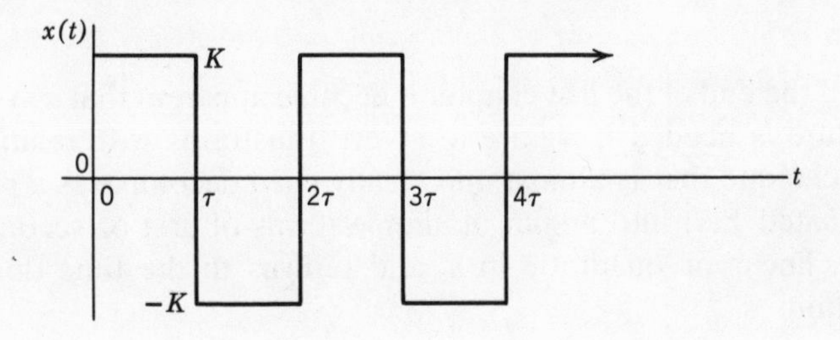

Fig. 3–6. A repeated step function.

4 *Inverse Transformation*

Toward the end of the last chapter it became apparent that a systematic procedure is needed if we are to invert transforms with relative ease. The technique that is almost universally used decomposes a relatively complicated $Y(s)$ into a sum of simple terms of first or second order, that is, linear or quadratic in s, and returns to the time domain by inspection.

4-1. PARTIAL FRACTION EXPANSION

As an illustration of the standard inversion procedure, let us see how we could solve for the time response, $\hat{y}(t)$, given the s-domain expression

$$Y(s) = \frac{a}{(\tau_1 s + 1)(\tau_2 s + 1) \cdots (\tau_\nu s + 1)}$$

$$= \frac{\alpha}{(s + \lambda_1)(s + \lambda_2) \cdots (s + \lambda_\nu)} \tag{4-1}$$

where each λ is the reciprocal of the corresponding time constant, and $\alpha = a/\tau_1\tau_2 \cdots \tau_\nu = a\lambda_1\lambda_2 \cdots \lambda_\nu$. Such a factored form arises, for example, when an impulse $a\delta(t)$ acts on a cascade consisting of simple first-order components. However, with some algebraic work, equation (4–1) is also applicable if the basic starting point is a higher order differential equation such as

$$\frac{d^\nu \hat{y}}{dt^\nu} + a_{\nu-1}\frac{d^{\nu-1}\hat{y}}{dt^{\nu-1}} + \cdots + a_0\hat{y} = \hat{x}(t) \tag{4-2}$$

In this case, a polynomial transfer function will result from the Laplace transformation:

$$Y(s) = \frac{1}{s^{\nu} + a_{\nu-1}s^{\nu-1} + \cdots + a_0} X(s) \tag{4–3}$$

but because any νth-order polynomial can be factored into ν first order binomials, it is always possible to reduce equation (4–3) to the form of (4–1). The algebraic importance of the λ's lies in the fact that $s = -\lambda_1, -\lambda_2, \cdots, -\lambda_\nu$ are the roots of the equation:

$$s^{\nu} + a_{\nu-1}s^{\nu-1} + \cdots + a_0 = (s + \lambda_1)(s + \lambda_2) \cdots (s + \lambda_\nu) = 0$$

In the procedure called **partial fraction expansion,** $Y(s)$ is expanded as a sum of simple terms, each of which contains one of the denominator factors of equation (4–1):

$$Y(s) = \frac{K_1}{s + \lambda_1} + \frac{K_2}{s + \lambda_2} + \cdots + \frac{K_\nu}{s + \lambda_\nu} \tag{4–4}$$

The various K's are constants which must be found to complete this expansion. They are most easily evaluated by applying the following argument: The equality must hold for all s; let us then make comparisons of the two sides of the equation at those s values that are most convenient. Since the various terms are all alike in form, we need only complete the first computation as a model. To find K_1: (1) Multiply both sides of the equation by $(s + \lambda_1)$

$$\frac{\alpha}{(s + \lambda_2) \cdots (s + \lambda_\nu)} = K_1 + \frac{K_2(s + \lambda_1)}{(s + \lambda_2)} + \cdots + \frac{K_\nu(s + \lambda_1)}{(s + \lambda_\nu)}$$

(2) Evaluate both sides at $(s + \lambda_1) = 0$; that is at $s = -\lambda_1$

$$\frac{\alpha}{(-\lambda_1 + \lambda_2) \cdots (-\lambda_1 + \lambda_\nu)} = K_1$$

Thus we have the first constant, and in like manner each of the others should follow. The time-domain response can now be found by inspection:

$$\hat{y}(t) = \mathscr{L}^{-1}[Y(s)] = \mathscr{L}^{-1}\left[\frac{K_1}{s + \lambda_1}\right] + \mathscr{L}^{-1}\left[\frac{K_2}{s + \lambda_2}\right] + \cdots + \mathscr{L}^{-1}\left[\frac{K_\nu}{s + \lambda_\nu}\right]$$

$$= K_1 e^{-\lambda_1 t} + K_2 e^{-\lambda_2 t} + \cdots + K_\nu e^{-\lambda_\nu t} \tag{4–5}$$

Although this procedure is generally applicable to any $Y(s)$ with a polynomial denominator, we need to pay special attention to those cases in which repeated roots or complex roots are found. Because of their very common occurrence, a discussion of possible zero roots is also included in the following, although it may be noted that this is only a special case of the more general development for distinct roots.

ZERO ROOTS

The three-vessel cascade problem set up in Section 2–1 is only slightly different from the general formulation just discussed. For a step-forcing function this third-order system may be written as

$$Y(s) = \frac{a}{(\tau_1 s + 1)(\tau_2 s + 1)(\tau_3 s + 1)s} = \frac{a\lambda_1\lambda_2\lambda_3}{(s + \lambda_1)(s + \lambda_2)(s + \lambda_3)s}$$

from which it is apparent that one of the roots is zero. Otherwise this equation is entirely similar in form to equation (4–1). It may be expanded as

$$Y(s) = \frac{K_1}{s + \lambda_1} + \frac{K_2}{s + \lambda_2} + \frac{K_3}{s + \lambda_3} + \frac{K_4}{s}$$

giving

$$\hat{y}(t) = K_1 e^{-\lambda_1 t} + K_2 e^{-\lambda_2 t} + K_3 e^{-\lambda_3 t} + K_4 \qquad (4\text{–}6)$$

Since K_1, K_2, and K_3 can be evaluated from the non-zero roots no further comment is needed. The term containing K_4 is a bit different in form but will yield to the same procedure as follows: (1) Multiply both sides of the equation by s. [This may be thought of as multiplication by $(s + \lambda_4)$ where $\lambda_4 = 0$.]

$$\frac{a\lambda_1\lambda_2\lambda_3}{(s + \lambda_1)(s + \lambda_2)(s + \lambda_3)} = \frac{K_1 s}{s + \lambda_1} + \frac{K_2 s}{s + \lambda_2} + \frac{K_3 s}{s + \lambda_3} + K_4$$

(2) Evaluate both sides at $s = 0$:

$$\frac{a\lambda_1\lambda_2\lambda_3}{\lambda_1\lambda_2\lambda_3} = K_4 = a$$

Repeated Roots

An example of a denominator with a repeated root is illustrated in equation (3–12), developed for the ramp response of a well-stirred vessel

$$Y(s) = \frac{a}{s^2(\tau s + 1)} = \frac{a\lambda}{s^2(s+\lambda)} \tag{4–7}$$

If we proceeded according to the prior scheme, unmodified, we would consider two of the expansion factors to have identical denominators. Since such terms can always be added together, one of the roots would be masked. To obtain the most general expansion, terms are chosen which contain the various powers of the repeated factor. From equation (4–7) for example:

$$Y(s) = \frac{K_1}{s} + \frac{K_2}{s^2} + \frac{K_3}{s+\lambda} \tag{4–8}$$

(1) Multiply both sides of the equation by s^2:

$$\frac{a\lambda}{s+\lambda} = K_1 s + K_2 + \frac{K_3 s^2}{s+\lambda}$$

(2) Evaluate both sides at $s = 0$

$$a = K_2$$

This approach will not work to find K_1. (Try it and see.) It can be adapted, however, if both sides of equation (4–8) are first differentiated with respect to s:

$$\frac{-a\lambda}{(s+\lambda)^2} = K_1 + \frac{d}{ds}\left(\frac{K_3 s^2}{s+\lambda}\right) = K_1 + s^2 \frac{d}{ds}\left(\frac{K_3}{s+\lambda}\right) + \frac{K_3}{s+\lambda}\frac{d}{ds}(s^2)$$

Evaluation at $s = 0$ now gives $K_1 = -(a/\lambda)$. The end result is

$$\begin{aligned} \hat{y}(t) &= K_1 + K_2 t + K_3 e^{-\lambda t} \\ &= -\frac{a}{\lambda} + at + \frac{a}{\lambda} e^{-\lambda t} \\ &= a\tau\left(-1 + \frac{t}{\tau} + e^{-t/\tau}\right) \end{aligned}$$

COMPLEX ROOTS

The occurrence of complex roots is found in the last example of the group in Section 3–6. For a sinusoidal-forcing function:

$$Y(s) = \frac{a\omega}{(s^2+\omega^2)(\tau s+1)} = \frac{a\omega\lambda}{(s^2+\omega^2)(s+\lambda)} \tag{4–9}$$

The quadratic term could be factored to give

$$Y(s) = \frac{a\omega\lambda}{(s-j\omega)(s-j\omega)(s+\lambda)} = \frac{K_1'}{s-j\omega} + \frac{K_2'}{s+j\omega} + \frac{K_3}{s+\lambda} \tag{4–10}$$

but, although this is a perfectly legitimate procedure, it will give complex K's and complex exponents for the $\hat{y}(t)$ time function. In Problem 4–1 we will examine the implications of this finding. For our present purposes, however, it is much easier to make use of our prior results and expand $Y(s)$ as

$$Y(s) = \frac{K_1\omega + K_2 s}{s^2+\omega^2} + \frac{K_3}{s+\lambda}$$

The form of the quadratic term is suggested by equation (3–10) which gives the result

$$\hat{y}(t) = K_1 \sin \omega t + K_2 \cos \omega t + K_3 e^{-\lambda t} \tag{4–11}$$

The constants K_1 and K_2 can be determined by the now-standard technique for distinct roots: (1) Multiply both sides of the equation by $s^2 + \omega^2$

$$\frac{a\omega\lambda}{s+\lambda} = K_1\omega + K_2 s + K_3 \frac{s^2+\omega^2}{s+\lambda}$$

(2) Evaluate both sides at $(s^2 + \omega^2) = 0$; that is, at $s = \sqrt{-\omega^2} = \pm j\omega$

$$\frac{a\omega\lambda}{j\omega+\lambda} = K_1\omega + K_2 j\omega \tag{4–12}$$

We observe that the two constants we seek would be available in this equation if the denominator of the left-hand term were rationalized. This is the technique that moves the irrational (imaginary) term from the denominator of a fraction to the numerator. A comparison of equations (4–9) and (4–10) suggests how this may be done: Multiplying a complex quantity by its conjugate results in a real quantity. Applying this to the left side of equation (4–12) gives

$$\left(\frac{a\omega\lambda}{j\omega+\lambda}\right)\left(\frac{-j\omega+\lambda}{-j\omega+\lambda}\right)=\frac{a\omega\lambda^2-a\omega^2\lambda j}{\omega^2+\lambda^2}=\frac{a\lambda^2}{\omega^2+\lambda^2}\omega-\frac{a\lambda\omega}{\omega^2+\lambda^2}j\omega$$

A term-by-term comparison with the right side of equation (4–12) shows that

$$K_1=\frac{a\lambda^2}{\omega^2+\lambda^2}$$

$$K_2=\frac{-a\lambda\omega}{\omega^2+\lambda^2}$$

An alternative statement to Equation (4–11) is

$$\hat{y}(t)=K\sin(\omega t+\phi)+K_3e^{-\lambda t}$$

When this form is preferred, the constants K and ϕ are found from K_1 and K_2 by relations (3–9).

$$K=\sqrt{K_1^2+K_2^2}=a\sqrt{\lambda^2/(\omega^2+\lambda^2)}=a\frac{1}{\sqrt{\omega^2\tau^2+1}} \tag{4–13}$$

$$\phi=\arctan\frac{K_2}{K_1}=\arctan\frac{-\omega}{\lambda}=-\arctan\omega\tau$$

4–2. CLOSED-LOOP ANALYSIS

The procedure of the last section is completely adequate for treating $Y(s)$ functions arising from forward-path cascades for any of the inputs we have considered. We need now to show how partial fraction expansion is applied to closed-loop analysis. To do this, let us examine first, equation (2–22) which provides an s-domain description of the response to a servo-loop command:

$$Y(s)=\frac{G_cG_vG}{1+G_cG_vGH}R(s)$$

From our prior discussion we may expect that the forward-path cascade is of the form

$$G_c G_v G = \frac{\alpha}{(s+\lambda_1)(s+\lambda_2)\cdots(s+\lambda_\nu)}$$

The measuring transducer might also contribute one or more factors to the result. Suppose that

$$H(s) = \frac{\beta}{(s+\lambda_T)}$$

Then by substitution and rearrangement

$$Y(s) = \frac{\alpha(s+\lambda_T)}{(s+\lambda_1)(s+\lambda_2)\cdots(s+\lambda_\nu)(s+\lambda_T)+\alpha\beta}R(s)$$

Notice that this denominator is not in factored form because of the added constant ($\alpha\beta$). It can be put in such a form though by expanding the indicated product, adding ($\alpha\beta$), and factoring the resulting polynomial. Setting the product of factors equal to zero gives:

$$\begin{aligned}&(s+\lambda_1)(s+\lambda_2)\cdots(s+\lambda_\nu)(s+\lambda_T)+\alpha\beta\\ &=(s+\mu_1)(s+\mu_2)\cdots(s+\mu_n)=0\end{aligned} \tag{4–14}$$

an equation of higher order and with different roots than the original λ's.

Another difference that shows up in this closed-loop equation is the appearance of a function of s in the numerator of $Y(s)$. This function is not necessarily of order one, as can be seen by postulating a more complex $H(s)$ than was done above or by studying in detail the closed-loop regulator described by equation (2–21):

$$Y(s) = \frac{-G}{1+G_c G_v G H}U(s)$$

In these cases, a more complicated numerator will develop, providing in general an expression such as

$$Y(s) = \frac{\alpha(s+\lambda_T)(s+\lambda_1)(s+\lambda_2)\cdots}{(s+\mu_1)(s+\mu_2)\cdots(s+\mu_n)}U(s)$$

or, in polynomial form

$$Y(s) = \alpha \frac{s^m + b_{m-1}s^{m-1} + \cdots + b_0}{s^n + a_{n-1}s^{n-1} + \cdots + a_0} U(s)$$

Regarding the procedure of partial fraction expansion, no essential modification is needed, although for this case there may be considerable numerical difficulty in finding the μ's, the roots of equation (4–14). Since this transfer function is general in form, it is convenient to use

$$F(s) = \alpha \frac{s^m + b_{m-1}s^{m-1} + \cdots + b_0}{s^n + a_{n-1}s^{n-1} + \cdots + a_0} \tag{4–15}$$

in discussing the properties of closed loops. Note, for example, that the denominator polynomial is the same whether the closed loop is a servo or regulator system. The difference between these two cases only appears in the numerator of $F(s)$; consequently, it can only affect numerically the various K's in the expansion. The all-important denominator of $F(s)$, the closed-loop transfer function, is called the **characteristic polynomial**. Correspondingly, equation (4–14) is the **characteristic equation** and the μ's are **characteristic roots**.

The form of the response will depend on the nature of the characteristic roots. As before, the factors: s, $(s+\mu)$, and $(s^2+\omega^2)$ may arise for roots that are zero, real, and imaginary respectively. One or more of these may be repeated. In addition, it is now possible for a new form to arise from the factoring procedure. If the characteristic polynomial has roots that are complex, conjugate factors will appear as

$$\left(\frac{1}{s+\mu-j\omega}\right)\left(\frac{1}{s+\mu+j\omega}\right) \tag{4–16}$$

Although it is entirely proper to work with these in the expansion procedure, much of the complex algebra can be avoided by retaining a single quadratic term in place of the two factors as was done in dealing with equation (4–9). Expanding (4–16) and regrouping the terms gives

$$\frac{1}{s^2 + 2\mu s + \mu^2 + \omega^2} = \frac{1}{(s+\mu)^2 + \omega^2} \tag{4–17}$$

This suggests a partial fraction expansion term:

$$\frac{K_1\omega + K_2(s+\mu)}{(s+\mu)^2 + \omega^2}$$

which can be inverted by inspection from the result of problem 3–3.

$$\mathscr{L}^{-1}\left[\frac{K_1\omega+K_2(s+\mu)}{(s+\mu)^2+\omega^2}\right]=e^{-\mu t}(K_1\sin\omega t+K_2\cos\omega t)$$
$$=Ke^{-\mu t}\sin(\omega t+\phi)$$

where K and ϕ are as defined by equation (3–9). A quadratic factor of the characteristic polynomial may not immediately appear in the form of equation (4–17), but this is never a limitation, since by completing the square any quadratic factor may be put in this form. Complex roots could also occur from the forward-path analysis, if one of the blocks represented an oscillatory, second-order device. This, however, is a relatively rare occurrence in chemical engineering apparatus. Typically, those second-order systems that do occur in the forward path give quadratics that are factorable into two real first-order terms.

4–3. STABILITY

There is another result of utmost importance that commonly arises in closed-loop analysis. Consider the implication of finding, during a numerical study of a system, that one of the factors is of the form $1/(s-\mu)$ or $1/[(s-\mu)^2+\omega^2]$. In the time domain, these factors would produce terms of the form $Ke^{+\mu t}$ and $Ke^{+\mu t}\sin(\omega t+\phi)$ respectively. Because of the positive exponents, these terms continue to grow with time, and the solution would show:

$$\hat{y}(t)\to\infty,\qquad t\to\infty$$

In this circumstance the response is said to be *unstable*. Physically this means that the response signal would continue to grow in magnitude until it reached a value where the original equations were no longer valid.

A response is **stable** if it remains bounded (finite) for all bounded inputs. But since bounded inputs (e.g., step, sinusoid) never contribute factors having positive roots, unstable responses can only arise from the roots of the characteristic equation. This argument shows that the property of stability or instability is really a characteristic of the system, not the particular bounded input chosen. As a result, we often refer to stable *systems* instead of stable *responses*. The two are essentially interchangeable for linear systems, although, of course, even a stable system can produce an unstable response if it is forced by an unbounded input (say, a ramp).

Since the stability of linear systems can be divorced from specific inputs, it is most convenient to study system stability by examining the closed-loop transfer function. While it is also possible to speak of stability with regard to forward-path cascades, the discussion is trivial in virtually all practical cases of importance in chemical engineering since the individual G's are almost always stable. It is when closed loops are considered that stability becomes a meaningful concern, for it is commonly the case that a closed loop is unstable, even though it is composed entirely of stable components. The focus is then on the closed-loop transfer function $F(s)$, or, more specifically, on its denominator. Other names for the characteristic roots come from complex variable theory. They are the *zeros* of the characteristic polynomial or the *poles* of $F(s)$, i.e., the values of s at which $F(s) \to \infty$. It is worth noting again that the characteristic equation of a system is the same, regardless of whether $F(s)$ is derived for a servo loop or a regulator: a system stable for a reference input change is stable for any other loop disturbance, and vice versa.

4-4. THE CHARACTERISTIC ROOTS

By now it should be evident why the term "characteristic" is used to describe the transfer-function denominator and its roots. The emphasis has been on stability, that is, on the signs of the roots, but equally important is the fact that the same characteristic determines the nature of these roots – whether they are real or complex. This last factor fixes the form of the response. The various possibilities are presented in summary form in Table 4-1 together with notes on stability. From the table or from the prior discussion it may be concluded that a sufficient and necessary condition for stability is that the real parts of all characteristic roots be negative. If at least one root has a positive real part, the system is unstable. A zero root will not cause instability unless it is repeated. Complex roots always contribute oscillatory behavior which dies out more or less rapidly, according to the relative magnitudes of μ and ω. By analogy to the behavior of common mechanical devices, this effect is called damping, and one speaks of **underdamped** (oscillatory) and **overdamped** (nonoscillatory) responses. These ideas can be made quantitative by defining the parameters

$$\omega_n = \sqrt{\omega^2 + \mu^2}$$
$$\zeta = \mu / \omega_n \tag{4-18}$$

where ζ is called the **damping factor** or **damping coefficient,** and ω_n is

TABLE 4–1
The Properties of Various Characteristic Roots

	Factor of Characteristic Polynomial	Characteristic Root(s)	Algebraic Contribution to Response Equation	Stability	Root location in *s*-plane	Form of Contribution to Response Curve
Distinct Roots	$(s+\mu)$	$s=-\mu$	$Ke^{-\mu t}$	Stable if $\mu \geqslant 0$	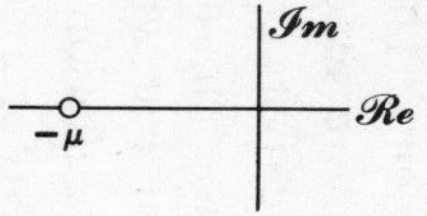	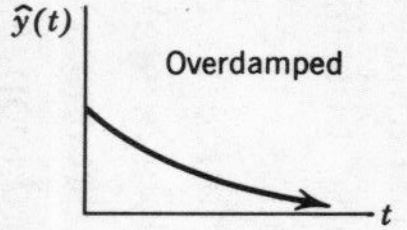 Overdamped
				Unstable if $\mu < 0$	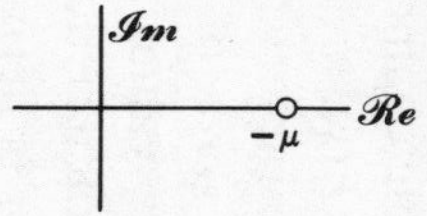	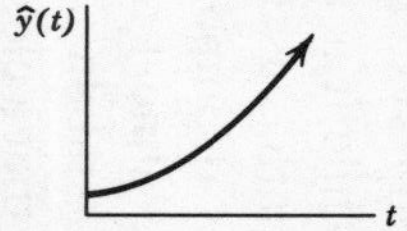
	$(s^2+\omega^2)$	$s=\pm j\omega$	$K \sin \omega t$	Marginally stable	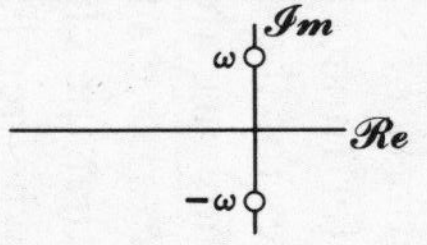	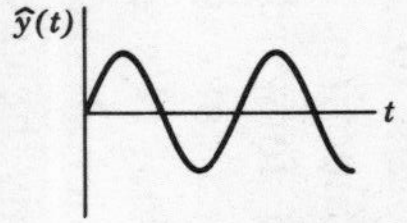
	$(s+\mu)^2+\omega^2$	$s=-\mu \pm j\omega$	$Ke^{-\mu t} \sin(\omega t+\phi)$	Stable if $\mu > 0$	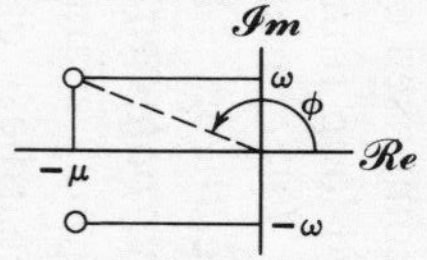	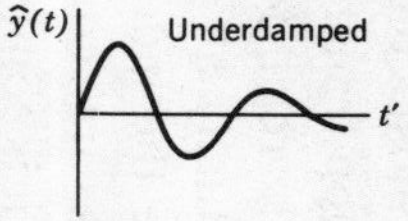 Underdamped
				Unstable if $\mu < 0$	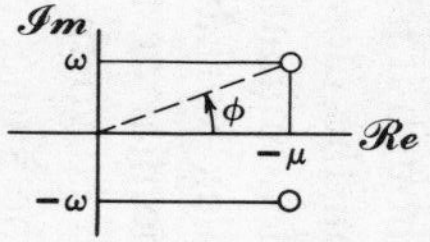	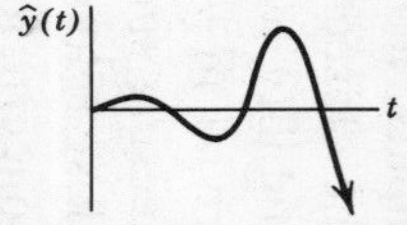

TABLE 4–1 (Continued)
The Properties of Various Characteristic Roots

	Factor of Characteristic Polynomial	Characteristic Root(s)	Algebraic Contribution to Response Equation	Stability	Root location in s-plane	Form of Contribution to Response Curve
Distinct Root	s	$s = 0$	K	Always stable	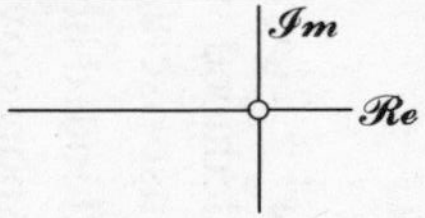 $\mathscr{I}m$, $\mathscr{R}e$	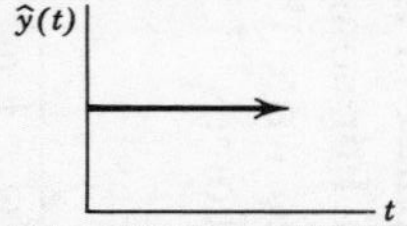 $\hat{y}(t)$, t
Repeated Roots	s^2	$s = 0, 0$	$K_0 + K_1 t$	Never stable	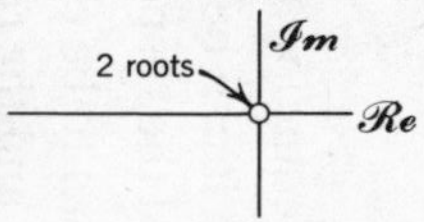 2 roots; $\mathscr{I}m$, $\mathscr{R}e$	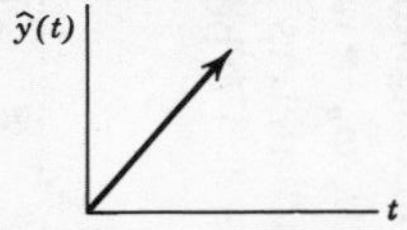 $\hat{y}(t)$, t
	$(s+\mu)^2$	$s = -\mu, -\mu$	$e^{-\mu t}(K_0 + K_1 t)$	Stable if $\mu > 0$	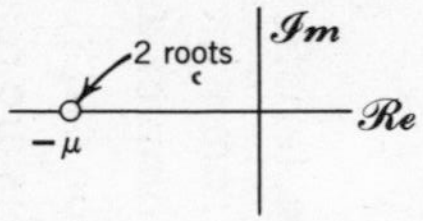 2 roots; $-\mu$; $\mathscr{I}m$, $\mathscr{R}e$	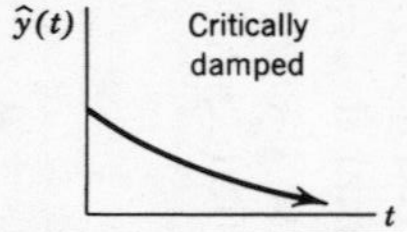 $\hat{y}(t)$, t; Critically damped
	$(s+\mu)^n$	$s = -\mu, -\mu, \ldots$ (n roots)	$e^{-\mu t}(K_0 + K_1 t + \cdots + K_{n-1} t^{n-1})$	Stable if $\mu > 0$	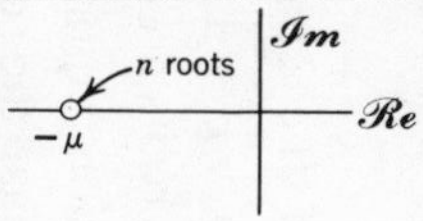 n roots; $-\mu$; $\mathscr{I}m$, $\mathscr{R}e$	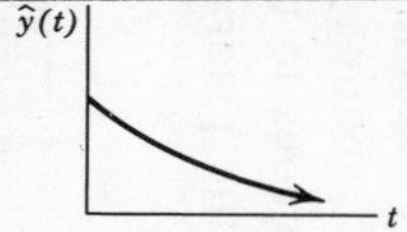 $\hat{y}(t)$, t

the undamped natural frequency. The significance of this name can be appreciated by noting that if $\mu \to 0$, $\omega_n \to \omega$. For some computations it is advantageous to use these parameters to write the second-order factor. Then the quadratic (equation 4–17) becomes

$$\frac{1}{(s+\mu)^2+\omega^2}=\frac{1}{s^2+2\mu s+\mu^2+\omega^2}=\frac{1}{s^2+2\zeta\omega_n s+\omega_n{}^2} \qquad (4\text{–}19)$$

The roots of the characteristic equation: $s^2+2\zeta\omega_n s+\omega_n{}^2=0$ are $s=-\zeta\omega_n \pm \omega_n\sqrt{\zeta^2-1}$, from which it can be deduced without difficulty that, if $\zeta < 1$, roots are complex and the response oscillatory.

The definition (equation 4–18) has to be extended however, if $\zeta > 1$, since in this case the roots are real and the response overdamped. This is most readily done by the observation that a quadratic characteristic equation with real roots can always be written as

$$\left(s+\frac{1}{\tau_1}\right)\left(s+\frac{1}{\tau_2}\right)=s^2+\left(\frac{1}{\tau_1}+\frac{1}{\tau_2}\right)s+\frac{1}{\tau_1\tau_2}=0$$

Comparison with equation (4–19) shows that: $\zeta=(\tau_1+\tau_2)/2\sqrt{\tau_1\tau_2}$ and $\omega_n=1/\sqrt{\tau_1\tau_2}$. The case of $\zeta=1$ is more a mathematical statement than a physical reality, since it corresponds to the extremely unlikely occurrence of two real, identical roots. Such a system is said to have **critical** damping.

Purely imaginary roots contribute undamped oscillatory behavior. Since a periodic response is bounded (with respect to amplitude, not time), it is considered to be within the category of stable behavior. To indicate that it is essentially different from a damped response, such a system is sometimes called **marginally stable**, or, if the decaying form of the damped response is to be emphasized, this latter response is called **asymptotically stable**. These distinctions become especially important in analyzing nonlinear systems.

4–5. DESIGN CONSIDERATIONS

After a system designer has assured himself that his system is stable, he must face a somewhat subtler problem. To the extent that the system parameters are under his control, he will be able to fix the characteristic roots, and by so doing will determine the form of transient responses. In a specific situation, which of the curves of Table 4–1 is a desirable form? Are oscillations good or bad? The answer depends on whether or not a certain degree of overshoot is especially damaging to a system, technically or economically speaking. It is not difficult to find examples of both cases.

Suppose, for example, that the control system is to regulate the temperature of a catalytic chemical reactor. Perhaps the activity and life of the relatively expensive catalyst are extremely sensitive to overheat. Then any temperatures above the set point are to be avoided if at all possible, and oscillatory behavior is not acceptable. An overdamped response is called for. Under other conditions, where prolonged negative deviations are just as damaging as overshoot, the long tail of the overdamped curve is to be avoided, and a slightly underdamped (oscillatory) curve will be wanted. The choice between these alternatives is a matter of judgment on the part of the engineer.

This discussion may be related to the *s*-plane root locations shown in Table 4–1. As $\omega \rightarrow 0$, the response tends toward the overdamped behavior. If ω is relatively dominant and $|\mu|$ small, the behavior becomes increasingly oscillatory and, in the limit, entirely undamped for $\mu = 0$. The degree of oscillatory response can also be expressed quantitatively by the angle ϕ, as shown on Table 4–1. This angle measures the root position between the extremes of overdamped and entirely undamped behavior, and allows a geometric interpretation of the damping factor:

$$\zeta = \frac{\mu}{\omega_n} = \frac{\mu}{\sqrt{\omega^2 + \mu^2}} = -\cos\phi$$

It should be noted that this use of ϕ is entirely consistent with that of equation (4–13), since

$$\text{arc tan}\frac{-\omega}{\mu} = \text{arc cos}\frac{-\mu}{\sqrt{\omega^2 + \mu^2}}$$

4–6. A NUMERICAL EXAMPLE

To illustrate the analysis of a system by a study of its characteristic roots, consider a feedback servo loop which is to control *y(t)*, the concentration of a critical trace component at the exit of a tubular mixing section (see Fig. 4–1*a*). Kramers and Alberda[1] have shown experimentally that under laminar flow conditions the response of this device can be approximated quite well by a three-vessel cascade model such as led to the transfer function in equation (2–4), but with $\tau_1 = \tau_2 = \tau_3 = \tau$:

[1]Kramers, H., and G. Alberda, *Chem. Eng. Sci.*, **2**, 173 (1953), see p. 178.

$$\frac{Y(s)}{Z(s)} = G(s) = \frac{1}{(\tau s + 1)^3}$$

where $z(t)$ is the concentration at the inlet to this section, most conveniently adjusted by manipulating the flowrate of the trace component

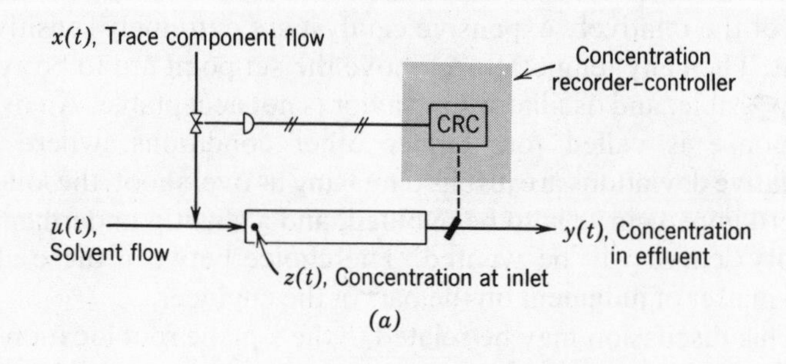

(a)

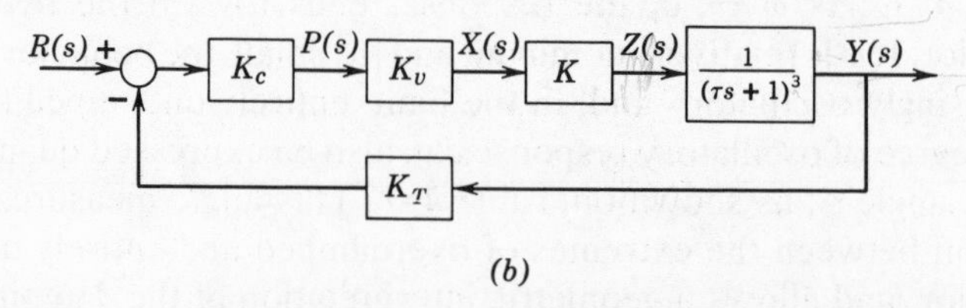

(b)

Fig. 4–1. Pictorial and block diagram of a concentration-servo loop. (a) Pictorial flow sheet. (b) Block diagram.

that enters the main solvent stream. Assume for the sake of simplicity that the manipulating flowrate x is related to the concentration z by the constant transfer function

$$\frac{Z(s)}{X(s)} = K \text{ (moles/ft}^3\text{)/(ft}^3\text{/min)} \tag{4–20}$$

The loop is closed by using the following components:

(1) A fast-acting measuring transducer which probes the needed concentration and reports it as a proportional electrical feedback signal: $H(s) = K_T$ mv/(moles/ft³).

(2) A proportional electric-to-pneumatic controller with an adjustable proportional gain setting: $G_c(s) = K_c$ psi/mv.

(3) A fast-acting linear valve which is used to manipulate the trace component flowrate: $G_v(s) = K_v$ (ft³/min)/psi. The entire system is shown in Fig. 4–1*b* in block-diagram form.

According to equation (2–22), we can predict the dependence of $Y(s)$ on $R(s)$ by

$$Y(s) = \frac{K_c K_v K/(\tau s + 1)^3}{1 + K_c K_v K K_T/(\tau s + 1)^3} R(s)$$

$$= \frac{K_c K_v K}{(\tau s + 1)^3 + K_c K_v K K_T} R(s)$$

Let us choose likely values for the several constants, leaving the controller gain for detailed study. Let $K_v = 0.1$ (ft³/min)/psi, $K = 0.01$ (mole/ft³)/(ft³/min), $K_T = 1000$ mv/(mole/ft³), $\tau = 0.5$ hr. Then:

$$Y(s) = \frac{0.008\, K_c}{(s + 2)^3 + 8K_c} R(s)$$

which has characteristic equation

$$(s + 2)^3 + 8K_c = 0 \tag{4–21}$$

This equation has great similarity to the left side of equation (4–14), however, it contains the adjustable controller gain K_c rather than fixed system constants. Expanding:

$$Y(s) = \frac{0.008K_c}{s^3 + 6s^2 + 12s + 8 + 8K_c} R(s) \tag{4–22}$$

To factor the characteristic polynomial as indicated by equation (4–14), it is necessary to specify K_c numerically. If $K_c = 1$ psi/mv, the characteristic equation becomes

$$s^3 + 6s^2 + 12s + 16 = (s + 4)(s^2 + 2s + 4) = 0$$

with roots $s = -4, -1 \pm \sqrt{3}j$. Note that a quadratic factor was used to handle the complex roots.

At this point it is convenient to find the system response to a specific input. To get rapid concentration buildup, it is proposed to turn up the set point on the controller in a step of size $\hat{r} = r_o$. Then $R(s) = r_o/s$, and

$$Y(s) = \frac{0.008}{(s^2 + 2s + 4)(s + 4)} \frac{r_o}{s}$$

By partial fraction expansion and inverse transformation

$$Y(s) = \frac{K_1\omega + K_2\,(s+1)}{(s+1)^2+3} + \frac{K_3}{s+4} + \frac{K_4}{s}$$

$$\hat{y}(t) = Ke^{-t}\sin(\omega t + \phi) + K_3e^{-4t} + K_4 \qquad (4\text{–}23)$$

The constants in this solution can be evaluated in the customary manner (this is one of the problems at the end of this chapter), but if our interest is only in the matter of stability, this computation is clearly unnecessary, since the system stability is assured by the negative exponentials in equation (4–23) and does not depend on the constant coefficients. In fact, the partial fraction expansion and inverse transformation are both unnecessary, since we knew the characteristic roots to have negative real parts.

To continue the stability analysis, consider the solution for $K_c = 8$. The characteristic equation is now

$$s^3 + 6s^2 + 12s + 72 = (s+6)(s^2+12) = 0$$

which has roots $s = -6$, $\pm 2\sqrt{3}j$. With purely imaginary roots the system is marginally stable. Finally, if $K_c = 27$, the analysis yields

$$s^3 + 6s^2 + 12s + 224 = (s+8)(s^2 - 2s + 28) = 0$$

For this case the three roots are $s = -8$, $1 \pm 3\sqrt{3}j$ and since the complex roots have positive real parts, the system is unstable.

4–7 THE ROOT LOCUS

The results of a study such as the one carried out in the last section can be summarized very advantageously on a graph. The point of interest is to locate the characteristic roots as a function of the parameter, K_c. Our results to this point are shown by the circles in Fig. 4–2. The solid line in the same figure shows the **root locus** that is generated by allowing K_c to assume values from 0 to ∞. The branches of the root locus can be graduated as shown according to the values of K_c. It should be noted that all three roots remain in the left half plane for $0 \leqslant K_c < 8$, and the system is stable. If $K_c > 8$, the two complex roots have positive real parts and the system is unstable. The marginal value of $K_c = 8$ produces undamped oscillations. In the limit of $K_c = 0$, the closed loop reverts back to the forward-path cascade, since the feedback action is interrupted at the controller (see Fig. 4–1). Accordingly, the μ roots are identical to the λ's of the three-vessel model at this K_c. For this reason, the branches of the root locus start from a common point in this example. This is not generally the case, and is caused here by the coincidence of a triple root.

There are a number of available short-cuts[2,3] which make it possible to sketch the root locus without the necessity of repeatedly solving the characteristic equation. These will not be developed here, but it is worth noting how a designer might make use of a root-locus plot. Suppose first that both positive and negative errors are permissible and that a slightly oscillatory step response is desirable. From Fig. 4–2 at $K_c = 1$

$$\zeta = -\cos\phi = 0.5$$

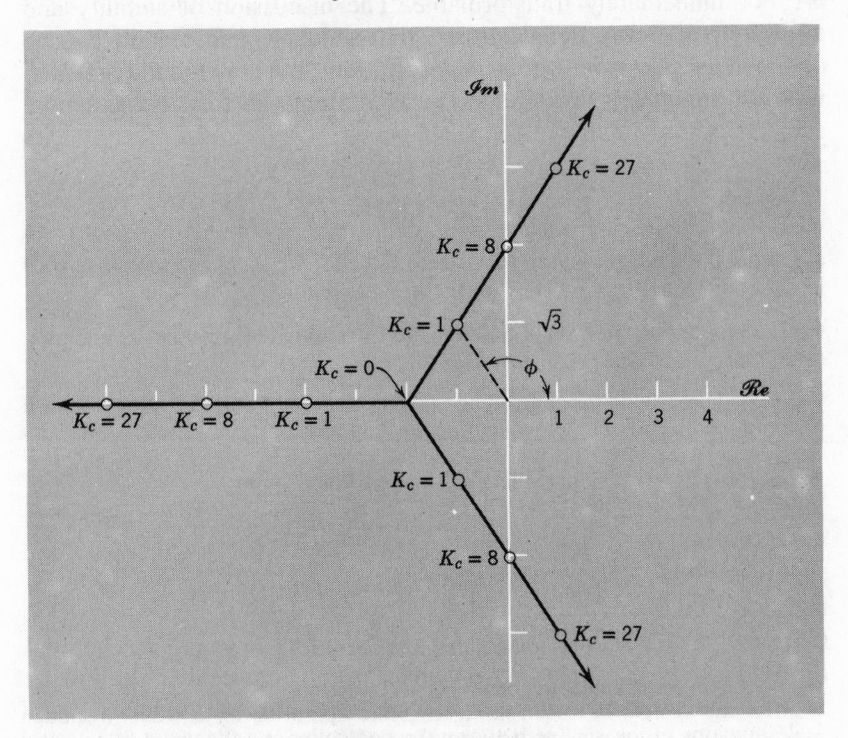

Fig. 4–2. The root locus for equation (4–21).

---

[2]Raven, F. H., *Automatic Control Engineering,* McGraw-Hill, New York, 1961, p. 114.

[3]Gille, J. C., M. J. Pellegrin, and P. Decaulne, *Feedback Control Systems,* McGraw-Hill, New York, 1959, p. 239.

an acceptable result. Suppose, on the other hand, that an overdamped response is essential. Then, since there is no $K_c > 0$ for which all roots lie on the real axis, the basic design must be altered, probably by introducing a more sophisticated controller.

REMARKS

This chapter and the two preceding ones contained techniques sufficient to solve a very wide class of linear problems. Several major items could not be fully explored, however, without seriously digressing from the primary points of emphasis. Although it was noted that only linear equations with constant coefficients can be transformed, no approach was even suggested for dealing with systems whose equations are not immediately transformable. The discussion of stability and characteristic roots demonstrated that valuable information can be obtained directly from s-domain descriptions, but here too the potential was not adequately exploited. These matters will form the essential subjects of study in the following chapters.

EXERCISES

4–1. Find the K's of equation (4–10) and solve for $\hat{y}(t)$. Can you reconcile your answer with equation (4–11) by using the Euler relation?

4–2. Complete the analysis of Section 4–6 by finding the constants of equation (4–23). For numerical results use $r_0 = 600$ mv.

4–3. A regulator loop for controlling the temperature of a water bath v, consists of components with the following transfer functions:

$$G_c \text{ (controller)} = 50 \text{ psi/mv}$$

$$G_v \text{ (valve)} = \frac{1}{10s + 1} \text{ (ft}^3\text{/min)/psi}$$

$$G \text{ (water bath)} = \frac{1}{25s + 1} \text{ °F/(ft}^3\text{/min)}$$

$$H \text{ (thermocouple)} = 0.02 \text{ mv/°F}$$

where the time constants are in units of seconds.

After the system has been in steady-state operation for a while, a sudden leak develops in the air line between the controller and the valve. It acts as a step disturbance of size $\hat{u}(t) = 0.5$ psi.

(a) Draw a block diagram showing this disturbance as $U(s)$. Write the equation relating $V(s)$ to the disturbance variable $U(s)$, in terms of the various transfer functions, and solve for $\hat{v}(t)$. Sketch a graph showing how $\hat{v}(t)$ varies in response to the disturbance. In particular show whether oscillations result, and whether the temperature returns to its original steady state. Identify any asymptote value numerically.

(b) Sketch the root locus for this closed-loop system considering K_c for the controller as a variable. For what K_c, if any, does the system become unstable? For what K_c oscillatory?

4–4. Find the inverse transform of

$$Y(s) = \frac{1}{2s^2(s^2+9)}$$

Hint: Try the substitution $s^2 = \sigma$

4–5. Find the inverse transform of

$$Y(s) = \frac{s^2+5}{(s+1)(s^3+2s^2+5s)}$$

4–6. Two well-mixed tanks of 20 ft³ and 5 ft³ respectively are connected in series. They are initially filled with pure water and then operate with a steady flow: 10 ft³/min is pumped into the first tank, between the tanks, and out of the second tank. The concentration of the feed solution x is varied and you are asked to study the responses of the intermediate concentration z and the final exit concentration y. Does it matter whether the larger or smaller tank is first? How would your answers change, if both tanks had equal volume (12.5 ft³ each)?

4–7. When a thermometer at 92°F is placed in a bath at 212°F, the initial temperature rise is noted to be 4°F/sec. What is the time constant of the thermometer assuming it is a first-order device? What will the thermometer read after one minute? If the initial rate of 4°F/sec were maintained, how long would it take for the thermometer to read 212°F? If the thermometer remains in its original position, but the bath temperature is increased from 92°F at a uniform rate of 4°F/sec, what is the true bath temperature after one minute? What is the thermometer reading after one minute? What is the **dynamic error** after one minute (the difference between the reading and the true bath temperature)?

4–8. A regulator loop is to control the level in a system such as that shown in Fig. 2–5. The vessel cross-sectional area is 4 ft² and an available level-sensitive transducer can be characterized by the transfer function $H=2$ psi/ft. In steady-state operation, the inflow to the vessel through the control valve just balances the effluent flow of 10 ft³/min, to maintain a level of 10 ft. Find the level response of the closed loop to an effluent flow impulse: $u = 4\delta(t)$ ft³ if the loop is closed through a pneumatic-electric controller with transfer function $G_c = 16$ volts/psi and an electric motor-driven valve with transfer function

$$G_v = \frac{0.5}{s}\ \text{(ft}^3\text{/min)/volt}$$

Sketch your result as level versus time.

4-9. (a) Re-examine the previous problem if the loop is closed by an all-pneumatic controller, $G_c = K_c$ psi/psi, and a pneumatic diaphragm valve with transfer function

$$G_v = \frac{1}{0.25s + 1} \text{ (ft}^3\text{/min)/psi}$$

Solve and sketch results for $K_c = 1.5, 2, 10$. How does the controller output pressure vary with time? How would the level vary if the same disturbance were introduced to the uncontrolled system?

(b) How would your answers change (all pneumatic control) for an effluent flow step disturbance from 10 ft^3/min to 14 ft^3/min.

(c) Sketch the root locus for this closed-loop system considering K_c for the controller as a variable. For what K_c, if any, does the system become unstable? For what K_c, oscillatory?

5 *Linearization and Regulator Control*

The block-diagram algebra so convenient for cascades and feedback loops, the characteristic roots used to study stability, and the various other techniques that are based on Laplace transformation and s-domain analysis are all limited in their applicability to constant coefficient, linear systems. Because of this, the distinction between linear and nonlinear systems is more than merely one of convenience. The plain fact is that while we have powerful methods with which to solve linear problems and will find further strength in the chapters to come, there is no comparable general treatment available for nonlinearities.

At this point it is worthwhile comparing our methods of analysis with the realities of the chemical engineer's world. Consider the following observations: (1) Mass and heat transfer correlations based on dimensionless groups always present nonlinear relations, since without exception fractional exponents are found. (2) Pressure drop computations at high Reynolds numbers depend on the square of flowrate. (3) Chemical kinetic equations of the simplest kind usually involve nonlinear forms such as equation (1–10); furthermore, even if the kinetics are first order ($n = 1$), a most significant nonlinearity shows up in the Arrhenius dependence of k on temperature:

$$r = k_0 e^{-Q/v} y^n \tag{5–1}$$

(4) common control valves show parabolic, semilogarithmic, and other nonlinear characteristics; often these nonlinearities are desirable, and are intentionally included in the design of such hardware.

In this chapter we will be concerned with a method of approximation called **linearization.** We will show how apparently insurmountable nonlinear mountains can be reduced to linear molehills. In essence, since we do not have tools for handling the real problem, we recast it in a form for which we do have tools. When this has been done we will ask ourselves about the nature of this approximation and explore the conditions of operation under which it would be expected to be most satisfactory.

5-1. APPROXIMATION AT A POINT

Obviously, a nonlinear curve cannot be approximated by a straight line over its entire range. In Fig. 5-1, for example, a characteristic

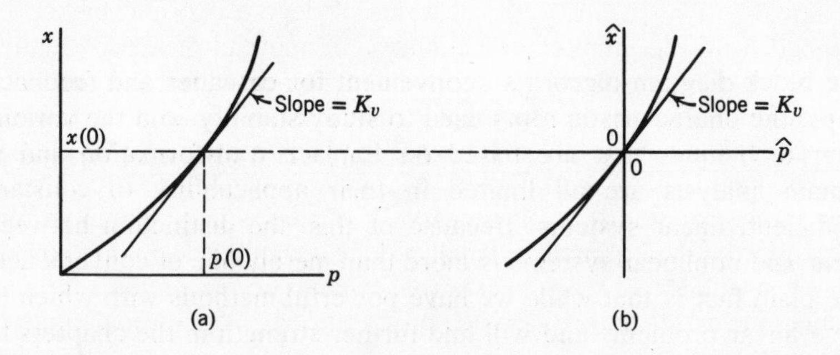

Fig. 5-1. Linearization of a valve characteristic. (a) Original variables. (b) Deviation variables.

curve is shown for a valve, the nonlinear counterpart of Fig. 2-8. The straight line clearly approximates the curve very well when the variables are close to their initial values, $x(0)$ and $p(0)$. Since the line is tangent to the curve at this point, the slope of the line K_v must be exactly $\left(\frac{dx}{dp}\right)_0$, the zero subscript indicating time zero. In the neighborhood of this point

$$\hat{x} = \left(\frac{dx}{dp}\right)_0 \hat{p} = K_v\hat{p} \tag{5-2}$$

and with the proper interpretation of K_v we have salvaged equation (2-15). We now need to ask how good is good; that is, quantitatively, what error is involved in this linearization? Using the fact that x is a continuous function of p (with continuous derivatives), we can write an equation for $\hat{x}$ by using a Maclaurin expansion about the initial condition:

$$\hat{x} = \hat{x}(0) + \left(\frac{dx}{dp}\right)_0 \hat{p} + \tfrac{1}{2}\left(\frac{d^2x}{dp^2}\right)_0 \hat{p}^2 + \cdots$$

But since $\hat{x}(0) = 0$:

$$\hat{x} = \left(\frac{dx}{dp}\right)_0 \hat{p} + \tfrac{1}{2}\left(\frac{d^2x}{dp^2}\right)_0 \hat{p}^2 + \cdots$$

Comparing this equation with equation (5–2) shows the true nature of the linearization: to linearize, all terms of degree two and higher are dropped from the infinite series. The same method of approximation can be applied to functions of more than one variable. The total derivative coefficients are then replaced by a series of partial derivatives for each of the hat variables. This will be shown by examples later in this chapter. It is to be expected that systems which operate close to their initial conditions at all times will be particularly adaptable to a linear approximation since for small enough deviations all higher powers will be negligible. This suggests that a good regulator loop is more readily linearized than a servo loop operating over a wide range of command signals.

But what if the variables are related through a differential equation rather than a simple algebraic relation? In this case it is sometimes possible to identify an intermediate variable such that the over-all dependence is split into a linear differential equation and a nonlinear algebraic relation. For the nonlinear pneumatic valve, for example, we may use the valve stem position, $m(t)$, for this purpose. Suppose that the linear relation between pressure and valve stem position is

$$\tau_v \frac{d\hat{m}}{dt} + \hat{m} = K_p \hat{p}(t) \tag{5–3}$$

and the nonlinear, time-independent part relates flowrate to valve position by $x = f(m)$. When linearized this becomes

$$\hat{x} = \left(\frac{dx}{dm}\right)_0 \hat{m} = K_m \hat{m}$$

Equations (5–3) and (5–4) may be combined directly to give

$$\tau_v \frac{d\hat{x}}{dt} + \hat{x} = K_m K_p \hat{p} = K_v \hat{p}$$

or the same result can be shown by a block diagram as in Fig. 5–2. As the valve motor is made faster, the time constant τ_v is reduced. In the limit $\tau_v \rightarrow 0$ and the transfer function $G_v(s) \rightarrow K_v$.

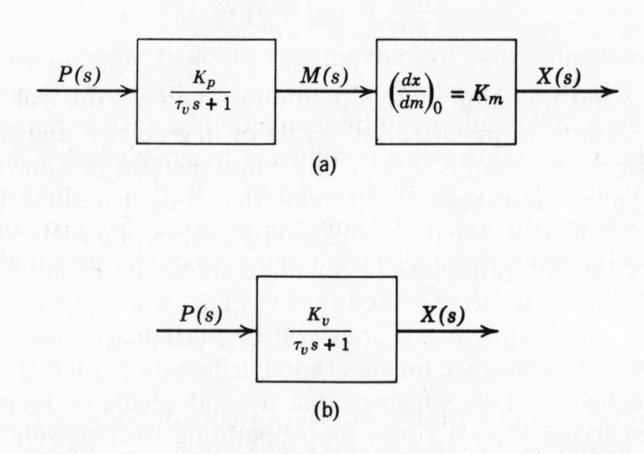

Fig. 5–2. Alternative block diagrams for a nonlinear valve. (a) Cascade representation. (b) Single block representation.

In treating many nonlinearities, it is not possible to split up the problem into such convenient segments. In the next section, we study a nonlinear differential equation directly, without recourse to the device of an intermediate variable.

5–2. NONLINEAR CHEMICAL KINETICS

We return to equation (1–9) which was derived by a material balance on a well-stirred reactor with a nonlinear reaction rate $r(y)$:

$$V \frac{dy}{dt} = qx - qy - Vr \tag{5–5}$$

In preparation for transformation and block algebra, we introduce the hat variables:

$$y = y - y(0)$$
$$x = x - x(0)$$
$$r = r - r(0)$$

to obtain:

$$V\frac{d\hat{y}}{dt} = q\hat{x} - q\hat{y} - V\hat{r} + \Big[qx(0) - qy(0) - Vr(0)\Big] \tag{5–6}$$

We now recognize that the advantages of block algebra will be lost unless the bracketed constants of equation (5–6) can be dropped, and ask how this simplification can be justified. The answer again emphasizes regulator operation, for it is sufficient to establish that the system was in a steady-state condition prior to $t = 0$, that is, that at $t = 0^-$, $(dy/dt) = 0$. Since the material balance (equation 5–5) must hold before $t = 0$, as well as after, the steady-state requirement assures that

$$V\frac{dy}{dt}(0^-) = 0 = qx(0^-) - qy(0^-) - Vr(0^-) \tag{5–7}$$

Comparing this result with the bracket of equation (5–6), it is evident that the desired simplification can be made if

$$x(0) = x(0^-)$$
$$y(0) = y(0^-)$$
$$r(0) = r(0^-)$$

Exceptions to these identities can occur only for discontinuous functions; thus, any ambiguities can be avoided by defining the input deviation as $x = x - x(0^-)$. We will do this routinely in subsequent derivations. With the bracket dropped, equation (5–6) reduces to

$$V\frac{dy}{dt} = qx - qy - Vr \tag{5–8}$$

To this point the relationship is still nonlinear in y, but from the previous findings on linearization, we may write

$$r = \left(\frac{dr}{dy}\right)_0 y$$

A simple substitution into equation (5–8) gives the linear equation

$$V\frac{d\hat{y}}{dt} = q\hat{x} - q\hat{y} - V\left(\frac{dr}{dy}\right)_0 \hat{y} \tag{5–9}$$

Defining

$$\tau = \frac{V}{q + V\left(\frac{dr}{dy}\right)_0}$$

$$K = \frac{q}{q + V\left(\frac{dr}{dy}\right)_0}$$

and transforming leads to a first-order result:

$$Y(s) = \frac{K}{\tau s + 1} X(s)$$

5–3. TIME-VARYING COEFFICIENTS

To illustrate a supplemental approach that must be called upon when time-varying coefficients or product nonlinearities arise, consider the concentration response of a reactor effluent when the constant-volume system is forced by a change in flowrate $q(t)$ at constant inlet concentration a:

$$V\frac{dy}{dt} = aq(t) - q(t)y - Vr \tag{5–10}$$

Such an equation is most readily handled by the substitution of a combination variable: $z = qy$. Then as usual, we define:

$$\hat{y} = y - y(0)$$
$$\hat{q} = q - q(0^-)$$
$$\hat{z} = z - z(0^-)$$
$$\hat{r} = r - r(0)$$

and obtain by substitution:

$$V\frac{d\hat{y}}{dt} = a\hat{q} - \hat{z} - V\hat{r} + \left[aq(0^-) - z(0^-) - Vr(0)\right] \tag{5–11}$$

We may linearize $\hat{r}$ as was done above, but for $\hat{z}$ we must retain the linear terms of the Maclaurin expansion in two variables:

$$\hat{z} = \left(\frac{\partial z}{\partial y}\right)_0 \hat{y} + \left(\frac{\partial z}{\partial q}\right)_0 \hat{q} = q(0^-)\hat{y} + y(0)\hat{q} \tag{5–12}$$

The constant coefficients are now the partial derivatives evaluated at the steady state of $t = 0^-$. Substitution in equation (5–11) will produce an equation ready for transformation, since as expected the bracket of constants in equation (5–11) is zero if regulator action is assumed prior to any disturbance. The linear result:

$$V\frac{d\hat{y}}{dt} = \left[a - y(0)\right]\hat{q} - \left[q(0^-) + V\left(\frac{\partial r}{\partial y}\right)_0\right]\hat{y}$$

gives $Y(s) = [K/(\tau s + 1)]\, Q(s)$ where

$$K = \frac{a - y(0)}{q(0^-) + V\left(\frac{\partial r}{\partial y}\right)_0}$$

$$\tau = \frac{V}{q(0^-) + V\left(\frac{\partial r}{\partial y}\right)_0}$$

We have noted two circumstances associated with regulator operation that are very fortunate. First, by narrowing the range over which system variables are likely to roam, linear approximations are favored. Secondly, groupings of system constants that arise from initial conditions are identically zero, provided that a system is in a steady state just before an upset. Hereafter, unless otherwise stated, we will naturally assume that such a steady state exists at $t = 0^-$. Consequently, it will not be necessary to explain in every problem why the use of hat variables permits us to drop all constant terms. The justification in each case will be the (very reasonable) steady-state assumption that is made here.

5–4. LINEARIZATION IN SIMULTANEOUS EQUATIONS

In the chemical-reactor discussion just completed, it was assumed that the reaction rate r was a function only of reactant concentration y. A more realistic treatment must recognize that r is also a function of temperature v. In this section we include this consideration by writing the unsteady-state energy balance for a well-stirred reactor, as well as the now familiar material balance. The energy balance equation is the same as previously derived in Problem 1–8 for a heated vessel, but a term, ΔHr, must be added to account for heat liberated by reaction.

$$V\frac{dy}{dt} = qx - qy - Vr$$
$$\rho V C_p \frac{dv}{dt} = \rho q C_p(v_i - v) + hA(v_A - v) + \Delta HVr \tag{5–13}$$

As before, we wish to find a transfer function between the input $X(s)$ and the output $Y(s)$.

Analysis of these equations may now proceed according to the pattern of the last section. Define the usual hat variables and restrict the case to regulator operation where a steady state exists at $t = 0^-$. Then:

$$V\frac{d\hat{y}}{dt} = q\hat{x} - q\hat{y} - V\hat{r}$$
$$\rho V C_p \frac{d\hat{v}}{dt} = -(\rho q C_p + hA)\hat{v} + \Delta HV\hat{r} \tag{5–14}$$

The only nonlinear terms in these equations are the chemical rate terms which include $\hat{r}$. We may linearize this term as was done in Section (5–3), retaining the linear terms of the Maclaurin expansion in two variables:

$$\hat{r} = \left(\frac{\partial r}{\partial y}\right)_0 \hat{y} + \left(\frac{\partial r}{\partial v}\right)_0 \hat{v} \tag{5–15}$$

The constant coefficients are again partial derivatives to be evaluated at the original steady state. Substituting equation (5–15) in (5–14) produces a set of simultaneous linear equations.

$$V\frac{d\hat{y}}{dt} = q\hat{x} - q\hat{y} - V\left(\frac{\partial r}{\partial y}\right)_0 \hat{y} - V\left(\frac{\partial r}{\partial v}\right)_0 \hat{v}$$
$$\rho V C_p \frac{d\hat{v}}{dt} = -(\rho q C_p + hA)\hat{v} + \Delta HV\left(\frac{\partial r}{\partial y}\right)_0 \hat{y} + \Delta HV\left(\frac{\partial r}{\partial v}\right)_0 \hat{v} \tag{5–16}$$

which transforms and rearranges to:

$$Y(s) = \frac{K_1}{\tau_1 s + 1} X(s) - \frac{K_2}{\tau_1 s + 1} V(s)$$

$$V(s) = \frac{K_3}{\tau_2 s + 1} Y(s) \tag{5–17}$$

The constants K_1, K_2, K_3, τ_1, and τ_2 are collections of the various system parameters. Their evaluation is left as an exercise for the reader. Equations (5–17) may be shown as either of the block diagrams in Fig. 5–3.

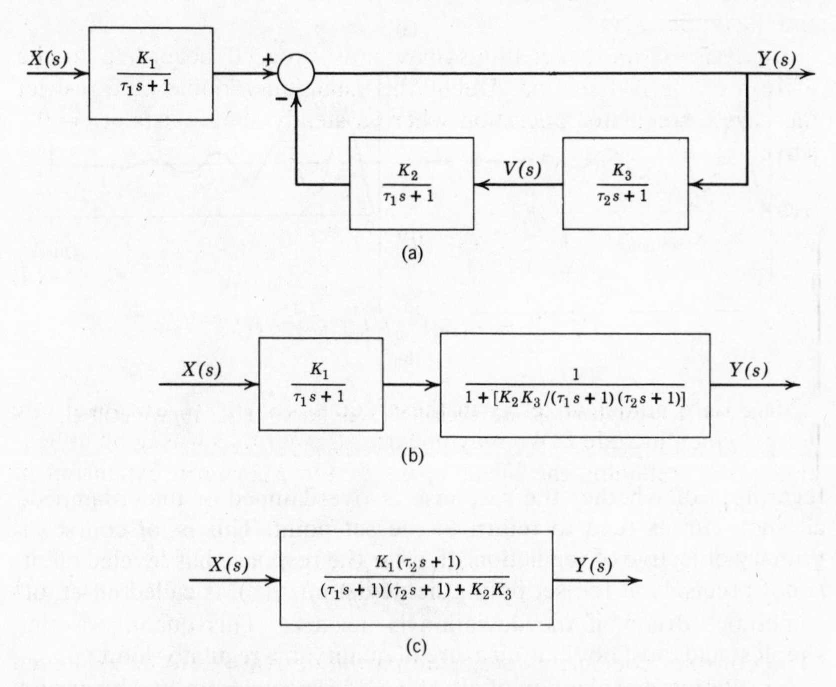

Fig. 5–3. Alternative block diagrams of equations (5–17). (a) All variables shown explicitly. (b) The temperature variable eliminated. (c) A single block.

5–5. OFFSET AND THE FINAL-VALUE THEOREM

The object of regulator operation is to hold a critical variable constant in spite of various loop disturbances. To the extent that the design is successful, the system variables will show greater or lesser excursions from the intended set point. A typical step-response curve for some control variable y might be expected to look like one of those in Fig. 5–4. The curves chosen for the illustration are oscillatory, but

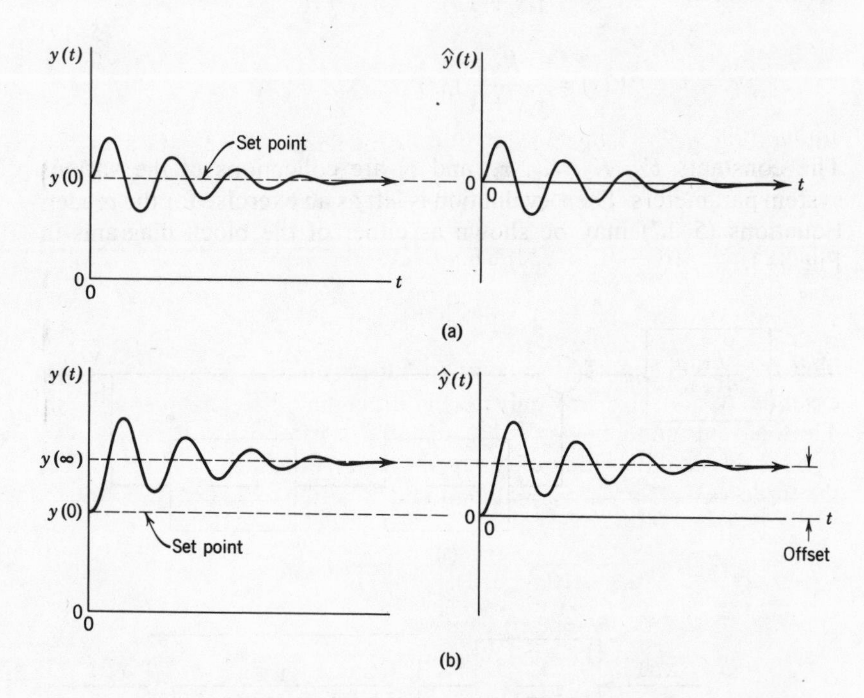

Fig. 5–4. Typical step response regulator curves. (a) No Offset. (b) With Offset.

regardless of whether the response is overdamped or underdamped, all such curves tend to return to the set point. This is, of course, a primary objective of regulation. If, after the response has leveled off, it is not precisely at the set point, the deviation, $\hat{y}(\infty)$, is called **offset**, or sometimes **droop**, if the deviation is negative. This quantity is the simplest and most obvious measure of quality in a regulator loop.

A brute-force evaluation of offset would proceed from $Y(s)$ by partial fraction expansion, inverse transformation, and evaluation of $\hat{y}(\infty)$ by $\lim_{t\to\infty} \hat{y}(t)$. However, since it is the final value of $\hat{y}(t)$ that is sought, rather than the details of the approach to this steady state, it is desirable to short-cut the laborious transform inversion and evaluate $\hat{y}(\infty)$ directly. We show how this may be done in this section, which might appropriately be subheaded: *How to Suceed Without Really Trying*. Consider the equality

$$\mathscr{L}\left[\frac{d\hat{y}}{dt}\right] = \int_0^\infty \frac{d\hat{y}}{dt} e^{-st}\, dt = sY(s)$$

In the limit as $s \to 0$

$$\int_0^\infty \frac{d\hat{y}}{dt}\, dt = \lim_{s\to 0} sY(s)$$

Integrating the left side and substituting the limits of integration

$$\lim_{t\to\infty} \hat{y}(t) - \hat{y}(0) = \lim_{s\to 0} sY(s)$$

which, since $\hat{y}(0) = 0$, gives the **final-value theorem**:

$$\hat{y}(\infty) = \lim_{t\to\infty} \hat{y}(t) = \lim_{s\to 0} sY(s) \tag{5–18}$$

This result will enable us to compute offsets directly from $Y(s)$, but it is essential to note that it is only a valid procedure if $\hat{y}(t)$ has a finite limit. The theorem cannot be applied to unstable or marginally stable systems.

As a simple illustration of the final-value theorem, let us find $\hat{y}(\infty)$ for the three-vessel forward cascade forced by a step of size a.

$$Y(s) = \frac{a}{(\tau_1 s + 1)(\tau_2 s + 1)(\tau_3 s + 1)s}$$

$$\hat{y}(\infty) = \lim_{s\to 0} sY(s) = \lim_{s\to 0} \frac{a}{(\tau_1 s + 1)(\tau_2 s + 1)(\tau_3 s + 1)} = a$$

This answer is in accord with the prediction of equation (4–6) as $t \to \infty$, but by using equation (5–18) no formal inversion was necessary. An application to a closed-loop regulator problem is elaborated in the next section.

5–6. A NUMERICAL EXAMPLE

To consolidate the developments on linearization and to highlight some of the difficulties peculiar to a closed-loop regulator problem, we return here to the study of the tubular mixer of Fig. 4–1. This time we hold the reference signal at a fixed set point, but allow for possible disturbances in the mainstream solvent flow $u(t)$.

To properly relate u and x to z, we can make use of the nonlinear algebraic material balance applicable at the inlet to the tube:

$$\frac{\rho x}{M} = z(u + x) \tag{5–19}$$

where ρ and M are the density and molecular weight of the pure trace component. Linearization of (5–19) gives

$$\hat{z} = \left(\frac{\partial z}{\partial x}\right)_0 \hat{x} + \left(\frac{\partial z}{\partial u}\right)_0 \hat{u} = K_x\hat{x} + K_u\hat{u}$$

$$Z(s) = K_x X(s) + K_u U(s) \tag{5–20}$$

The partial derivatives must be found numerically by either experiment, or direct calculation from:

$$\left(\frac{\partial z}{\partial x}\right)_0 = K_x = \frac{\rho}{M}\frac{u(0)}{[u(0)+x(0)]^2}$$

$$\left(\frac{\partial z}{\partial u}\right)_0 = K_u = -\frac{\rho}{M}\frac{x(0)}{[u(0)+x(0)]^2} \tag{5–21}$$

Equation (5–20) yields the block diagram, Fig. 5–5, and permits the closed-loop block diagram, Fig. 5–6. If $\hat{u}(t) = 0$, this diagram reduces

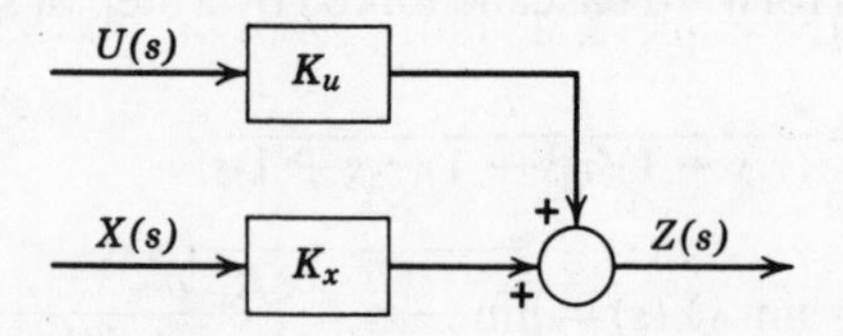

Fig. 5–5. Block diagram from equation (5–20).

again to the servo loop of Fig. 4–1*b*. By comparison, it is evident that K_x is exactly the constant K of equation (4–20).

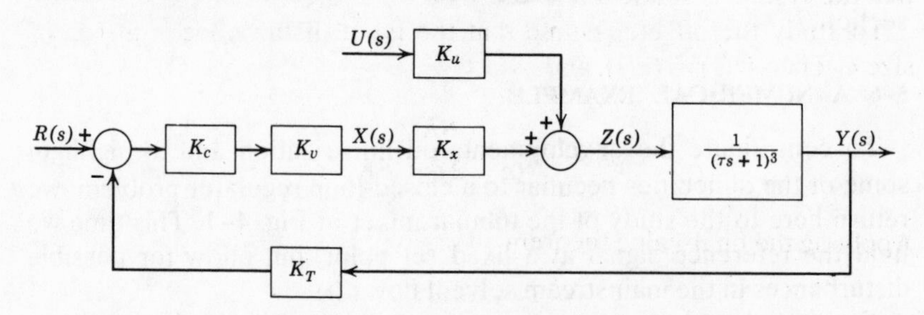

Fig. 5–6. Block diagram of concentration-control loop with flow disturbance.

It should be noted that the units of the disturbance $u(t)$ are not immediately compatible with those of x, the manipulating variable in the loop, since a change in the solvent flow does not affect the control variable to the same extent as a similar change in the trace component flowrate. From this viewpoint the blocks K_x and K_u act in effect as conversion factors (with units), essential ingredients of this analysis. This requirement is commonly encountered in process-control studies, but it rarely occurs in servo design, because the reference input is of necessity expressed in the same units as the error signal of the loop. In the earlier servo-loop analysis, for example, it was apparent that the input r was to be measured in millivolts, since this was the unit specified for the electric-to-pneumatic controller.

From Fig. 5–6 the effect of a disturbance on the control variable may be written by inspection as

$$Y(s) = \frac{K_u/(\tau s+1)^3}{1 + K_c K_v K_x K_T/(\tau s+1)^3} U(s)$$

$$= \frac{K_u}{(\tau s+1)^3 + K_c K_v K_x K_T} U(s) \tag{5–22}$$

By substituting the numerical values given for the constants in Section 4–6:

$$Y(s) = \frac{8K_u}{(s+2)^3 + 8K_c} U(s)$$

As might have been anticipated from the earlier emphasis, the characteristic polynomial for this system is identical to that derived earlier for servo operation. With no further computation then, it may be noted that the system is stable if $0 \leqslant K_c < 8$.

To study the offset, assume that the input disturbance is a step of size a. Then $U(s) = (a/s)$, and

$$Y(s) = \frac{8K_u}{(s+2)^3 + 8K_c} \frac{a}{s}$$

Applying the final-value theorem

$$\hat{y}(\infty) = \lim_{s\to 0} sY(s) = aK_u \frac{1}{1+K_c} \tag{5–23}$$

a result which suggests several important points. It is clear that the system will show a finite offset regardless of the controller gain K_c but that the size of the offset can be reduced by increasing this setting. If $K_c = 0$, the solution corresponds to that for the uncontrolled plant; evidently, the degree of offset reduction that can be attributed to the control action is in the factor: $1/(1 + K_c)$. Since any $K_c > 8$ produces instability for the problem at hand, the maximum offset reduction possible is by a factor of 1/9. If the offset is small, the system is said to show great **accuracy**. Since accuracy is a desirable feature, it seems quite reasonable to demand high controller gain. In fact, why not set the control for the maximum gain available on the given hardware? The answer to this question is to be found in the stability analysis where it was shown that the system becomes unstable at $K_c > 8$. If the designer insists on high accuracy, he may encounter stability problems. Conversely, a choice of controller gain far from the stability limit will produce a system with relatively poor accuracy. This difficulty is sometimes called the **stability-accuracy dilemma**. Although it was illustrated here by a specific example, it is, in fact, the major focus of all closed-loop design, regardless of the control action or system chosen.

5-7. INTEGRAL CONTROL

A major drawback of simple proportional control is the offset that always follows a sustained disturbance. This result can be avoided by including integration in the control. To illustrate this effect, consider the proportional controller of the last problem to be replaced by an (idealized) integral controller, a device which acts according to the input-output relation:

$$\hat{p} = K_i \int_0^t \hat{e}\, dt$$

$$\frac{d\hat{p}}{dt} = K_i \hat{e} \tag{5-24}$$

$$P(s) = \frac{K_i}{s} E(s) = G_c E(s)$$

The transfer function $G_c = (K_i/s)$. Referring back to Fig. 5-6, the closed-loop equation (5-22) may be modified to

$$Y(s) = \frac{K_u/(\tau s + 1)^3}{1 + K_i K_v K_x K_T / s(\tau s + 1)^3} U(s)$$

With numerical values:

$$Y(s) = \frac{8sK_u}{s(s+2)^3 + 8K_i} U(s) \tag{5-25}$$

Including the step disturbance:

$$Y(s) = \frac{8sK_u}{s(s+2)^3 + 8K_i} \frac{a}{s}$$

By the final value theorem:

$$\hat{y}(\infty) = \lim_{s \to 0} s\, Y(s) = 0 \tag{5-26}$$

It may be concluded that integral control eliminates offset. For this reason, this mode of control is also called **reset** control.

REMARKS

By focusing attention on some of the special features of regulator analysis we have in this chapter been able to bring the power of linear analysis to bear on nonlinear problems. It was shown by the final-value theorem that the laborious details of transform inversion can often be avoided, but the s-domain description is still used primarily as an intermediate step, not a basis for direct numerical computation. Such a direct s-domain analysis will be developed next, because without this tool a good framework is lacking in which to discuss, among other things, the performance and design of real controllers. When this is done the simple proportional and integral modes of control will be no less important, but we will not be limited to these idealizations.

EXERCISES

5-1. Evaluate the constants in equation (5–17) in terms of the system parameters. Are there any values of K_2 and K_3 that would make the loop of Fig. 5–3*a* unstable or oscillatory? Find the response of $\hat{y}(t)$ to the impulse $\hat{x}(t) = 0.2\ \delta(t)$ moles/ft³ and sketch your result if: $K_1 = 30$, $K_2 = 2$ moles/ft³°F, $K_3 = 0.5$°F ft³/mole, $\tau_1 = 6$ hr, $\tau_2 = 1$ hr.

5-2. Consider the numerical example of Section 5–6. Is the closed loop stable for $K_c = -\frac{1}{2}$ or for $K_c = -1$? What effect would a negative K_c have on offset?

5-3. Use the result (equation 1–19) to show that

$$\hat{y}(0^+) = \lim_{t \to 0} \hat{y}(t) = \lim_{s \to \infty} sY(s)$$

This is called the **initial-value theorem.** Use this theorem to prove that if equation (4–15) is to represent a realizable system, the polynomial exponents of $F(s)$ must be restricted by: $m < n$. The term **realizable** as used here means that the step response of the system is continuous at $t = 0$; i.e., $y(0^+) = y(0^-)$.

5–4. A control loop is composed of four elements represented by the following transfer functions:

$$\text{Controller: } G_c(s) = K_c \text{ psi/psi}$$

$$\text{Final Control Element: } G_v(s) = \left(\frac{3}{1 + 5s}\right)\text{(gal/min)/psi}$$

$$\text{Process: } G(s) = \left(\frac{0.25}{1 + s + 25s^2}\right) \text{ ft/(gal/min)}$$

$$\text{Measuring Element } H(s) = 0.5 \text{ psi/ft}$$

The control variable (the process output) is to be held at 8 ft, with offset not to exceed 2.0 ft. The maximum step disturbance expected is equivalent to 10 gal/min. What proportional gain would you recommend? Show that the system becomes unstable for any $K_c > 1.167$. What is the offset for this value of K_c? Would you recommend changing either the valve size or transducer sensitivity?

5–5. Apply the final-value theorem to the closed loop of Fig. 2–11. Let $G_v = K_v$, $G(s) = 8/(s + 2)^3$, $H = K_T$. Take G_c to be an ideal proportional controller, and consider a step disturbance for $\hat{u}(t)$. What offset results? Repeat the analysis for an ideal integral plus proportional controller

$$G_c = K_c\left(1 + \frac{1}{\tau_i s}\right)$$

and for an ideal integral controller

$$G_c = \frac{K_i}{s} = \frac{K_c}{\tau_i s}$$

5–6. Geerlings and Kramers[1] studied the $NaOH - CO_2$ neutralization in a continuous-flow, pilot-size apparatus (Fig. 5–7). They used mechanical

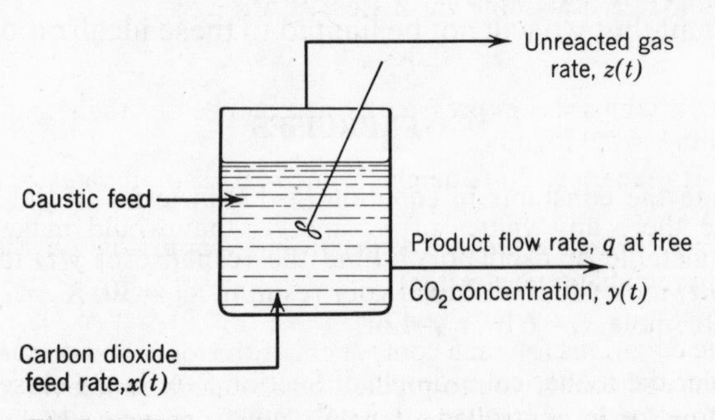

Fig. 5–7. The system used by Geerlings and Kramers.

[1]Geerlings, M. W., *Plant and Process Dynamic Characteristics,* Academic Press, New York, 1957, p. 124.

agitation to intimately mix pure CO_2 feed with the liquid. Because the neutralization reaction is virtually instantaneous, the chemical rate r may be treated as a constant in the dynamic material balance:

$$V\frac{dy}{dt} = x - z - qy - Vr$$

Assuming that z is an unknown nonlinear function of x and y, find the transfer function: $G(s) = Y(s)/X(s)$ by linearization. Experimentally, it is observed that z is almost independent of x. How does this simplify $G(s)$?

5–7. A stream of water is fed to a process vessel from a constant head tank. The flowrate is found to vary however, because of large downstream pressure fluctuations. It is therefore suggested that a control loop be installed to maintain the flow steady at $x = 10$ ft³/min. A venturi (1-in.-throat diameter, instantaneous response) is to be placed in the feed line as the measuring element; a diaphragm motor valve will act as the final control element [first-order element, 5-sec time constant, $K_v = 2$ (ft³/min)/psi]; a proportional controller is available. Draw a block diagram showing input and output for each part of the loop. Identify any nonlinear elements. Find the transfer function of each element in the loop and show appropriate units (use a linearization procedure for any nonlinear elements). What transfer function would enable you to predict the flow change resulting from a change in set point?

5–8. The level of water in a vessel is controlled by manipulation of a pneumatic valve on the inlet line. The **load** on the system (disturbance) is the effluent flow which discharges through an adjustable orifice in the bottom of the vessel. The control loop contains the following components:

Controller: Proportional, set at 25% P.B.; input span, zero to 20 psig; output span, zero to 20 psig.

Valve: The valve stem position responds to the diaphragm pressure (3 to 15 psig) with a first-order time constant of 10 sec; the flow through the valve x, is a parabolic function of the valve stem position m:

$$x = 0.004m^2 + 0.6m$$

where both variables are expressed as percentages of their maximum value. The maximum $x = 20$ ft³/min.

Vessel: 5-ft diameter; 20-ft height; orifice is 1.5-in. diameter; level control at 10 ft.

Measuring Element: Pressure transmitting diaphragm on the bottom of vessel; no appreciable time constant.

Linearize the equations for each component of the loop, and derive the transfer functions that will enable you to predict the change in tank level resulting from changes in load or in controller set point. What can you say about the loop stability?

5–9. The differential equation that describes the thermal behavior of a jacketed, well-mixed vessel is

$$\frac{dv}{dt} = \frac{q(v_i - v)}{V} - \frac{hA(v - v_A)}{\rho V C_p}$$

Derive this equation by an energy balance. Assuming ρ, V, C_p, A to be constant, derive transfer functions between:

(a) Feed temperature and effluent temperature.
(b) Heat transfer coefficient and effluent temperature.
(c) Flowrate and effluent temperature.

For which of these is linearization necessary?

5–10. To control the effluent temperature of a jacketed, well-mixed vessel in spite of disturbances in the feed temperature v_i, it is common to manipulate the heat transfer coefficient h, by means of the coolant flowrate x. The relationship between h and x is the nonlinear algebraic equation

$$h = ax^{0.8}$$

Taking the parameters V, A, p, C_p, and v_A to be constant, linearize the system and draw a regulator-loop block diagram. Find the constants in the transfer functions $V(s)/V_i(s)$ and $V(s)/X(s)$ in terms of the system parameters.

5–11. Stewart, Sliepcevich, and Puckett[2] have made frequency response measurements on a system such as described in Problem 5–9. Their results indicated first-order behavior (time constant of 25 sec) when the flowrate was forced to obtain temperature response. They used water feed to a one liter autoclave at a mean rate of 5.44 lb/hr. Find the heat transferred in Btu/hr °F assuming the heat transfer area is 0.2 ft².

5–12. Evaluate K and τ for the first-order transfer function derived in Section 5–2, if $V = 100$ ft³, $q = 50$ ft³/hr, $y(0) = 0.25$ moles/ft³, and the chemical rate is given by:

(*a*) The equation: $r = 2y^{1.5}$ moles/hr ft³
(*b*) The following steady-state measurements.

y, moles/ft³	r, moles/hr ft³
0.05	0.45
0.10	0.64
0.15	0.78
0.20	0.89
0.25	1.00
0.30	1.10

5–13. If the reactants for a reversible chemical reaction:

$$A + B \rightleftharpoons C$$

are fed in stoichiometric proportion, the isothermal rate is characterized by the equation:

---

[2]Stewart, W. S., C. M. Sliepcevich, and T. H. Puckett, *Chem. Eng. Prog. Symp. Ser. No. 36*, **57**, 119 (1961).

$$r = 0.50y_1^2 - 0.25y_2$$

where y_1, y_2 are the respective concentrations of reactant and product in moles/ft^3 and r is the rate in moles/hr ft^3. Show that material balances on reactant and product can yield the simultaneous equations:

$$V\frac{dy_1}{dt} = qx_1 - qy_1 - Vr$$

$$V\frac{dy_2}{dt} = qx_2 - qy_2 + Vr$$

What transfer functions would enable you to calculate the responses of y_1 and y_2 to a step change in the feed concentration x_1?

Consider a well-stirred reactor of 200 ft^3 volume in which the above reaction is to be carried out. A steady state is established by feeding A and B at concentrations: $x_1 = x_2$, at a total flow rate (in and out) of 100 ft^3/hr. In this steady condition the concentrations of reactants A and B in the reactor are 0.30 moles/ft^3 each and the concentration of product C is 0.06 moles/ft^3. Use the final-value theorem to find the offset, $\hat{y}_1(\infty)$, following a step disturbance of size: $\hat{x}_1 = 0.04$ moles/ft^3. Is the system oscillatory? Is it stable?

5–14. Consider a process vessel which receives gas at w_i lb/min and discharges to the atmosphere at a rate of w lb/min. Assume that the changes are slow enough to be isothermal, and that the pressure drops are small enough to permit use of the incompressible flow equation:

$$w = k\sqrt{(p - p_o)p}$$

where k = a constant
p = pressure in the vessel
p_o = atmospheric pressure

Use a material balance and the ideal gas law to derive a transfer function: $P(s)/W_i(s)$.

6 *Frequency-Response Analysis*

Among the several inputs considered in detail in Chapter 3 the sine-wave input was discussed as having a particular importance: it could serve as a component of an arbitrary input. It is true that the same could be said of the step function, since an arbitrary curve can just as well be approximated by a series of small finite steps, but the sinusoid has another important characteristic. When a stable linear system is forced sinusoidally, it shows transient behavior for a limited time depending on initial conditions, and then it responds sinusoidally. If this statement seems obvious, recall that it is not generally true for other simple inputs. The response to a step change in the input flow to a storage vessel, for example, is not a step in level, but rather a ramp. Furthermore, even for systems in which a step input does cause a step response (after transients have died), the constant response is per se devoid of any dynamic information. Although the sinusoidal form passes through all linear operations unscathed, the wave does change in dimensions and position on the time axis, providing valuable information on the system involved. Using the sinusoidal analysis allows us to wash out all initial-condition effects, and still retain dynamic behavior for study. Before we go on, the reader will want to see the reasoning behind the claims already made.

6-1. THE BASIC RELATIONSHIPS

Letting $G(s)$ be the transfer function for any linear system, we elect to study the input–output relationship for the particular $\hat{x}(t) = a \sin \omega t$, $X(s) = a\omega/(s^2 + \omega^2)$.

$$Y(s) = G(s)\,X(s) = \frac{a\omega}{s^2 + \omega^2}G(s) \tag{6–1}$$

If the characteristic roots of the system are distinct, a partial fraction expansion yields

$$Y(s) = \frac{K_1\omega + K_2 s}{s^2 + \omega^2} + \frac{K_3}{s + \lambda_3} + \frac{K_4}{s + \lambda_4} + \cdots \tag{6–2}$$

from which

$$\begin{aligned} \hat{y}(t) &= K_1 \sin \omega t + K_2 \cos \omega t + K_3 e^{-\lambda_3 t} + K_4 e^{-\lambda_4 t} + \cdots \\ &= K \sin(\omega t + \phi) + K_3 e^{-\lambda_3 t} + K_4 e^{-\lambda_4 t} + \cdots \end{aligned} \tag{6–3}$$

The exponential terms evidently represent the transients referred to previously. For a stable system they will die out as $t \to \infty$, leaving the sinusoid as the only time-varying result. The same argument also applies if repeated or complex roots occur, as can be confirmed by a brief review of Table 4–1. If the system has a zero root, an additive constant will appear in the result. Now, it remains only to find K and ϕ (or what amounts to the same thing, K_1 and K_2) in terms of the input amplitude a and the system parameters in $G(s)$. Following the established procedure for evaluating constants in a partial fraction expansion, K_1 and K_2 are found by multiplying both sides of equations (6–1) and (6–2) by the factor $(s^2 + \omega^2)$:

$$a\omega\, G(s) = K_1\omega + K_2 s + (s^2 + \omega^2)\frac{K_3}{s + \lambda_3} + \cdots \tag{6–4}$$

and evaluating this expression at the s value where $(s^2 + \omega^2) = 0$, that is, at $s = j\omega$:

$$a\omega G(j\omega) = K_1\omega + K_2 j\omega$$

$$G(j\omega) = \frac{K_1}{a} + \frac{K_2}{a}j \tag{6–5}$$

In effect, this equation shows us that to find K_1 and K_2, we can work from $G(s)$ as follows: (1) Substitute $s = j\omega$ to produce $G(j\omega)$; (2) rearrange this complex expression to the form of the right side of equation (6–5); (3) identify K_1 and K_2 by equating the real part of $G(j\omega)$ with (K_1/a) and the imaginary part with (K_2/a). The tedious part of this manipulation is item (2), since this will usually involve considerable arithmetic and a rationalization step [see the section following equation (4–12) for an example].

We can also deal with this procedure in a more concise notation by using the geometric properties of $G(j\omega)$: since it is a complex quantity, it can be thought of as a vector in the complex plane, with components (K_1/a) and (K_2/a) on the real and imaginary axes, as in Fig. 6–1. But

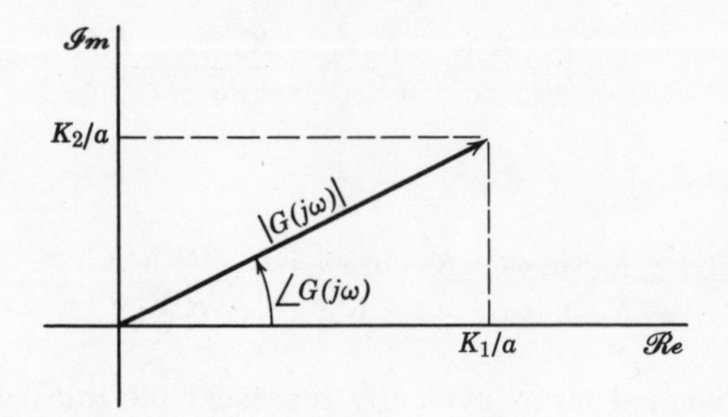

Fig. 6–1. Vector notation for a complex number.

such a vector can equally well be described by its magnitude (length) and angle. Using the notation

$$\begin{aligned} \text{magnitude} &= |G(j\omega)| \\ \text{angle} &= \angle G(j\omega) \end{aligned} \tag{6–6}$$

the geometry of Fig. 6–1 gives

$$|G(j\omega)| = \sqrt{\left(\frac{K_1}{a}\right)^2 + \left(\frac{K_2}{a}\right)^2} = \frac{\sqrt{K_1^2 + K_2^2}}{a}$$

$$\angle G(j\omega) = \arctan \frac{(K_2/a)}{(K_1/a)} = \arctan (K_2/K_1)$$

Combining these results with the relations of equation (3–9):

$$|G(j\omega)| = \frac{K}{a}$$

$$\angle G(j\omega) = \phi \tag{6–7}$$

This discussion may be concluded, therefore, by the following observations. After a more or less brief transient period, a linear system forced sinusoidally will respond sinusoidally. The output wave will have the same frequency as the input, but will differ in amplitude and phase according to the system transfer function $G(s)$. The ratio of the two amplitudes will be equal to the magnitude of the complex quantity $G(j\omega)$ while the associated angle is equal to an angular shift by which the output wave will lag the input. If the input and output waves are compared on a single time scale they will appear as Fig. 6–2 (the transient parts are omitted). Recall that in general the units of x and y are different. An application to a familiar system is useful to illustrate this result.

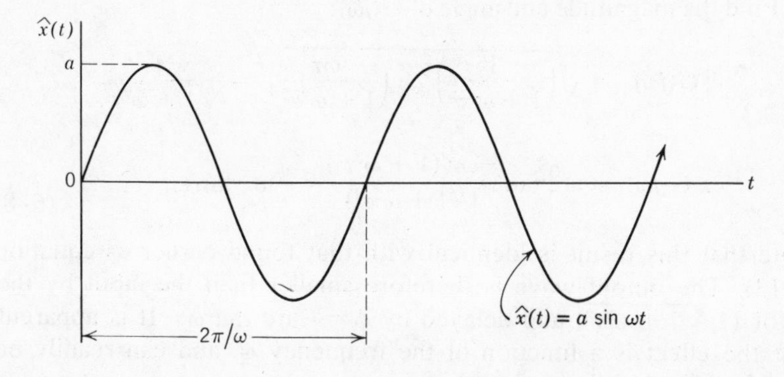

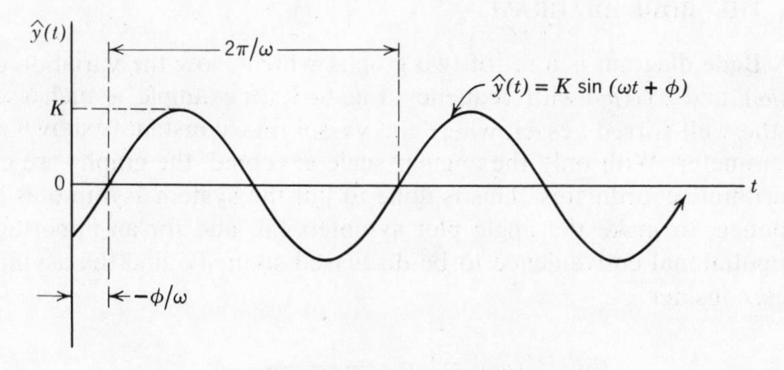

Fig. 6–2. Frequency-response curves.

6–2. THE WELL-STIRRED VESSEL REVISITED AGAIN

We consider the input concentration to our familiar well-stirred vessel to be forced sinusoidally. Starting from

$$G(s) = \frac{1}{1 + \tau s}$$

(1) Let $s = j\omega$:

$$G(j\omega) = \frac{1}{1 + \tau(j\omega)}$$

(2) Rationalize the denominator:

$$G(j\omega) = \frac{1}{1 + \omega\tau j}\frac{1 - \omega\tau j}{1 - \omega\tau j} = \frac{1}{1 + \omega^2\tau^2} - \frac{\omega}{1 + \omega^2\tau^2}j$$

(3) Find the magnitude and angle of $G(j\omega)$:

$$|G(j\omega)| = \sqrt{\left(\frac{1}{1 + \omega^2\tau^2}\right)^2 + \left(\frac{\omega\tau}{1 + \omega^2\tau^2}\right)^2} = \frac{1}{\sqrt{1 + \omega^2\tau^2}}$$

$$\angle G(j\omega) = \text{arc tan}\frac{-\omega\tau/(1 + \omega^2\tau^2)}{1/(1 + \omega^2\tau^2)} = -\text{arc tan}\ \omega\tau \tag{6-8}$$

Note that this result is identical with that found earlier as equation (4–13). The output wave is therefore smaller than the input by the factor $(1/\sqrt{1 + \omega^2\tau^2})$ and delayed by $\phi = -\text{arc tan}\ \omega\tau$. It is apparent that the effect is a function of the frequency ω, and can readily be exhibited graphically.

6–3. THE BODE DIAGRAM

A **Bode** diagram is a set of two graphs which show the variation of $|G(j\omega)|$ and $\angle G(j\omega)$ with frequency. Fig. 6–3, for example, is such a set for the well-stirred vessel, where the vessel time constant is shown as a parameter. With only the angular scale excepted, the graphs are on logarithmic coordinates. This is done to put the system asymptotes in evidence, to make the angle plot symmetrical, and for an important computational convenience to be discussed soon. To find the asymptotes, consider:

$$\lim_{\omega\to 0}|G(j\omega)| = \lim_{\omega\to 0}\frac{1}{\sqrt{1 + \omega^2\tau^2}} = 1$$

$$\lim_{\omega\to 0}\angle G(j\omega) = \lim_{\omega\to 0}\ \text{arc tan}\,(-\omega\tau) = 0$$

$$\lim_{\omega\to\infty}\angle G(j\omega) = \lim_{\omega\to\infty}\ \text{arc tan}\,(-\omega\tau) = -90° \tag{6-9}$$

and also, since

$$\log|G(j\omega)| = \log\frac{1}{\sqrt{1 + \omega^2\tau^2}} = -\log\sqrt{1 + \omega^2\tau^2}$$

the high-frequency asymptote of $\log |G(j\omega)|$ is

$$\lim_{\omega\to\infty} \log |G(j\omega)| = \lim_{\omega\to\infty} (-\log \sqrt{1+\omega^2\tau^2}) = -\log \omega\tau$$
$$= -\log \omega - \log \tau \qquad (6\text{–}10)$$

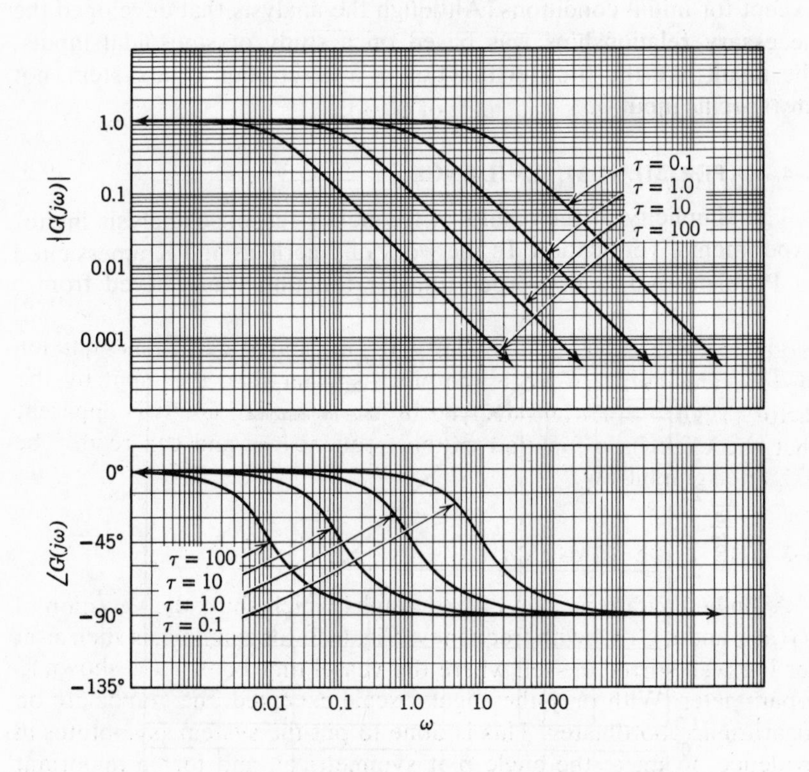

Fig. 6–3. Bode diagrams for first-order systems.

Therefore, on the log-log coordinates chosen, this curve approaches a straight line of slope $= -1$. The asymptotes will intersect where $\log 1 = -\log \omega\tau$; that is, where $\omega = (1/\tau)$. This frequency is called the **corner** or **break frequency** of the system. It is at this frequency that $\angle G(j\omega) = -45°$, as can be confirmed by equation (6–8).

In electrical engineering terminology, and in some other fields, it is customary to express the magnitude scale in units of **decibels**, defined by

$$D = 20 \log |G| \qquad (6\text{–}11)$$

This usage has the advantage (or possibly, the disadvantage) of absorbing the logarithmic relationship in the new unit. It is somewhat analogous to the pH scale commonly used in acid-base chemistry.

The Bode plot is in essence a graph of the transfer function, and like any algebraic statement of $G(s)$ it describes a linear system completely, except for initial conditions. Although the analysis that developed the necessary relationships was based on a study of sinusoidal inputs, the result like the transfer function is a description of a system, not any specific input.

6–4. EXPERIMENTAL EVIDENCE

The simplicity of the results of frequency-response analysis invites experimental verification. In the work of Geerlings and Kramers cited in Problem 5–6, a first-order transfer function was derived from a

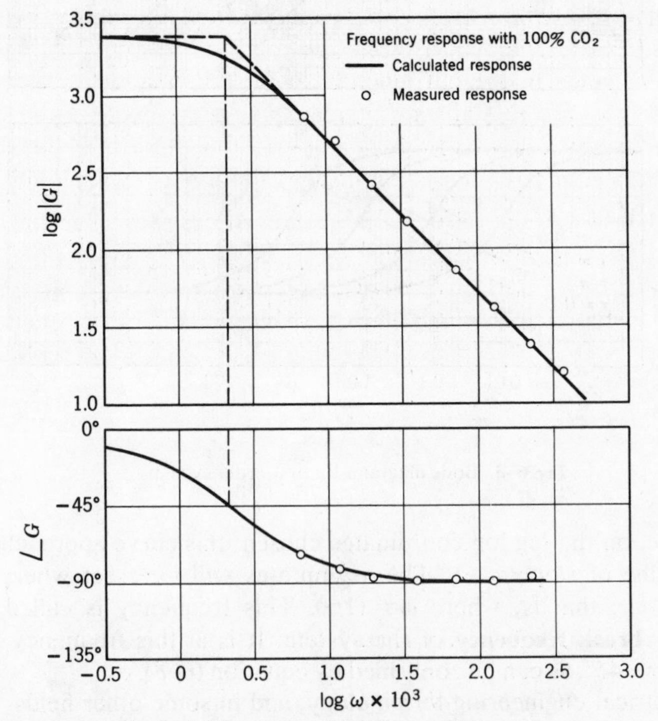

Fig. 6–4. The results of Geerlings and Kramers.

study of NaOH—CO_2 neutralization. By introducing the pure gas at a sinusoidally varying rate, and continuously monitoring the solute concentration in the effluent liquid, the frequency-response data were obtained that are reproduced in Fig. 6–4. It is clear that the measurements are consistent with the first-order model shown by the solid lines on the same diagram. The ordinate scale used by Geerlings and Kramers includes a transducer constant which entered in measuring effluent concentration.

6–5. GRAPHICAL COMPUTATIONS

In Section 2–1 a transfer function was derived for a system that consisted of three subsystems in series. This combination of three first-order systems produced a third-order system, over-all, in the form of equation (2–4). In expanded form it is:

$$G(s) = \frac{1}{\tau_1\tau_2\tau_3 s^3 + (\tau_1\tau_2 + \tau_2\tau_3 + \tau_1\tau_3)s^2 + (\tau_1 + \tau_2 + \tau_3)s + 1}$$

Rather than resort to a brute-force evaluation of $|G|$ and $\angle G$ (for a Bode plot), we can easily use our previous results by recalling the observation made in the introduction to this chapter with regard to sinusoidal response to sinusoidal forcing. Precisely because the sine-wave form is retained as the signal passes through each of the three vessels in question, $\hat{x}(t)$, $\hat{z}(t)$, $\hat{w}(t)$, and $\hat{y}(t)$, differ only in amplitude and phase.

$$\begin{aligned} \hat{x}(t) &= a \sin \omega t \\ \hat{z}(t) &= a_1 \sin (\omega t + \phi_1) \\ \hat{w}(t) &= a_2 \sin (\omega t + \phi_2) \\ \hat{y}(t) &= a_3 \sin (\omega t + \phi_3) \end{aligned} \qquad (6\text{–}12)$$

$$\begin{aligned} |G_1| &= \frac{a_1}{a} \qquad \angle G_1 = \phi_1 \\ |G_2| &= \frac{a_2}{a_1} \qquad \angle G_2 = (\phi_2 - \phi_1) \\ |G_3| &= \frac{a_3}{a_2} \qquad \angle G_3 = (\phi_3 - \phi_2) \end{aligned} \qquad (6\text{–}13)$$

Over-all, the signals $\hat{x}(t)$ and $\hat{y}(t)$ are related as

$$|G| = \frac{a_3}{a} \qquad \angle G = \phi_3$$

Therefore, it is clear that if $G = G_1G_2G_3$ then

$$\begin{aligned} |G| &= |G_1|\,|G_2|\,|G_3| \\ \angle G &= \angle G_1 + \angle G_2 + \angle G_3 \end{aligned} \qquad (6\text{–}14)$$

or, put into words, individual transfer functions in a cascade may be combined by multiplying the magnitudes and adding the angle contributions of the respective parts. Applied to the particular system of three vessels, this rule provides

$$|G| = \frac{1}{\sqrt{1+\omega^2\tau_1^2}} \frac{1}{\sqrt{1+\omega^2\tau_2^2}} \frac{1}{\sqrt{1+\omega^2\tau_3^2}}$$

$$\angle G = -\text{arc tan } \omega\tau_1 - \text{arc tan } \omega\tau_2 - \text{arc tan } \omega\tau_3$$

Although it is possible to proceed algebraically, this would lose one of the most important advantages of the Bode diagram. Rather, we prefer to compute graphically, by adding the contributions of G_1, G_2, and G_3. For numerical illustration purposes, let us choose: $\tau_1 = 0.5$ hr, $\tau_2 = 1.0$ hr, $\tau_3 = 4.0$ hr. The three Bode graphs are shown on Fig. 6–5. To combine these, we add the angles as indicated by equation (6–14). On Fig.

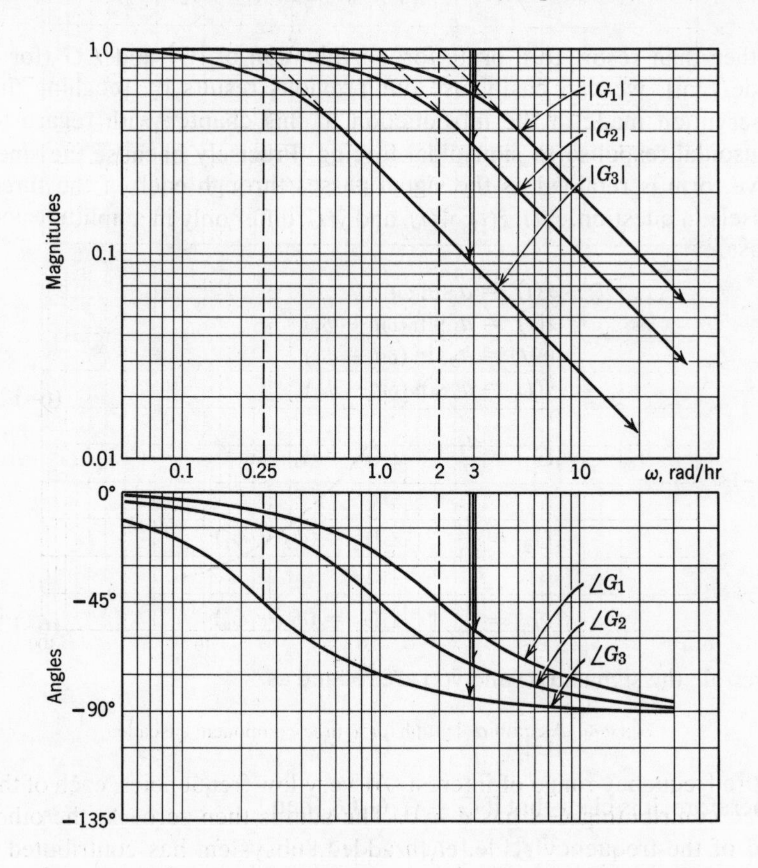

Fig. 6–5. The graphs of three first-order components superimposed.

6–5 each angle is a distance measured in the negative direction from the $\phi = 0$ reference line, so that it is necessary to add three distances at each ω. See, for example, the three arrows at $\omega = 3$. Their sum is $-213°$, the value of $\angle G$ at this frequency. In this manner, it is easy to cover the

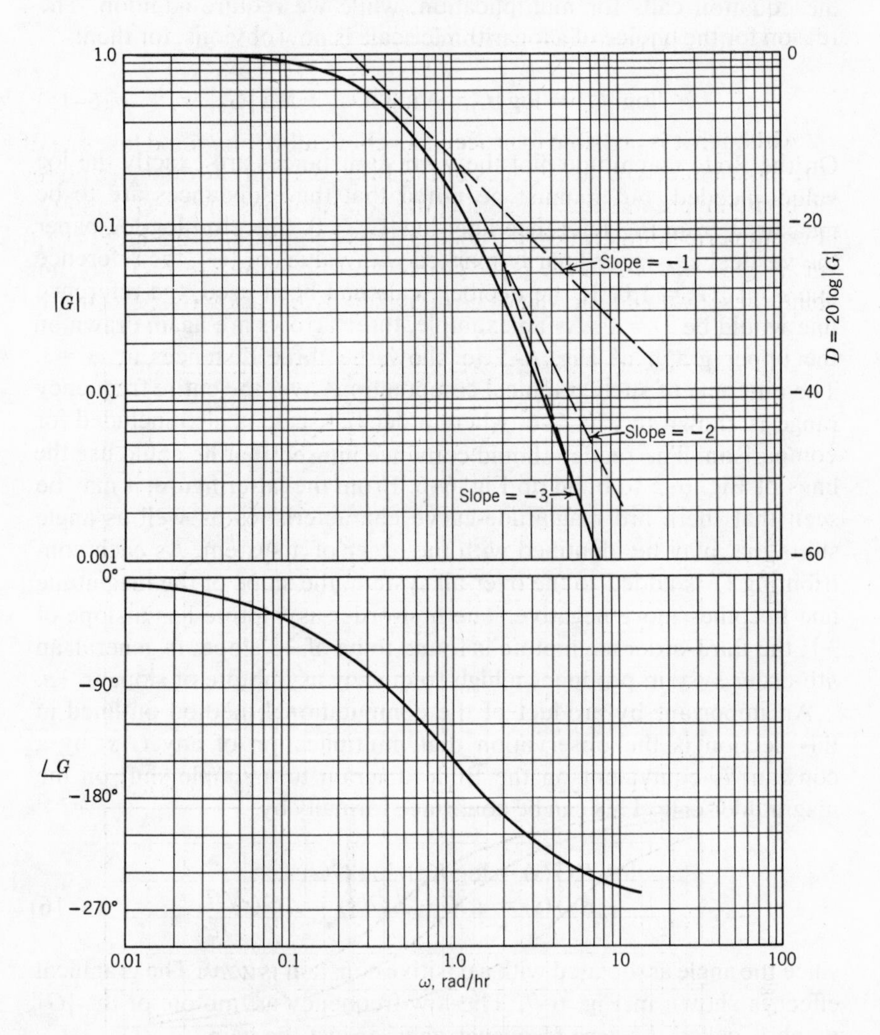

Fig. 6–6. A combined graph for a three-component cascade.

entire frequency range of interest. At very low frequencies, each of the three contributing G's has $\phi = 0$. The sum is then zero. At the other end of the frequency scale, each added subsystem has contributed a 90° phase lag. The third-order system thus shows an asymptote of

$-270°$. As might be expected, an nth-order system shows a lag of $n\pi/2$ as $\omega \to \infty$.

To obtain the corresponding combined magnitude plot, we refer to equation (6–14) again, and seek appropriate graphical distances. But the equation calls for multiplication, while we require addition. The reason for the choice of a logarithmic scale is now obvious, for then:

$$\log |G| = \log |G_1| + \log |G_2| + \log |G_3| \qquad (6\text{–}15)$$

On the Bode magnitude plot the vertical distances are exactly the log values needed, but it must be noted that these distances are to be measured from the reference line: $\log |G| = 0$. Since on log-log paper the vertical axis is ordinarily marked with values of $|G|$, the reference line is at $|G| = 1.0$. If the decibel scale had been used, the reference line would be $D = 0$. As an example, three arrows are again drawn on the upper graph of Fig. 6–5 to show the three distances at $\omega = 3$. The outcome of such graphical computations over the entire frequency range is shown in Fig. 6–6, where a decibel scale is also included for comparison. The reader should convince himself that he could use the lines of Fig. 6–5 to build up Fig. 6–6. From the latter figure, it may be seen that there are magnitude-curve characteristics as well as angle shifts that may be identified with the order of a system. As each contributing G is added to the over-all system, the slope of the magnitude line becomes more negative. The first-order asymptote has a slope of -1; the third-order asymptote is found to be of -3 slope; in general, an nth-order system produces a high-frequency asymptote of slope $= -n$.

An important by-product of the computational method outlined in this section is the observation that multiplication of any $G(s)$ by a constant is equivalent on the Bode diagram to a simple shift on the magnitude scale. This can be confirmed formally by

$$\begin{aligned} \log KG(s) &= \log K + \log G(s) \\ \angle KG(s) &= \angle K + \angle G(s) = \angle G(s) \end{aligned} \qquad (6\text{–}16)$$

since the angle associated with a positive constant is zero. The graphical effect is shown in Fig. 6–7. The low-frequency asymptote of the $|G|$ graph is called the **zero frequency gain**, or just the **gain**.

6–6 A STANDARD FIRST-ORDER GRAPH

For reference purposes, it is more convenient to have a single dimensionless Bode plot than individual curves for the various time constants and various gains. To achieve this it is only necessary to modify the frequency scale to include the time constant in the group $(\omega\tau)$ and to factor the gain out of $G(s)$. With these changes, the break

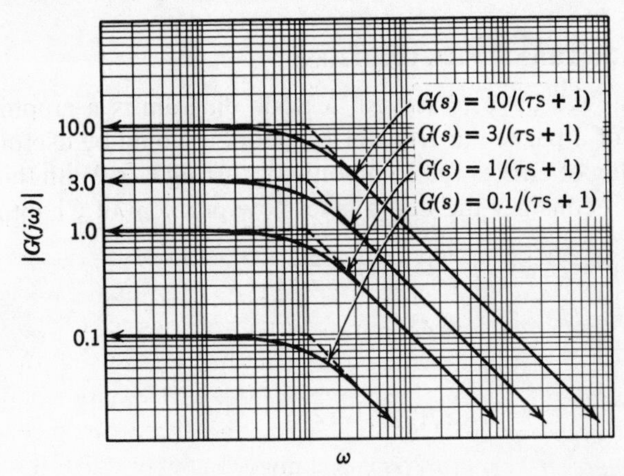

Fig. 6–7. Effect of gain-constant on Bode magnitude line.

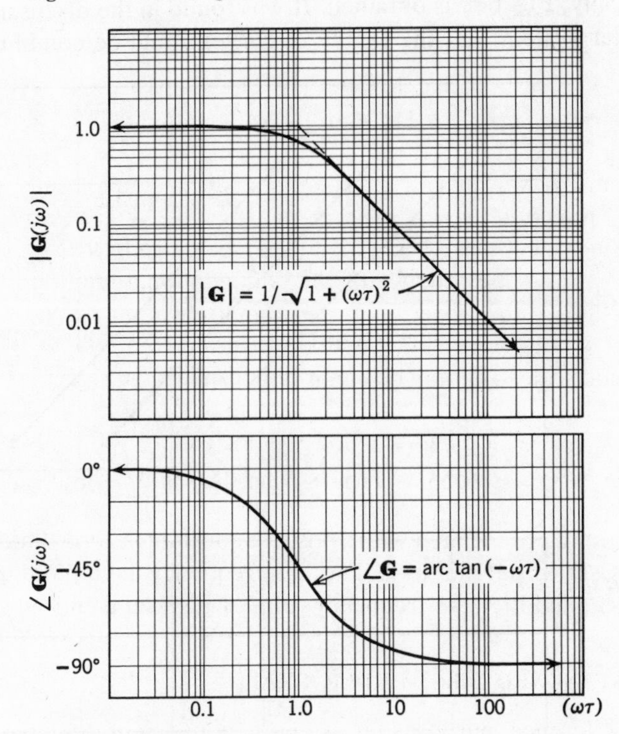

Fig. 6–8. Standard form of Bode plot for first-order system.

frequency is at $(\omega\tau) = 1$, as in Fig. 6–8, and the asymptote for $\omega \to 0$ returns to 1. A boldface **G** will be used to show that a standard form is meant: $\mathbf{G} = G/K$.

6–7. OTHER TRANSFER FUNCTIONS

Since, as we have observed, a Bode diagram is a graphical representation of a particular transfer function, it would be useful to have a brief catalog of curves for commonly occurring G's. With this object in mind, we reconsider the liquid level-flow problem of Chapter 2 where

$$G(s) = \frac{1}{As}$$

$$G(j\omega) = \frac{1}{A\omega j} = -\frac{1}{A\omega} j$$

$$|G(j\omega)| = \frac{1}{A\omega}$$

$$\angle G(j\omega) = -90^\circ \tag{6–17}$$

Graphically, Fig. 6–9 is obtained. It was found in the discussion of the first-order system that the family of curves could be combined into a

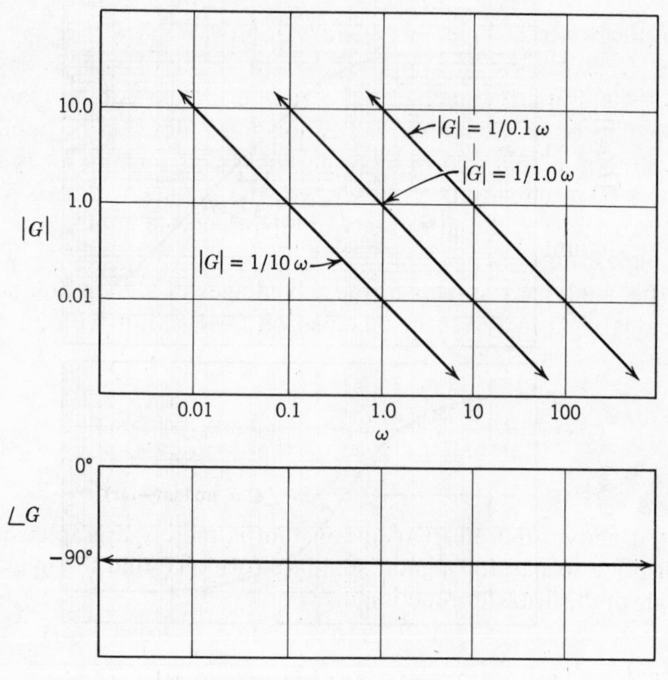

Fig. 6–9. Bode plot from $G(s) = 1/As$.

single standard curve, if the system parameter (the time constant) were combined with the frequency in a lumped abscissa scale. A similar advantage can be obtained for this Bode plot by using the product $(A\omega)$. The result is Fig. 6–10. The $\angle G$ graph remains unchanged.

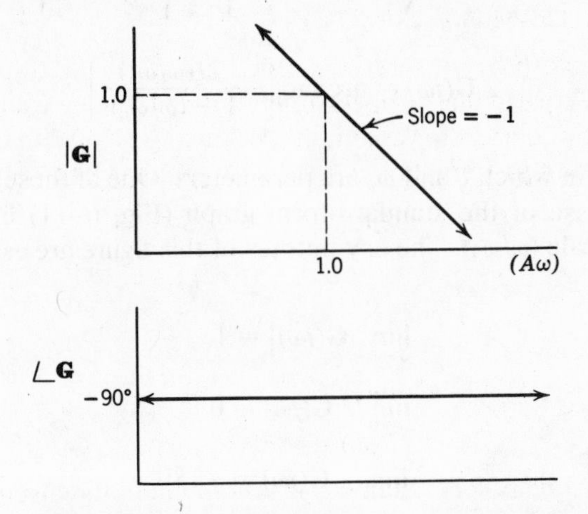

Fig. 6–10. Standard form of Bode plot for $G = 1/As$.

From the study of inverse transformation, we know that any polynominal $G(s)$ can be decomposed into a series of simpler factors, linear or quadratic. Conversely, a series of factors can be expanded algebraically, or as we found in Section 6–5, they can be combined graphically on a Bode plot. Since the linear components for real and zero roots have already been described, the picture will be complete if we make a last addition to our Bode plot catalog: a quadratic term with complex roots.

For this study, we anticipate the advantages of a good notation by writing this $\mathbf{G}(s)$ in the form of equation (4–19), but with an added constant:

$$\mathbf{G}(s) = \frac{\omega_n^2}{s^2 + 2\zeta\omega_n s + \omega_n^2} = \frac{1}{s^2/\omega_n^2 + 2\zeta s/\omega_n + 1} \tag{6–18}$$

As noted above, the effect of a constant is merely a graphical shift, a small price to pay for a good standard form. To find the magnitude and angle of this transfer function, use

$$\mathbf{G}(j\omega) = \frac{1}{-\omega^2/\omega_n^2 + 2\zeta j\omega/\omega_n + 1} = \frac{1}{[1 - (\omega/\omega_n)^2] + [2\zeta(\omega/\omega_n)]j}$$

Then:

$$|\mathbf{G}(j\omega)| = \frac{1}{\sqrt{\left[1 - (\omega/\omega_n)^2\right]^2 + \left[2\zeta(\omega/\omega_n)\right]^2}}$$

$$\angle \mathbf{G}(j\omega) = \text{arc tan}\left[-\frac{2\zeta(\omega/\omega_n)}{1 - (\omega/\omega_n)^2}\right] \tag{6-19}$$

expressions in which ζ and ω_n are parameters. One of these is absorbed in the abscissa of the standard-form graph (Fig. 6–11) by using the combined scale (ω/ω_n). The asymptotes of this figure are established as follows:

$$\lim_{\omega \to 0} |\mathbf{G}(j\omega)| = 1$$

$$\lim_{\omega \to 0} \angle \mathbf{G}(j\omega) = 0$$

$$\lim_{\omega \to \infty} \angle \mathbf{G}(j\omega) = -180°$$

and since

$$\log |\mathbf{G}(j\omega)| = -\log \sqrt{[1 - (\omega/\omega_n)^2]^2 + [2\zeta(\omega/\omega_n)]^2}$$

the high frequency asymptote of $|\mathbf{G}(j\omega)|$ is

$$\lim_{\omega \to \infty} \log |\mathbf{G}(j\omega)| = \lim_{\omega \to \infty} -\log \sqrt{[1 - (\omega/\omega_n)^2]^2 + [2\zeta(\omega/\omega_n)]^2}$$

$$= -2 \log \omega + 2 \log \omega_n \tag{6-20}$$

a straight line of slope = –2 on log-log coordinates. The second-order asymptotes will intersect where $\log 1 = -\log (\omega/\omega_n)^2$, that is, where $\omega = \omega_n$. At this frequency, $\angle \mathbf{G}(j\omega) = -90°$.

Although the second-order study was motivated by cases of complex roots ($\zeta < 1$), equations (6–19) are equally satisfactory for values of $\zeta > 1$. In this case the quadratic may be further factored to give two real roots, or the curves of Fig. 6–11 may be used.

6–8. THE NYQUIST DIAGRAM

In the arguments that accompanied Fig. 6–1, $G(j\omega)$ was presented as a vector having magnitude and associated angle. But since this vector is a function of frequency it will change direction and length.

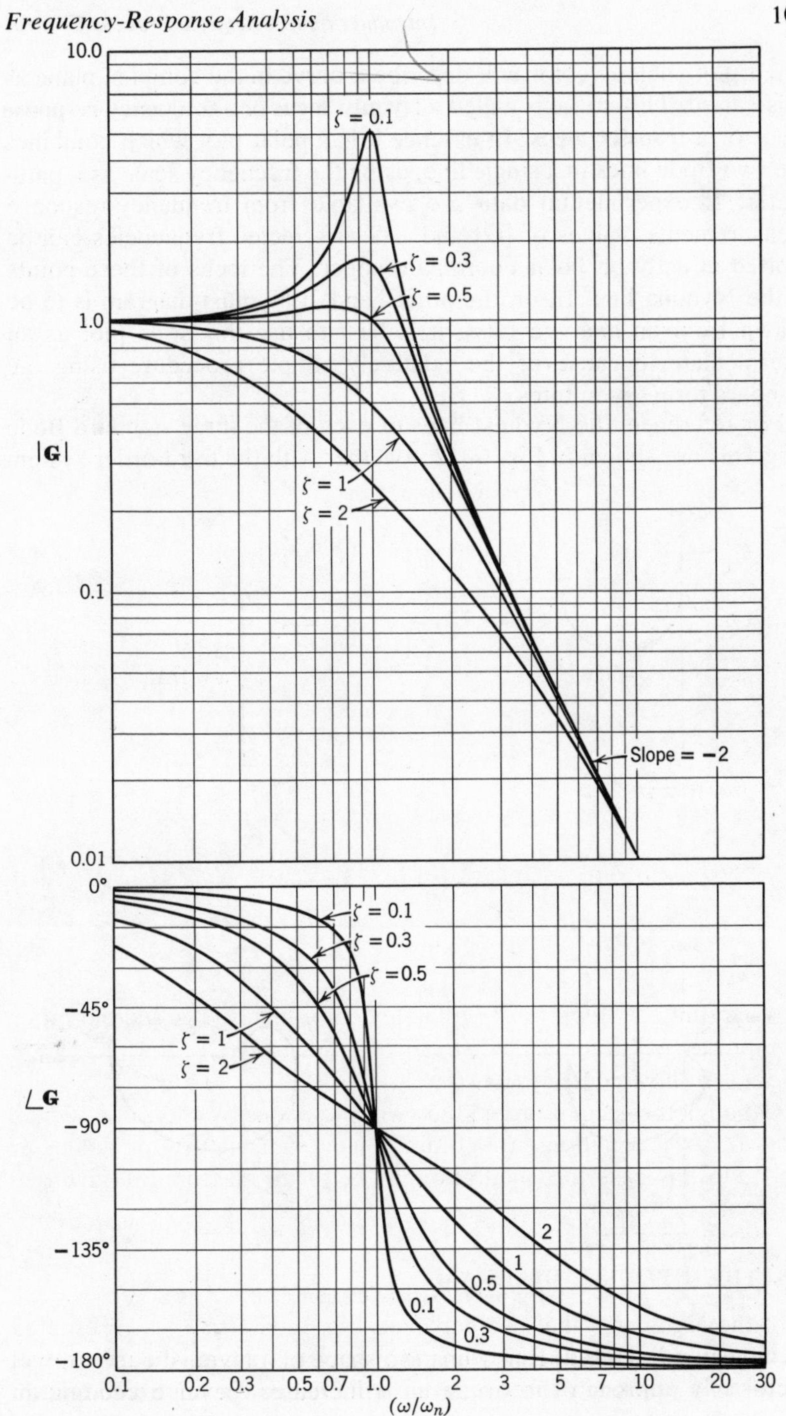

Fig. 6–11. Standard form of Bode plot for second-order system.

The tip of such a vector will describe a curve in the complex plane as ω is varied. This curve is called a **Nyquist locus** or a **frequency-response locus** or a **transfer locus.** In essence it is a polar plot which combines the two Bode lines in a single line, using the frequency scale as a parameter. If experimental data are available from frequency-response measurements, values of $|G|$ and $\angle G$ at selected frequencies can be plotted directly on polar coordinate paper. The locus of these points is the Nyquist line. If, on the other hand, a Nyquist diagram is to be drawn from an analytic $G(s)$, it is best to use the Bode plot as an intermediate, because of the relatively simple procedure using the standard form asymptotes.

For reference, the Nyquist lines of each of the three standard Bode diagrams are shown in Fig. 6–12, together with the third-order system

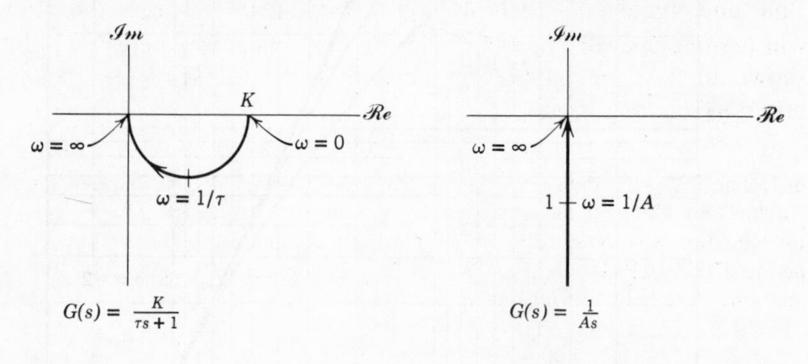

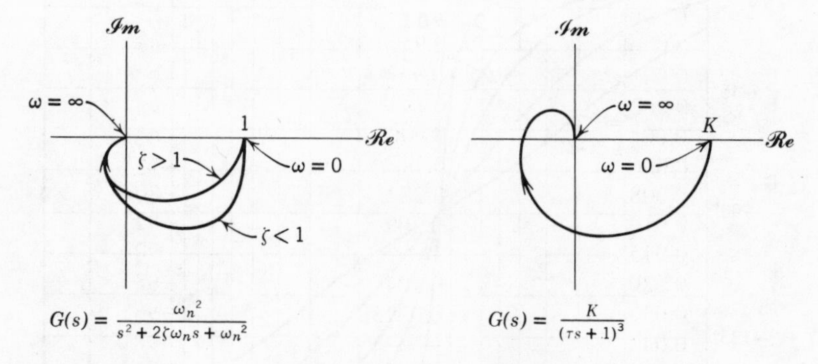

Fig. 6–12. Nyquist diagrams.

previously considered. Regarding the shape of a Nyquist curve, it will necessarily approach the origin as ω increases, never exceeding an angle of $-(n\pi/2)$ where n is the order of the system. If the system function has no poles at $s = 0$, the line will terminate for $\omega = 0$ at $\angle G = 0$ at a finite $|G|$; otherwise $|G|$ will increase without limit as $\omega \rightarrow 0$ and the line will asympotically approach one of the axes. Each integration in the function (repeated zero root) shifts the asymptote by $-90°$; thus, for a single s the approach is to $-90°$, for an s^2 term the approach is to $-180°$, etc.

REMARKS

The Bode plot is the connecting link between algebraic and graphical analysis, and between analytic equations and experimental data. It is remarkably adaptable to linear functions of any order, requiring only the proper combination of three standard form graphs. Although the Bode and Nyquist diagrams are equivalent in many respects, the latter will assume special importance in the next chapter, where it will be shown to have an intimate association with a closed-loop stability criterion.

EXERCISES

6–1. The following data are adapted from the experimental measurements of Taylor and Conover (as reported by Walsh and Hougen[1]). The object of investigation was to describe input and output concentration fluctuations of an agitated (177 RPM) mixing vessel of 26.2 gallon capacity. The flowrates in and out were held constant at 3.22 gal/min.

Frequency-Response Data

ω, rad/sec	$\|G\|$, dimensionless	$\angle G$, degrees
0.0001	——	−3
0.0005	0.955	−13
0.001	0.933	−25
0.002	0.773	−45
0.004	0.500	−62
0.006	0.347	−72
0.008	0.282	−80
0.010	0.209	−82
0.015	——	−90
0.020	0.104	−88
0.03	0.0773	−96
0.04	——	−98
0.05	0.0426	−109
0.06	0.0380	−106

[1] Walsh, R. A., and J. O. Hougen, *Chem. Eng. Prog.* **57**, 72 (1961).

(a) Prepare a Bode plot from the data. Is the system first-order? Explain. Would you expect first-order behavior? What is the system time constant? Does it check with the frequency-response data?

(b) When the Taylor and Conover data are extended to higher frequencies they show:

ω, rad/sec	$\lvert G \rvert$, dimensionless	$\angle G$, degrees
0.08	0.0214	−106
0.10	0.0191	−116
0.15	0.0129	−132
0.20	0.00870	−143
0.30	0.00500	−167
0.40	0.00346	—
0.50	0.00214	—
0.60	0.00166	—
0.70	0.00095	—
0.80	0.00080	—
0.90	0.00044	—
1.00	0.00033	—

Do these data change any conclusions that you drew from the previous data?

6–2. Referring to the thermometer of Problem 4–7, how rapid an input fluctuation is permissible: (a) to maintain perfect accuracy? (b) to maintain an output/input amplitude ratio = 0.9? (c) to maintain a phase lag not over 10°?

6–3. An On-Off controller maintains the temperature in a furnace between 900°F and 980°F, the sinusoidal oscillations occurring about once every two minutes. How accurate a record could be obtained using a first-order thermocouple with time constant equal to 10 sec? Would your result change significantly if the thermocouple were protected by a thermal well of one minute time constant? Assume the well is also first-order in its behavior.

6–4. Experimental measurements on a heat exchanger were made by Hearn[2] using the shell-side flowrate as input, and the tube effluent temperature as output. The exchanger had 4 tube passes (8 tubes/pass) and 12 baffles on the shell side. Hearn reports that his data may be described by the transfer function:

$$G(s) = \frac{K}{(1 + \tau_1 s)(1 + \tau_2 s)}$$

[2]Hearn, J. S., M. S. Thesis, St. Louis Univ., 1959.

Do the following frequency-response data (approximating Hearn's) fit this model? If so, estimate the values of K, τ_1, and τ_2.

Experimental Results

ω, rad/sec	$\lvert G \rvert$, °F/(gal/min)	$\angle G$, degrees
0.0022	—	−3
0.0030	—	−5
0.0042	—	−7
0.0050	0.48	—
0.0060	—	−8
0.0080	—	−10
0.0090	—	−13
0.011	0.46	−15
0.016	0.47	−22
0.023	0.46	−30
0.032	0.46	−44
0.046	0.37	−60
0.063	0.25	−77
0.094	0.16	−88
0.12	0.14	−91
0.18	0.096	−112
0.26	0.062	—
0.37	0.017	—

6–5. Sketch a Bode plot for the transfer function:

$$G(s) = \frac{1}{s^2 + 6s + 9}$$

by each of two methods: (*a*) find the damping coefficient and the natural undamped frequency, and use the generalized second-order Fig. (6–11); and (b) factor the quadratic term, and add the two first-order graphs. Do the results agree? Which method is simpler? Is the choice always available?

6–6. Given the four transfer functions:

$$G_1(s) = 1/(\tau s + 1)$$
$$G_2(s) = 1/(\tau s - 1)$$
$$G_3(s) = (\tau s + 1)$$
$$G_4(s) = (\tau s - 1)$$

(a) Show that: $|G_1| = |G_2| = 1/|G_3| = 1/|G_4|$, that: $\angle G_1 = -\angle G_2 = -\angle G_3 = \angle G_4$, and sketch Bode diagrams for each. (b) Sketch a Bode diagram for

$$G(s) = \frac{\tau s - 1}{\tau s + 1}$$

A system whose transfer function contains this factor is called a **non-minimum phase** system. Can you explain this designation?

6–7. Given the two transfer functions:

$$G_1(s) = \frac{1}{(s^2 + 2\zeta\omega_n s + \omega_n^2)}$$

$$G_2(s) = (s^2 + 2\zeta\omega_n s + \omega_n^2)$$

(a) Show that: $|G_1| = 1/|G_2|$, $\angle G_1 = -\angle G_2$. (b) Generalize this result and those of the previous problem to apply to any G's that are reciprocal to one another.

6–8. The control action of an idealized three-mode proportional plus integral plus derivative controller may be written as:

$$\hat{p} = K_c\left(\hat{e} + \frac{1}{\tau_i}\int_0^t \hat{e}\, dt + \tau_d \frac{d\hat{e}}{dt}\right)$$

where the three adjustable parameters are:

K_c = proportional gain
τ_i = integral time constant
τ_d = derivative time constant

and $\hat{p}$, $\hat{e}$ have the same meanings as in equation (2–24), (*a*) Show that in the s-domain this equation becomes

$$G_c(s) = \frac{P(s)}{E(s)} = \frac{K_c}{\tau_i s}\left(\frac{s^2 + 2\zeta\omega_n s + \omega_n^2}{\omega_n^2}\right)$$

and identify ω_n, ζ in terms of the adjustable control parameters. (b) Sketch this G_c on the Bode coordinates if $\tau_i = 2$ min., $\tau_d = 0.4$ min.

6–9. Typical experimental results on a pneumatic controller are shown in Fig. 6–13. (a) Does this controller exhibit proportional action over part of

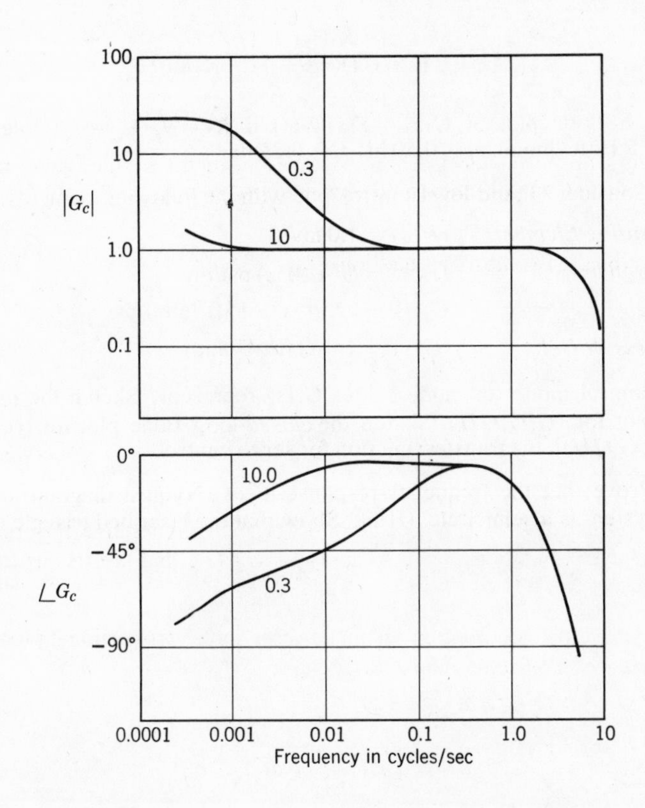

Fig. 6–13. Typical experimental frequency-response data for a pneumatic controller. Parameter is dial reading in minutes.

the frequency range? If so, what is the proportional gain? Does this controller exhibit integral action? If so, what is the integral time constant? Does this controller exhibit derivative action? If so, what is the derivative time constant? (*b*) Is the behavior of this controller consistent with the idealized $G_c(s)$ given in the previous problem or in Problem 5–5? Does it fit better the approximation:

$$G_c(s) = K\left(\frac{\tau_1 s + 1}{\tau_2 s + 1}\right)$$

If so, estimate K, τ_1, and τ_2.

6–10. In the chemical-reactor discussion that led to Fig. 5–3, it was shown by linearization that

$$Y(s) = \frac{K_1(\tau_2 s + 1)}{(\tau_1 s + 1)(\tau_2 s + 1) + K_2 K_3} X(s)$$

Sketch a Bode plot of $G(s) = Y(s)/X(s)$ if $K_1 = 9$, $K_2 = 7$ (moles/ft^3)/°F, $K_3 = 0.5$°F/(ft^3/mole), $\tau_1 = 0.50$ hr, $\tau_2 = 0.25$ hr.

6–11. Consider a liquid-level control loop with the following elements:

Measuring Element:	$H(s) = 1.0$ mv/ft
Controller:	$G_c(s) = (1 + .05s)$ psi/mv
Valve:	$G_v(s) = 125/(5s + 1)$(ft^3/min)/psi
Process Vessel:	$G(s) = 1/4\pi s$ ft/(ft^3/min)

What control mode (or modes) does $G_c(s)$ represent? Sketch the *open*-loop Bode plot for $(G_c G_v G H)$. Sketch the *closed*-loop Bode plot for $[(G_c G_v G)/(1 + G_c G_v G H)]$, the transfer function for servo control.

6–12. Prove that the frequency-response locus (Nyquist diagram) of a first-order system is a semicircle. (Hint: Show that the inscribed triangle is a right triangle.)

7 Graphical Stability Criteria

A major shortcoming of the stability analysis that studies the roots of the characteristic equation is its dependence on algebraic information. In dealing with complicated systems, it is often advantageous and sometimes essential to characterize a system by resort to experimental data. When this is the case, frequency-response measurements are most suitable, but the criterion which rested on the signs of the characteristic roots must now be translated into some related property of the Bode and Nyquist diagrams, curves which can arise from experiment.

7-1. THE MIKHAILOV CURVE

As a first step in the direction of graphical stability analysis, note that the characteristic polynomial

$$\Gamma(s) = s^n + a_{n-1}s^{n-1} + \cdots + a_0$$

$$= (s + \mu_1)(s + \mu_2) \cdots (s + \mu_n) \qquad (7\text{-}1)$$

can be plotted in the complex plane from its magnitude and angle:

$$|\Gamma(j\omega)| = |j\omega + \mu_1| \cdot |j\omega + \mu_2| \cdots |j\omega + \mu_n|$$

$$= \sqrt{\omega^2 + \mu_1{}^2} \cdot \sqrt{\omega^2 + \mu_2{}^2} \cdots \sqrt{\omega^2 + \mu_n{}^2}$$

$$\angle\Gamma(j\omega) = \angle(j\omega+\mu_1)+\angle(j\omega+\mu_2)+\cdots+\angle(j\omega+\mu_n)$$

$$= \arc\tan\frac{\omega}{\mu_1} + \arc\tan\frac{\omega}{\mu_2} + \cdots + \arc\tan\frac{\omega}{\mu_n}$$

$$= \theta_1 + \theta_2 + \cdots + \theta_n \tag{7-2}$$

This locus, called the **Mikhailov** curve, is a function of frequency in the same sense as the Nyquist locus of the last chapter. In fact the two have other similarities, but it is of great importance to recognize that the Nyquist curve describes a forward-path cascade, while the Mikhailov figure refers to the characteristic polynomial of a closed loop. As the parameter ω increases from zero to infinity, the vector representation of $\Gamma(j\omega)$ sweeps across the complex plane through an angle that is the sum of the terms in equation (7–2). Each stable root of the characteristic equation (see Table 4–1) will contribute a term with positive μ; the point $(j\omega + \mu)$ will appear in the first quadrant of the complex plane as in Fig. 7–1*a*. As ω increases in the range $0 \leqslant \omega < \infty$, the angle contribution θ_i increases by $\pi/2$ from (0° to 90°). On the contrary, each unstable root corresponds to a negative μ as shown in Fig. 7–1*b*. In this case the angle θ_i decreases $\pi/2$ from (180° to 90°) as ω increases in $0 \leqslant \omega < \infty$.

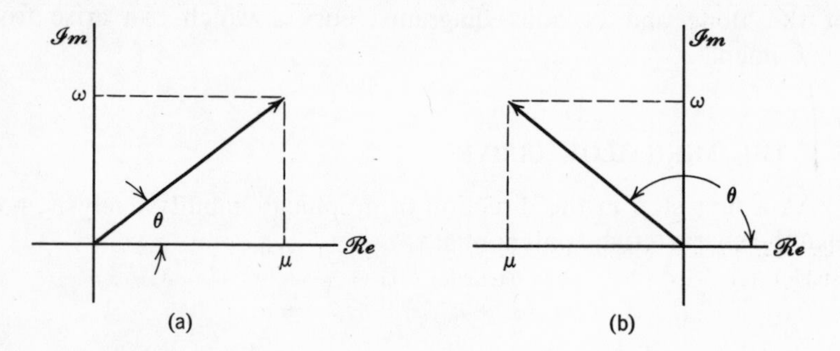

Fig. 7–1. Root location in the complex plane. (a) Positive μ (stable root). (b) Negative μ (unstable root).

This observation leads to a simple stability argument: in order that an nth-order characteristic equation have n stable roots, the $\angle\Gamma\,(j\omega)$ must increase through n quadrants as ω increases through $0 \leqslant \omega < \infty$. Every unstable root will decrease the total number of quadrants covered by two, since it has a negative effect over and above the removal of the positive contribution. It is therefore possible to establish whether or not a system is stable by inspection of the Mikhailov curve. Several samples are shown in Fig. 7–2.

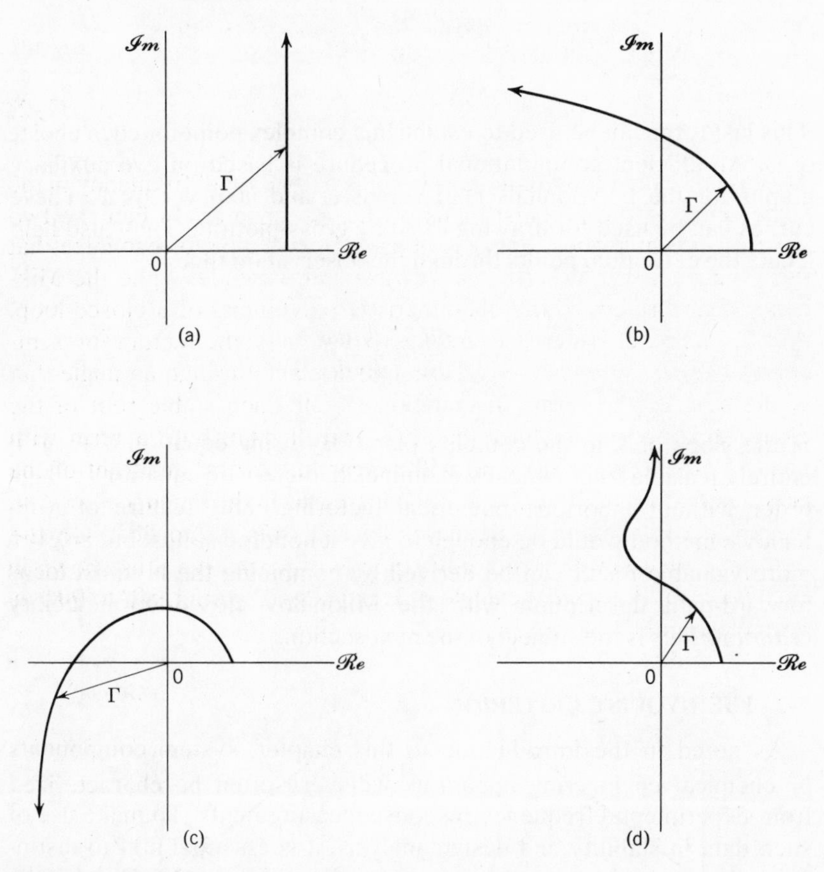

Fig. 7–2. Typical Mikhailov curves. a) $\Gamma = \tau s + 1$ (stable). (b) $\Gamma = s^2 + 2\zeta\omega_n s + \omega_n{}^2$ (stable). (c) $\Gamma = s^3 + 6s^2 + 11s + 6$ (stable). (d) $\Gamma = 2s^3 + s^2 + 23s + 66$ (unstable).

If it were necessary to write $\Gamma(s)$ in the factored form of equation (7–1) in order to draw the $\Gamma(j\omega)$ curve, there would be nothing gained, for the signs of the factors are already sufficient to establish stability or instability. It may be demonstrated that a factored form is not needed by writing

$$\Gamma(s) = a_0 + a_1 s + \cdots + a_{n-1} s^{n-1} + s^n$$

$$\Gamma(j\omega) = a_0 + a_1(j\omega) + \cdots + a_{n-1}(j\omega)^{n-1} + (j\omega)^n$$

$$= (a_0 - a_2\omega^2 + a_4\omega^4 - \cdots) + (a_1\omega - a_3\omega^3 + a_5\omega^5 - \cdots)j$$

$$= g(\omega) + h(\omega)j \tag{7-3}$$

This last form can be used to establish a complex point for each choice of ω. An efficient computational procedure is based on two auxiliary graphs for the polynomials $g(\omega)$ versus ω and $h(\omega)$ versus ω. These curves can be used for drawing $\Gamma(j\omega)$ by cross-plotting. They also help locate the extremum points through the observation that

$$\frac{dh}{dg} = \frac{dh/d\omega}{dg/d\omega}$$

is the slope of Γ in the complex plane. By using equation (7–3) it is entirely feasible to graphically examine characteristic equations of high order without laborious numerical factoring. This feature of Mikhailov's method would be enough to give it honored status, but an even more valuable result can be derived by combining the Nyquist locus forward-path description with the Mikhailov closed-loop stability criterion. This is the subject of the next section.

7–2. THE NYQUIST CRITERION

As noted in the introduction to this chapter, system components of chemical engineering apparatus will very often be characterized from experimental frequency response measurements. To make use of such data in stability and design analysis, it is essential first to distinguish between the open-loop transfer function, G_cG_vGH, and the forward-path transfer function, which depends on the loop input location. For a servo-loop we have called G_cG_vG the forward-path function, whereas for regulator loops in which the disturbance enters to directly affect the manipulating variable, the plant G is alone the forward-path transfer function.

Both the forward-path function and the open-loop function appear in any closed-loop expression. Considering a servo-loop, for example, the closed-loop transfer function is:

$$F(s) = \frac{G_cG_vG}{1 + G_cG_vGH} = \frac{\text{(forward-path function)}}{1 + \text{(open-loop function)}} \tag{7-4}$$

Writing the open-loop function as a ratio of polynomials:

$$G_c G_v G H = \frac{\Lambda(s)}{\Gamma(s)} \tag{7-5}$$

the closed-loop function is

$$F(s) = \frac{\Lambda/H\Gamma}{1+\Lambda/\Gamma} = \frac{\Lambda/H}{\Gamma+\Lambda} = \frac{\Lambda/H}{\Gamma_n} \tag{7-6}$$

where Γ and Γ_n are the characteristic polynomials for the open-and closed-loop transfer functions respectively. As was shown in Problem 5–3, the numerator polynomial of an open-loop function cannot be of order greater than that of the corresponding denominator. Therefore, Λ must be of order less than Γ, and their sum, Γ_n, must be a polynomial of the same order as Γ (the order is n).

From equation (7–6) we can write the auxiliary relation:

$$1 + \frac{\Lambda}{\Gamma} = \frac{\Gamma+\Lambda}{\Gamma} = \frac{\Gamma_n}{\Gamma}$$

By letting L represent the open-loop function $G_c G_v G H = \Lambda/\Gamma$, this can be condensed to

$$1 + L = \frac{\Gamma_n}{\Gamma} \tag{7-7}$$

which is in a form convenient for applying Mikhailov's criterion. Suppose that the open loop is known to be stable: then the Mikhailov curve of Γ passes through n quadrants. We are looking for closed-loop stability: then the Mikhailov curve of Γ_n must also pass through n quadrants. But since angles are to be subtracted in taking ratios of complex expressions, the vector (Γ_n/Γ) must sweep out $(n-n)=0$ net quadrants as $0 \leqslant \omega < \infty$. This will be the case if the curve of (Γ_n/Γ) does not enclose the origin. This conclusion is illustrated by Fig. 7–3*a* where curves for stable and unstable systems are shown.

By taking advantage of equation (7–7) this finding can be translated into a criterion for the open-loop function, for as this equation shows, the vector (Γ_n/Γ) differs from the vector L merely by a unit displacement in the complex plane. This is shown by Fig. 7–3*b*. If the (Γ_n/Γ) curve does not enclose the origin, the L curve will not enclose the -1 point. This discussion of stability may be summarized as the simplified[1] Nyquist criterion: a closed-loop control system is stable if (and only if) the open-loop Nyquist curve does not enclose the critical point at −1. Because this comparison is entirely graphical, it is ideally suited to treatment of experimental data.

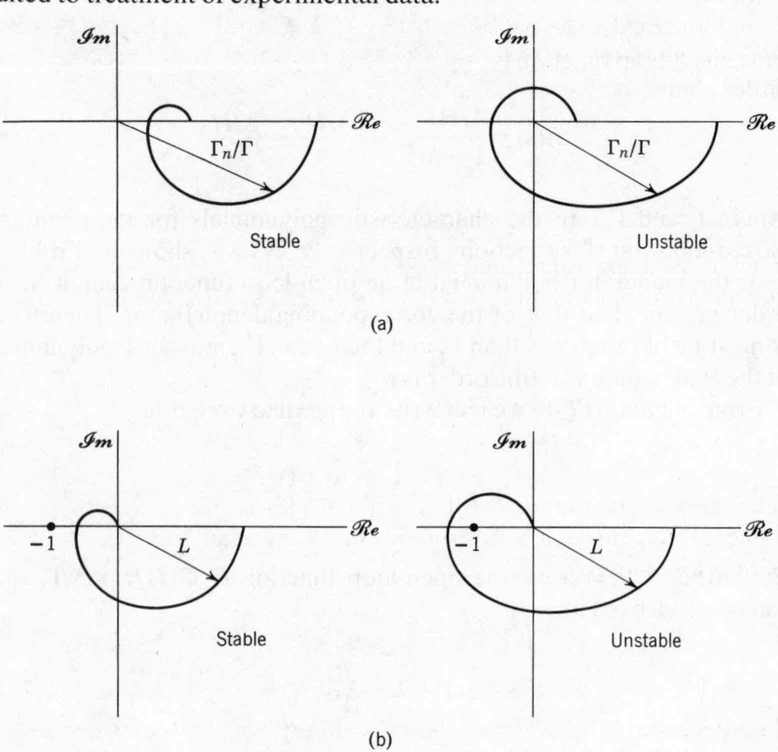

Fig. 7–3. The Nyquist criterion for closed-loop stability from open-loop data. (a) The ratio of Mikhailov curves: (Γ_n/Γ). (b) open-loop Nyquist curves: $L = G_cG_vGH$.

7–3. STABILITY ON THE BODE PLOT

The critical point at −1 in the complex plane can also be described by its magnitude (unity) and angle (−180°). If the open-loop Nyquist locus is not to enclose this point, $|L| < 1$ at $\angle L = -180°$. On the Bode coordinates, then, there will be a **critical frequency,** ω_c, at which the angle curve crosses the −180° level. The open-loop magnitude at

[1]There is a more general form of this criterion which can be applied even if the open-loop is unstable, provided the number of unstable open-loop poles is known; however, the simpler criterion developed here accounts for almost all single-loop problems of practical importance.

this frequency will establish stability or instability, according to its value relative to unity. It may be noted in passing that the product $L = G_c G_v GH$ will be dimensionless, regardless of the units associated with each transfer function.

A numerical example is instructive: in Chapter 4 a detailed study was made of the stability of a closed loop that contained the third-order plant

$$G(s) = \frac{1}{(\tau s + 1)^3}$$

The transducer, valve, and proportional controller contributed only constant transfer functions, so that the over-all open-loop function was

$$L(s) = G_c G_v GH(s) = \frac{K_c K_v K K_T}{(\tau s + 1)^3} = \frac{8K_c}{(s + 2)^3} \qquad (7\text{–}8)$$

The stability of the closed-loop system was found to depend on the value of K_c, through a consideration of the characteristic equation of the closed loop:

$$\Gamma_n(s) = (s + 2)^3 + 8K_c = 0 \qquad (7\text{–}9)$$

The decision as to whether the closed loop was stable or not rested on the signs associated with the real parts of the characteristic roots.

In this section a Bode plot comparison of the three cases previously studied is presented as Fig. 7–4. We observe the following: regardless of the controller gain, K_c, the critical frequency is $\omega_c = 2\sqrt{3}$. At this frequency, the magnitude values determine whether or not the closed loop is stable: at $K_c > 8$, unstable; at $K_c = 8$, marginally stable; at $K_c < 8$, stable. As is to be expected the result agrees with the prior stability analysis. By using the Bode plot of the open-loop transfer function, it was possible to avoid the tedious numerical methods needed to solve for the characteristic roots.

If it is more convenient to do so, the strengths of graphical analysis can also be found directly on the Nyquist coordinates. The three cases of this numerical example are shown in Fig. 7–5, where, of course, the conclusions are by now familiar: the curves indicate stability, marginal stability, and instability in that order, depending on whether or not the particular curve in question encloses the critical point. Since the system is third order, each curve approaches the origin along the −270° asymptote.

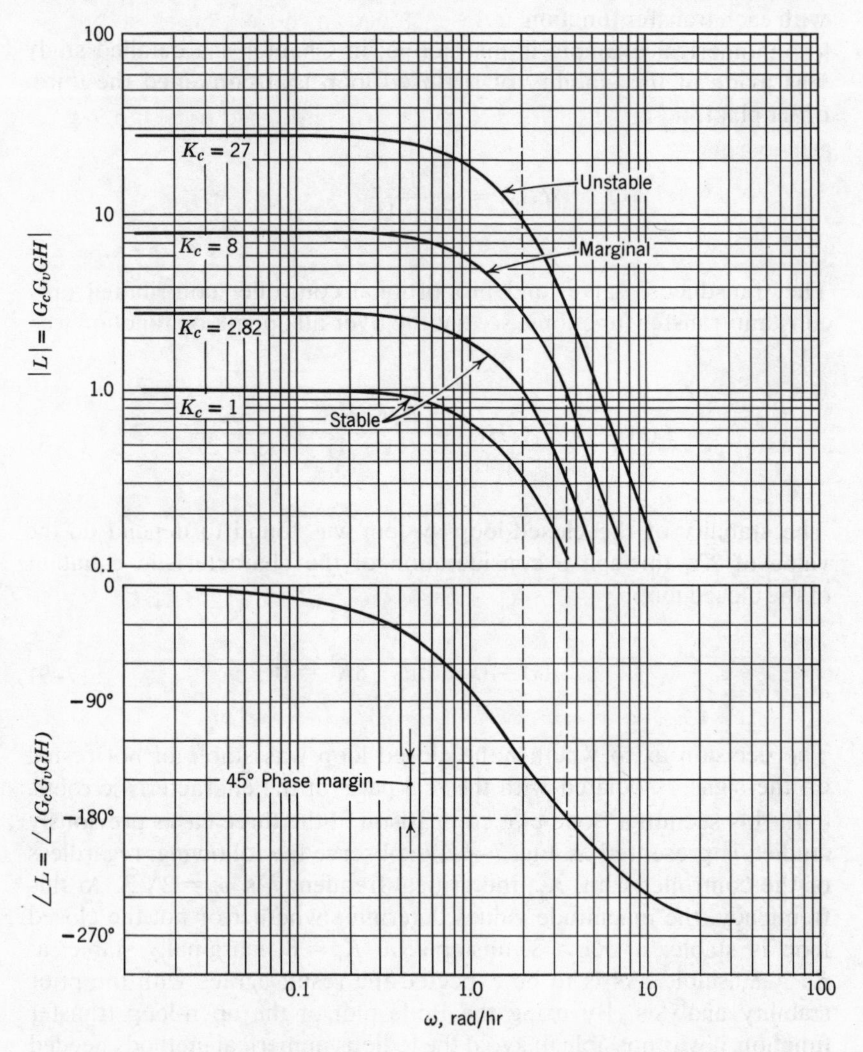

Fig. 7–4. Bode diagram for $L = G_cG_vGH = 8K_c/(s+2)^3$.

7–4. PHASE AND GAIN MARGINS

Returning to the stability discussion of Chapter 4, we may recall the need for compromise in the choice of loop gain. The essence of the stability-accuracy dilemma is that while a large K_c is needed to reduce offset (increase accuracy), the value of this parameter must be kept comfortably below the instability point. By referring to Fig. 7–4, it is clear that a safety factor can be included in the design by setting K_c lower than the marginal stability value by some arbitrary amount. If this safety factor is taken as 2.0, for example, the controller gain of Fig. 7–4 would be set at $K_c = 4$. Such a design is said to be based on a **gain margin**.

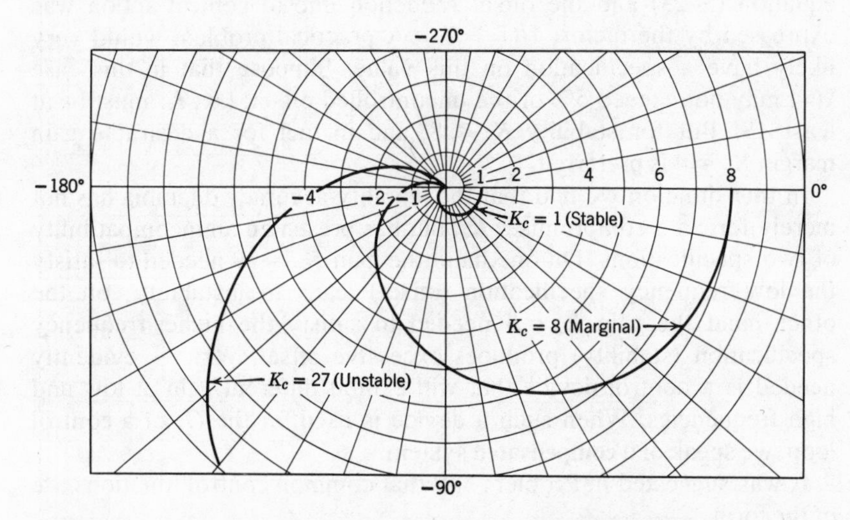

Fig. 7–5. Nyquist diagram for $L = G_cG_vGH = 8K_c/(s+2)^3$.

Alternatively, it is common to back away from marginal stability on the lower graph of the Bode pair. Instead of reducing the gain at the critical frequency, the design may be based on an arbitrary **phase margin** (angular safety factor) at which frequency $|L|$ is set equal to 1.0. A typical design basis might use a phase margin of 45°; that is, K_c would be chosen to give $|L| = 1$ at $\angle L = -180° + 45° = -135°$. Referring again to Fig. 7–4, this design is seen to give $K_c = 2.82$. Because of the arbitrary factors involved, the phase and gain margin designs are in principle equally valid. In view of the increased uncertainty associated with high-frequency experimental data, however, it is often the case that a designer can have more confidence in phase margin design, since it utilizes data over a smaller range of frequencies. Much larger gain or phase margins than those suggested above may be desirable if the experimental data are uncertain, or if the curve of L versus ω is not monotonically decreasing.

7–5. COMPENSATION

So far, attention has been focused on the high-frequency end of the Bode or Nyquist diagrams. This was necessary to assure stability and to provide a quantitative measure of relative stability via the gain or phase margins. But if we recall the stability-accuracy dilemma it is apparent that only half the job is done. In Chapter 5, the accuracy was evaluated by the final-value theorem. For the particular problem just considered the offset resulting from a disturbance step was given by equation (5–23) and the offset reduction due to control action was expressed by the factor, $1/(1+K_c)$. A practical problem would very likely have a specification on this value. Suppose that in this case $\hat{y}(\infty)$ may not exceed 5% of the uncontrolled offset; i.e., K_c must be at least 19. But for stability $K_c < 8$, and in fact for a desirable gain margin $K_c = 4$ is preferred.

In this situation we find that the stability-accuracy dilemma has not merely forced a compromise, K_c, but has presented an incompatibility of two specifications. On one hand the gain $K_c = 19$ needed to satisfy the low-frequency specification (offset) leads to instability; on the other hand the gain $K_c = 4$ needed to satisfy the higher-frequency specification (stability) produces excessive offset. What is evidently needed is a control device that will exhibit different gain at low and high frequencies. When such a device is used for the G_c of a control loop, we speak of a **compensated** system.

It was suggested in Problem 5–9 that common control functions are of the form

$$G_c(s) = K\frac{\tau_1 s + 1}{\tau_2 s + 1} \tag{7–10}$$

over a considerable frequency range. The behavior of this function may be studied most readily by examining first the limiting cases. If τ_2 is allowed to grow while τ_1 is kept small:

$$\lim_{\tau_2\to\infty} G_c(s) = K\left(\frac{\tau_1 s + 1}{\tau_2 s}\right) = \frac{K\tau_1}{\tau_2}\left(1 + \frac{1}{\tau_1 s}\right)$$

which is recognizable as ideal proportional plus integral control when $(K\tau_1/\tau_2)$ is identified with K_c and τ_1 with τ_i of Problem 5–5. If on the contrary τ_2 is made very small:

$$\lim_{\tau_2\to 0} G_c(s) = K(\tau_1 s + 1)$$

which is ideal proportional plus derivative action (see Problem 6–11).

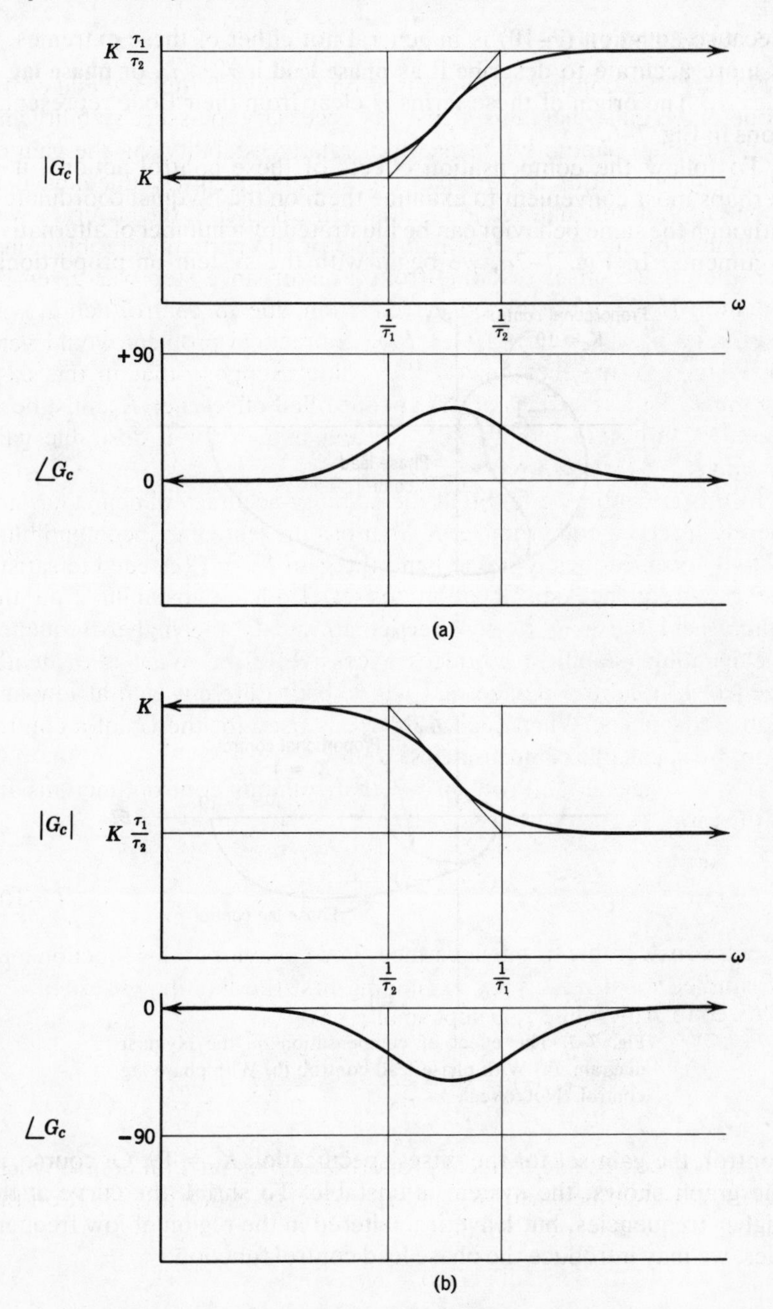

Fig. 7–6. Equation (7–10) on Bode coordinates. (a) Phase lead element ($\tau_2 < \tau_1$). (b) Phase lag element ($\tau_2 > \tau_1$).

Because equation (7–10) is in general not either of these extremes, it is more accurate to describe it as **phase lead** if $\tau_2 < \tau_1$, or **phase lag** if $\tau_2 > \tau_1$. The origin of these terms is clear from their Bode representations in Fig. 7–6.

To follow the compensation effects of these control actions, it is perhaps most convenient to examine them on the Nyquist coordinates, although the same behavior can be illustrated by a number of alternative arguments. In Fig. 7–7*a*, we begin with the system on proportional

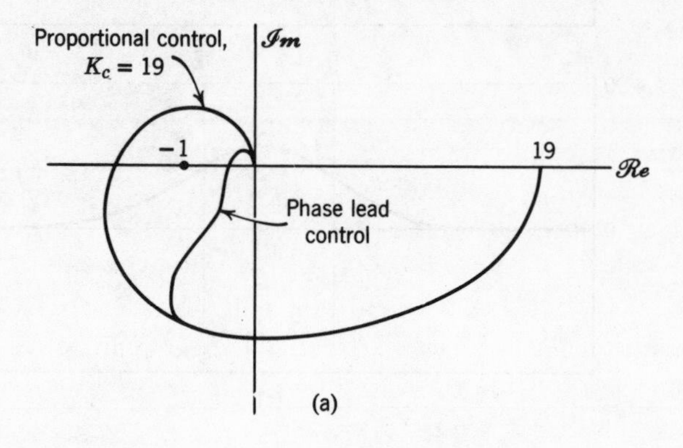

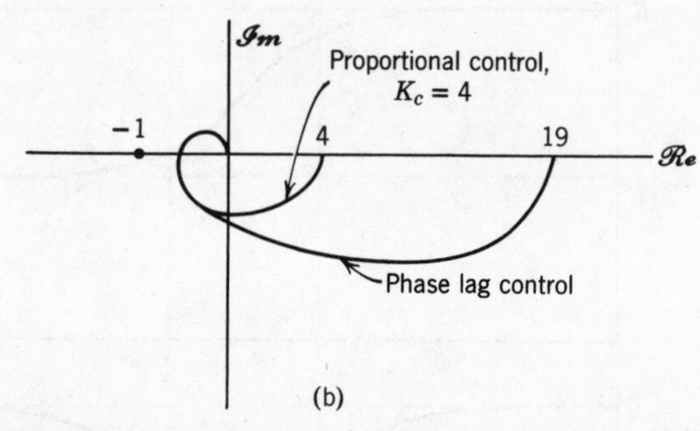

Fig. 7–7. The effect of compensation on the Nyquist diagram. (a) With phase lead control. (b) With phase lag control. (Not to scale.)

control, the gain set for the offset specification $K_c = 19$. Of course, as the graph shows, the system is unstable. To shrink the curve at the higher frequencies, but leave it unaltered in the region of low frequencies, we may introduce the phase lead control function:

$$G_c(s) = 19\left(\frac{\tau_1 s + 1}{\tau_2 s + 1}\right) \qquad \tau_2 < \tau_1 \tag{7–11}$$

The time constants are chosen so as to locate the hump in the phase lead curve in the neighborhood of the critical frequency. This tends to move ω_c toward higher frequencies where the magnitude of (G_vGH) is smaller. As shown, the result meets both specifications.

In the second case, Fig. 7–7*b*, the starting point is a system with adequate stability ($K_c = 4$), but showing unacceptable offset. By now augmenting the control action with a phase lag element

$$G_c(s) = 4\frac{\tau_2}{\tau_1}\left(\frac{\tau_1 s + 1}{\tau_2 s + 1}\right) \qquad \tau_2 > \tau_1 \tag{7–12}$$

it is possible to expand the low frequency end of the Nyquist curve, preserving meanwhile the same high-frequency characteristics. To keep ω_c from changing, the time constants must be chosen to position the phase lag bulge well below the critical frequency. To obtain a zero frequency gain of exactly $4\tau_2/\tau_1 = 19$, the ratio of the time constants should be $\tau_2/\tau_1 = 4.75$. The important point is that whereas our previous proportional-control design involved only expansion or shrinkage of the *entire* curve, the compensation effect changes the shape of the curve by modifying only a *part* of it.

EXERCISES

7–1. Show that the Mikhailov argument that centers about Fig. 7–1 is valid if μ is complex; that is, if two factors appear in $\Gamma(s)$ of the form: $(s + \mu + \beta j)(s + \mu - \beta j)$.

7–2. Show that the argument of Section 7–2 can be applied to a regulator loop, where

$$F(s) = \frac{G}{1 + G_c G_v G H}$$

Is the Nyquist criterion any different?

7–3. Draw the Mikhailov curve for the characteristic equation (7–9) for $K_c = 1, 8, 27$. What can you conclude about stability at these K_c values?

7–4. Design a control loop for the heat exchanger for which data were given in Problem 6–4. The following equipment is available.

Controller: P. B. dial from 0 to 10%; input span, 100 psi; output span, 20 psi.

Shell-side water valve: Linear pneumatic; diaphragm actuated; 3 to 15 psig, open to shut; flow is 50 gal/min when wide open.

Sensing element: Liquid-filled bulb; as temperature changes, the liquid expansion produces a linear pressure increase at 2 psi/°F. Assume negligible time lag for heat transfer to fluid in bulb.

Is the proposed controller adequate? Is your design based on a phase or gain margin? What controller setting would you use in each case?

7–5. Consider the previous problem from the point of view of transient response. Prepare a graph showing how the offset (in °F) will vary with % P. B. setting for a step change in load (disturbance) equivalent to 10 gal/min.

7–6. In Problem 7–4 it was assumed that the sensing element has a negligible time lag. A more realistic estimate might be to consider the bulb to be a first-order device with a 30-sec. time constant. Under these conditions, what proportional controller setting is marginal for stability? What would you recommend? What offset would result from a 10 gal/min load disturbance (step)?

7–7. In studying a chemical reactor having nonlinear kinetics, it is found that linearization about the steady state leads to the block diagram of Fig. 7–8

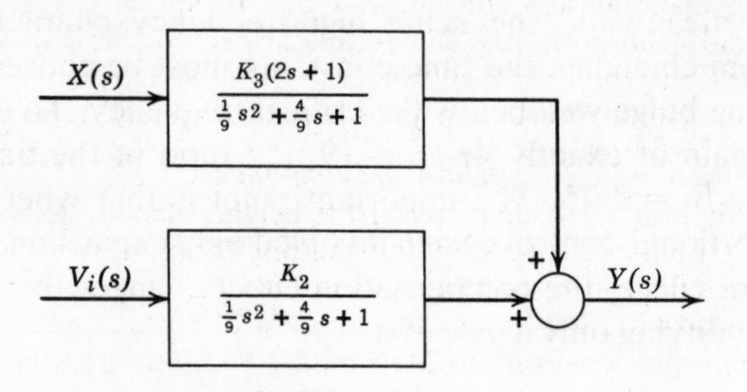

Fig. 7–8. Block diagram for a reactor.

where: x and y are the feed and product concentrations, mol/ft^3, v_i is the feed temperature, °F, $K_2 = -0.01$ (moles/ft^3)/°F, $K_3 = 0.33$ and the time constants are in hours. What is the significance of the negative sign on K_2?

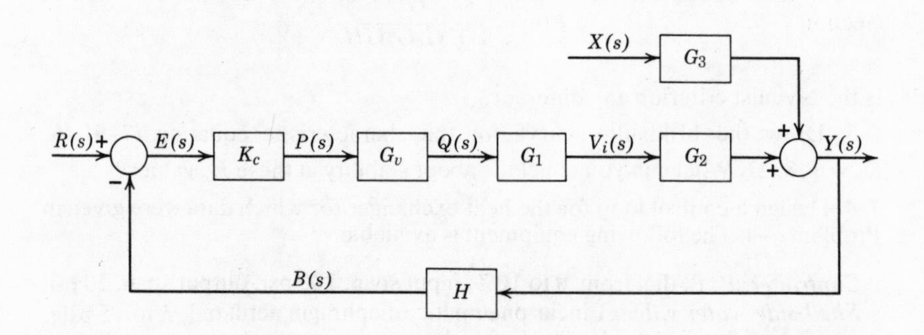

Fig. 7–9. Control loop for a reactor.

A shell-and-tube heat exchanger is connected to the reactor feed line and the loop is closed with appropriate transducer, valve, and controller, as shown in Fig. 7–9. Frequency-response measurements on the heat exchanger show that the effect of input shell-side flowrate q on the output tube-side temperature v_i, can be described by the transfer function:

$$G_1(s) = \frac{V_i(s)}{Q(s)} = \frac{K_1}{(\tau_1 s + 1)(\tau_2 s + 1)}$$

where: $K_1 = 2°\text{F/(gal/min)}$, $\tau_1 = 0.01$ hr, and $\tau_2 = 0.02$ hr. What controller setting K_c, would you recommend for design based on a 30° phase margin, if $G_v = K_v = -5$ (gal/min)/psi, and $H = K_T = 1000$ mv/(mol/ft³)? Why is K_v made negative?

7–8. The level of liquid in a vessel is to be controlled by manipulation of the inlet flowrate. The vessel acts as an alcohol reservoir for a subsequent reaction; it is to be pumped out at a constant rate of 7 ft³/min. Use the following data to recommend a proportional gain setting at each of the two settings of the integral time constant: $\tau_i = 0.30$ min, $\tau_i = 10$ min. Do your results support the contention that integral action tends to reduce system stability?

Data on Components

Tank Dimensions: 3 ft diameter; 10 ft height; alcohol density is 0.8 g/cc.

Measuring Element: Pressure transmitting diaphragm on the bottom of tank; estimated first-order time constant is 0.06 sec.

Valve: Linear with first order time constant of 50 sec; input span from 3 to 15 psig; output span from zero to 24 ft³/min.

Controller: Two-mode (proportional plus integral), for which Fig. 6–13 is given; input span from zero to 20 psig; output span from zero to 20 psig.

An engineer suggests that in this case an integral mode of control is not needed. Furthermore, he claims that the system will not show sustained offset *even with only proportional control.* Is he right? Explain.

7–9. Find suitable values for the time constants in equations (7–11) and (7–12) to produce the desired compensation in the problem presented in Section 7–5.

8 *Dead Time and Distributed Parameters*

There is a troublesome time delay common in chemical engineering systems that deserves special attention. It arises when a signal (output information) is physically carried between two points by a stream of material. Suppose that once again we direct our discussion in terms of the well-stirred vessel, but that for some good reason, the effluent concentration $y(t)$ must be measured at a point removed downstream by a distance L as illustrated in Figure 8–1. Perhaps the measuring probe

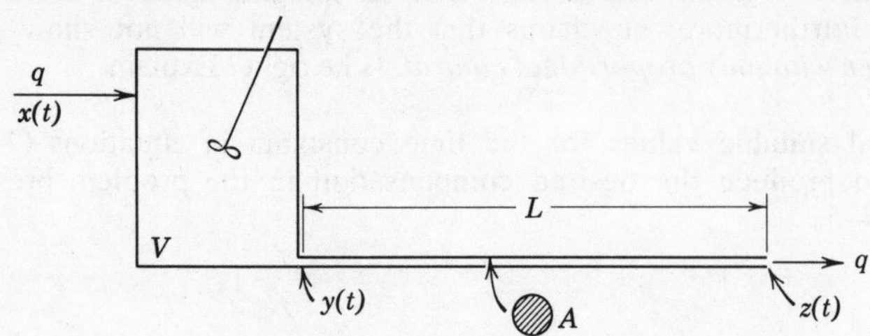

Fig. 8–1. A system with dead time.

is not operable at the high temperature existing in the vicinity of the vessel, or perhaps it is merely a matter of physical convenience. Then let us say that because of the time required for material to flow through the length of pipe, we measure $z(t)$, rather than $y(t)$. Sample curves which illustrate the relationship between these functions are shown in Fig. 8–2. The two curves are separated in the time direction by the **transportation lag**

$$\tau_0 = \frac{LA}{q} = \frac{V}{q} \tag{8–1}$$

where V is the pipe volume. **Dead time** and **distance-velocity lag** are other synonyms for τ_0. It may be confirmed from Fig. 8–2, that:

$$\hat{z}(t) = \hat{y}(t - \tau_0) \tag{8–2}$$

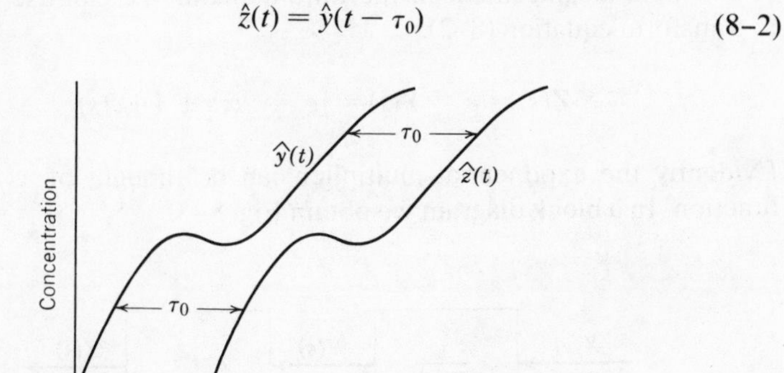

Fig. 8–2. A function displaced in time.

The transfer function between $X(s)$ and $Y(s)$ is of course the familiar first-order one. But how can we relate $Y(s)$ to $Z(s)$ in the s domain? To answer this question we must explore the transformation of a time-displaced function.

8–1. THE TIME-SHIFT THEOREM

Start with the definition:

$$\mathscr{L}[\hat{y}(t - \tau_0)] = \int_0^\infty \hat{y}(t - \tau_0)e^{-st}\,dt$$

Since τ_0 is constant, $dt = d(t - \tau_0)$, and

$$\mathscr{L}[\hat{y}(t - \tau_0)] = \int_0^\infty \hat{y}(t - \tau_0)e^{-st}\,d(t - \tau_0)$$

$$= e^{-s\tau_0}\int_0^\infty \hat{y}(t - \tau_0)e^{-s(t-\tau_0)}\,d(t - \tau_0)$$

$$= e^{-s\tau_0}Y(s) \tag{8–3}$$

The last step in this derivation may disturb the reader for a moment, unless he remembers that the variable of integration is a "dummy" in this transformation. It matters not whether the dummy is called t, or $(t - \tau_0)$, or λ: the integral ends up as a function of s. Note for example that

$$\int_0^\infty f(t)e^{-st}\,dt = \int_0^\infty f(\lambda)e^{-s\lambda}\,d\lambda = F(s)$$

The resulting equation (8–3) is called the **time-shift theorem.** In effect it says that multiplication by $e^{-s\tau_0}$ in the s domain is the counterpart of a simple displacement in the time domain. We can use this result to transform equation (8–2).

$$Z(s) = e^{-s\tau_0} Y(s) = [e^{-s\tau_0} /(\tau s + 1)]X(s) \tag{8–4}$$

Evidently the exponential multiplier can be thought of as a transfer function. In a block diagram we obtain Fig. 8–3.

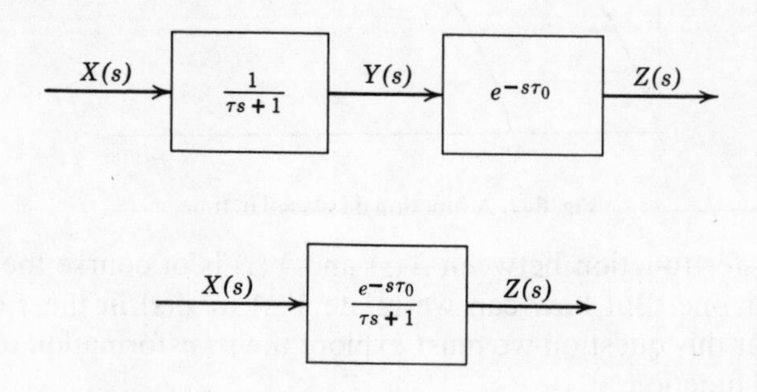

Fig. 8–3. Alternative block diagrams for a system with dead time.

8–2. BODE AND NYQUIST DIAGRAMS

The transfer function for dead time is the first of those we have encountered that is not a polynomial function of s. In spite of this, the function can be handled in the transformed domain through its Bode-plot properties. Consider

$$G(s) = e^{-s\tau_0}$$
$$G(j\omega) = e^{-j\omega\tau_0}$$

which by Euler's relation can also be written as

$$G(j\omega) = \cos \omega\tau_0 - j \sin \omega\tau_0$$

Then:

$$|G(j\omega)| = \sqrt{\cos^2\omega\tau_0 + \sin^2 \omega\tau_0} = 1$$

$$\angle G(j\omega) = \text{arc tan} \frac{-\sin \omega\tau_0}{\cos \omega\tau_0} = -\text{arc tan}(\tan \omega\tau_0) = -\omega\tau_0 \tag{8–5}$$

On a Bode diagram the magnitude of $G(s) = e^{-s\tau_0}$ is constant at unity, independent of frequency. The angle function is proportional to ω, the proportionality constant being $-\tau_0$. These curves are both shown on the usual coordinates in Fig. 8–4. It is most significant that unlike

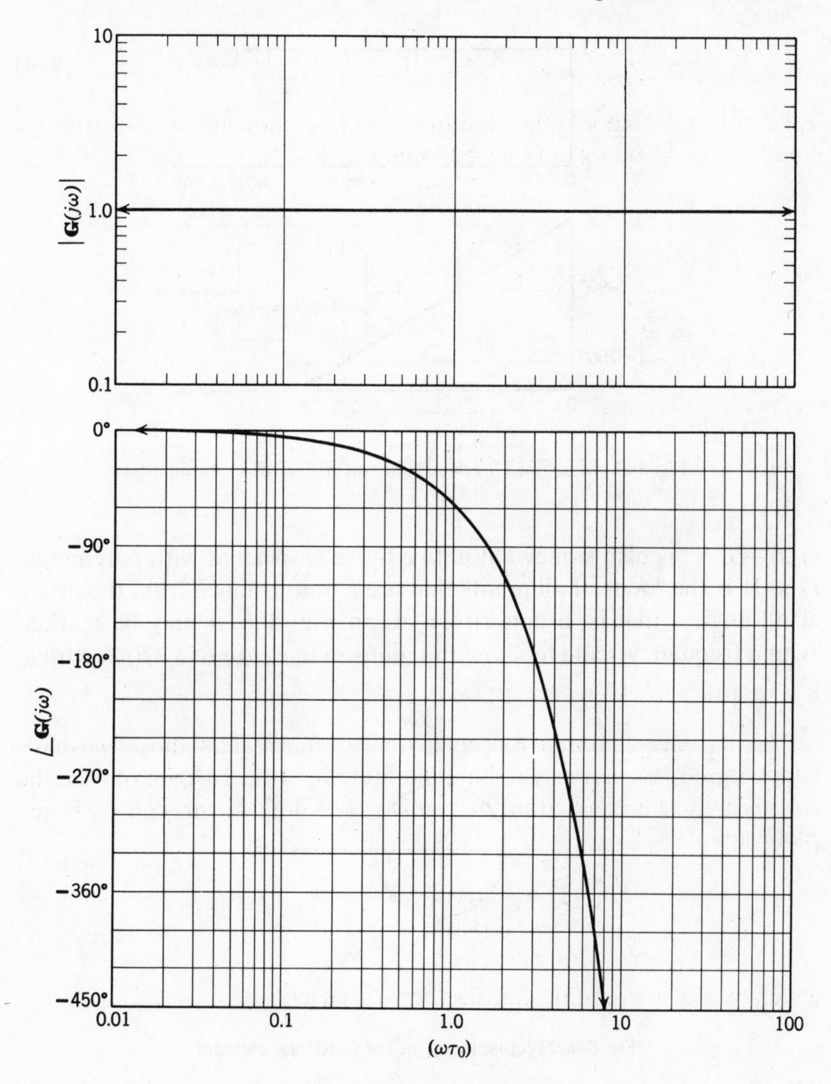

Fig. 8–4. Bode diagram for dead time.

the polynomial G's this function provides an angle-shift curve that does not show any asymptote at high frequencies. Sometimes it is useful to take advantage of the very simple linear $\angle G(j\omega)$ function by replotting these Bode lines on arithmetic coordinates instead of logarithmic. If this is done, Fig. 8–5 results. The Nyquist diagram for

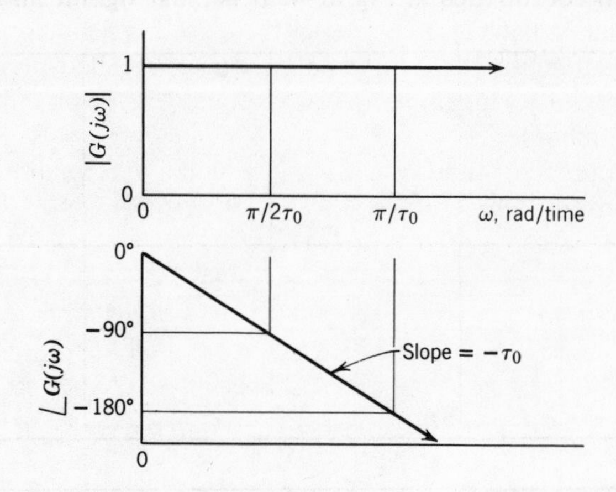

Fig. 8–5. Bode lines for dead time (on arithmetic co-ordinates).

$G(s) = e^{-\tau_0 s}$ is also somewhat unlike those associated with polynomial G's. It is the locus of all points that are a unit distance from the origin at all angles: that is, a unit circle. As in Fig. 8–6, it may be marked with a frequency scale to show the uniform increase of $\angle G(j\omega)$ with ω.

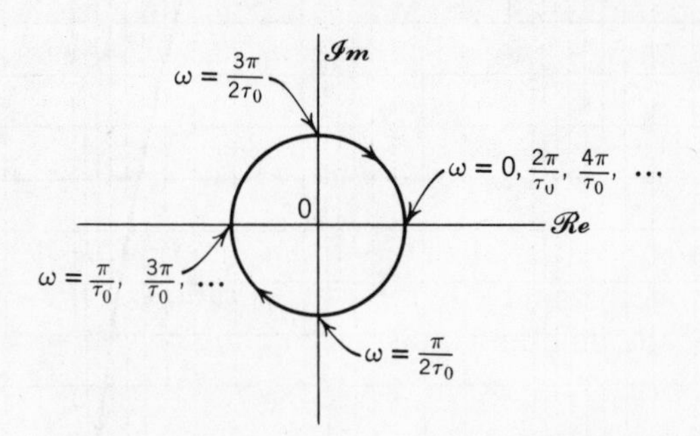

Fig. 8–6. Nyquist locus for the dead time element.

8–3. PLUG FLOW AND MIXING

Lest the reader get the mistaken impression that dead time is always the result of ignorance, oversight, or inhospitable conditions of measurement, it should be noted that the effect is on occasion inherent in the nature of a system, arising most commonly from convective transport. Chemical reactors, and various kinds of flow equipment are commonly tubular in form. If in addition the flowrate through the equipment has a flat velocity profile, the dynamic behavior essentially follows equation (8–2). Such a flow pattern is called **piston** or **plug** flow. It is found for example in packed beds and in pipe flow at high Reynolds numbers.

Consider a reactor tube (Fig. 8–7) in which a chemical reaction proceeds at constant temperature. To study the dynamics of this system,

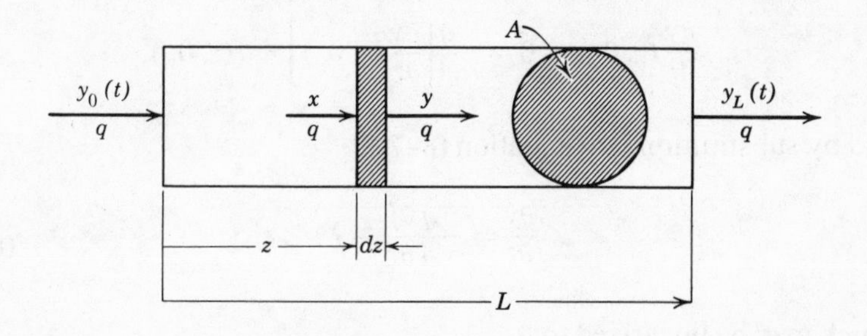

Fig. 8–7. A reactor tube.

we may neglect diffusional effects and start with a material balance similar to equation (1–9), however the accumulation, input, and output measures are now applied to a differentially small element of volume: $dV = A\,dz$. Furthermore, we must account for the dependence of concentration on both time and position, and use a partial differential notation:

$$dV\frac{\partial y}{\partial t} = qx - qy - r\,dV \tag{8–6}$$

where x is the concentration of the stream entering dV at some distance from the entrance z, and y is the concentration of the dV effluent at $(z + dz)$. Over the differential distance dz the change in concentration is

$$y - x = \frac{\partial y}{\partial z}\,dz$$

Substitution into equation (8–6) gives:

$$\frac{\partial y}{\partial t} = -\frac{q}{A}\frac{\partial y}{\partial z} - r \tag{8–7}$$

A system described in this manner by a partial differential equation is said to have a **distributed parameter,** in contradistinction to the ordinary differential equation **lumped parameter** model.

The deviation variables may now be referred to the condition before disturbance at any position:

$$\hat{y}(z,t) = y(z,t) - y(z,0)$$
$$\hat{r}(z,t) = r(z,t) - r(z,0^-)$$

By assuming a steady state before the disturbance:

$$\frac{\partial y}{\partial t}(z,0^-) = 0 = -\frac{q}{A}\left[\frac{\partial y}{\partial z}(z,0^-)\right] - r(z,0^-)$$

and by substitution into equation (8–7):

$$\frac{\partial \hat{y}}{\partial t} = -\frac{q}{A}\frac{\partial \hat{y}}{\partial z} - \hat{r} \qquad (8\text{–}8)$$

which may be linearized to:

$$\frac{\partial \hat{y}}{\partial t} = -\frac{q}{A}\frac{\partial \hat{y}}{\partial z} - \left(\frac{dr}{dy}\right)_0 \hat{y} \qquad (8\text{–}9)$$

by taking $(dr/dy)_0$ to be an average value over the length of the reactor.

In order to bring this discussion down to a specific problem, we may consider the input $\hat{y}(0,t)$ to be the forcing function and the effluent $\hat{y}(L,t)$ to be the response of interest. To derive a transfer function, we operate on equation (8–9) to obtain the ordinary differential equation:

$$sY(s) = -\frac{q}{A}\frac{dY(s)}{dz} - \left(\frac{dr}{dy}\right)_0 Y(s)$$

which may be rearranged to

$$\frac{dY(s)}{Y(s)} = -\frac{A}{q}\left[s + \left(\frac{dr}{dy}\right)_0\right] dz$$

Integrating between limits of $z = 0$ and $z = L$:

$$\frac{Y_L(s)}{Y_0(s)} = \exp\left\{-\frac{A}{q}\left[s + \left(\frac{dr}{dy}\right)_0\right]L\right\} = \exp\left\{-\tau_0\left[s + \left(\frac{dr}{dy}\right)_0\right]\right\}$$
$$= Ke^{-\tau_0 s} \qquad (8\text{–}10)$$

where the $Y(s)$ subscripts refer to output and input locations. The result is a dead-time element multiplied by a gain constant $K = \exp[-\tau_0(dr/dy)_0]$.

To establish the connection between a perfect mixer and the plug-flow device, consider a cascade of n perfect mixers of total volume V each of volume (V/n). If the constant flowrate q is the same to each vessel, the transfer function for such a cascade is

$$G(s) = \left[\frac{1}{(\tau_0/n)s + 1}\right]^n \tag{8-11}$$

where $\tau_0 = (V/q)$. This leads to the magnitude and angle:

$$|G(j\omega)| = \left[\frac{1}{\sqrt{1 + (\omega\tau_0/n)^2}}\right]^n$$
$$\angle G(j\omega) = -n \arctan(\omega\tau_0/n) \tag{8-12}$$

In the limit, as $n \to \infty$, $|G(j\omega)| \to 1$, and $\angle G(j\omega) \to -\omega\tau_0$, precisely the values found for dead time.[1] We find therefore that from this point of view, a plug-flow system can be thought of as consisting of an infinite number of infinitesmally small perfect mixers. This idea has been the basis of a number of chemical engineering analyses of packed bed behavior. Since real systems show neither plug flow nor perfect mixing, it is often helpful to describe practical devices in terms of equation (8–11) and a finite n. We saw an example of this in the earlier analysis of a tubular mixer whose behavior was approximated by a three-vessel cascade. In another experimental study Gray and Prados[2] found that packed gas absorption columns could be described with moderate success as consisting of $n = 30$ or 40 well-mixed stages.

The basic importance of dead time as an interpreting factor of mixing quality can be arrived at from another direction by referring to the experimental data of Kramers and Geerlings.[3] Their frequency response measurements on a well-stirred vessel are reproduced in Fig.

---

[1]The same result can be obtained more formally by

$$\lim_{n\to\infty} \left[\frac{1}{(\tau_0 s/n) + 1}\right]^n = e^{-\tau_0 s}$$

[2]Gray, R. I., and J. W. Prados, *A.I.Ch.E. Journal*, **9**, 211 (1963).

[3]Geerlings, M. W., *Plant and Process Dynamic Characteristics*, Academic Press, New York, 1957, p. 129.

8–8 to show that even this simple first order system exhibits dead time at high enough frequency. If all measurements had been carried out at $\omega\tau_r < 10$, the system would have appeared to be perfectly well mixed

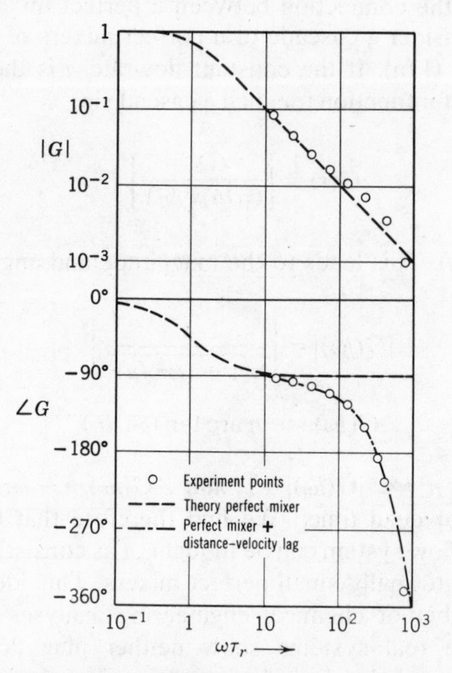

Fig. 8–8. Frequency-response data of Kramers and Geerlings. Vessel volume–8 liters; 3-bladed propeller of $\frac{1}{3}$ tank diameter and rotating at 300 rpm; $\tau_r = 600$ sec, $\tau_0 = 2.8$ sec.

(first order). Evidently, the high test frequencies produce disturbances that are rapid in comparison with the stirring speed. It may be concluded that any mixed vessel is only perfectly mixed over some region of input frequencies.

In a practical sense, then, the perfect mixer and the plug-flow model are extremes. Real systems are usually intermediate in character, unless pains are taken to approach one or the other limit. Combinations of these models have been used successfully to describe mixing in engineering equipment. As an example we may cite the work of Sinclair[4] who analyzed the mixing pattern in a vessel by formulating a model consisting of a first-order feedback path imposed on a tubular

[4]Sinclair, C. G., *A.I.Ch.E. Journal,* 7, 709 (1961).

plug-flow geometry. The details of Sinclair's model are shown pictorially in Fig. 8–9*a*. A quantitative description begins with a material balance at the inlet mixing point:

$$y_M(q_R + q) = qx + q_R y_R$$

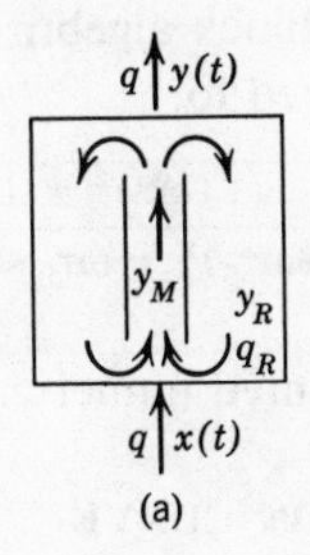

(a)

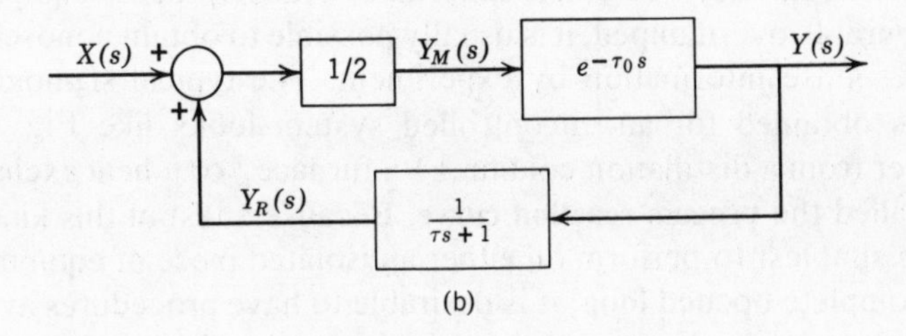

(b)

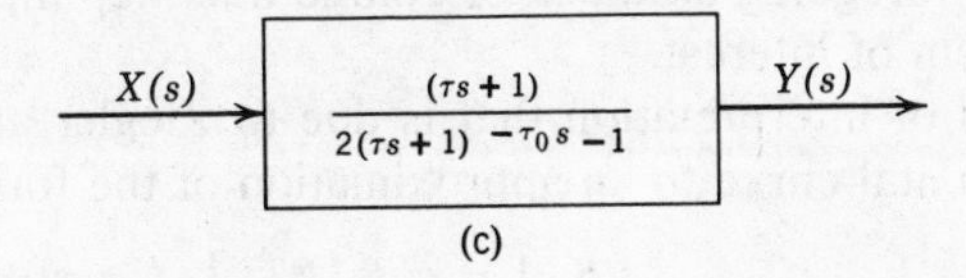

(c)

Fig. 8–9. Sinclair's formulation. (a) Pictorial representation; (b) combination of equations (8–13), (8–14), and (8–15); (c) simplified transfer function: $Y(s)/X(s)$.

The subscripts R and M refer to the recycle and mixed streams. If $q_R = q$; that is, the recycle rate is equal to the over-all throughput:

$$2y_M = x + y_R$$

$$Y_M(s) = \frac{1}{2}\left[X(s) + Y_R(s)\right] \qquad (8\text{–}13)$$

The forward path is a dead-time element:

$$Y(s) = Y_M(s)\, e^{-\tau_0 s} \qquad (8\text{–}14)$$

while the recycle effect is first order:

$$Y_R(s) = \frac{1}{\tau s + 1} \quad Y(s) \tag{8–15}$$

A step-by-step combination of the last three equations yields the diagram (Fig. 8–9*b*), which by block algebra leads to Fig. 8–9*c*. If $\tau = \tau_0$, the final result may be reduced to:

$$|G(j\omega)| = \sqrt{\frac{(\omega\tau)^2 + 1}{1 + 4\,[1 + (\omega\tau_0)^2 + \omega\tau_0 \sin \omega\tau_0 - \cos \omega\tau_0]}} \tag{8–16}$$

for which Sinclair has presented numerical results (see Problem 8–1).

8–4 THE PROCESS REACTION CURVE

It has been observed empirically that because process equipment is considerably overdamped, it is usually possible to obtain nonoscillatory step-response information by experiment. The typical sigmoid curve that is obtained for an uncontrolled system looks like Fig. 8–10*a*, whether from a distillation column,[5, 6] a furnace,[7] or a heat exchanger.[8] It is called the **process reaction curve**. Because a test of this kind is by far the simplest to perform on either an isolated piece of equipment or on a complete opened loop, it is desirable to have procedures available for interpreting such measurements and for using them for closed-loop design. The foregoing assumes of course that step inputs are feasible for the system of interest.

A method of interpretation that is due to Ziegler and Nichols[9] fits the experimental curve to an approximation of the form:

$$\hat{y}(t) = \begin{cases} aK[1 - e^{-(t-\tau_E)/\tau_F}] & t \geq \tau_E \\ 0 & t < \tau_E \end{cases} \tag{8–17}$$

which (except for the constant K) is the time domain equivalent of transfer function (equation 8–4), operating on the step input $\hat{x} = a$. The approximation-curve parameters are chosen by examining the

[5]Wilkinson, W. L., and W. D. Armstrong, *Plant and Process Dynamic Characteristics*, Academic Press, New York, 1957, p. 56.

[6]Baber, M. F., L. L. Edwards, Jr., W. T. Harper, Jr., M. D. Witte, and J. A. Gerster, *Chem. Eng. Prog. Symp. Ser. No. 36*, **57**, 148 (1961).

[7]Endtz, J., J. M. L. Janssen, and J. C. Vermeulen, *Plant and Process Dynamic Characteristics*, Academic Press, New York, 1957, p. 176.

[8]Sternmole, F. J., and M. A. Larson, *Ind. Eng. Chem. Fundamentals*, **2**, 62 (1963).

[9]Ziegler, J. G., and N. B. Nichols, *Trans. ASME*, **64**, 759 (1942).

intercepts of the tangent to the data at the point of inflection. As shown in Fig. 8–10*a*, the total span of *y* determines *K* (for a given *a*), and the intercept τ_E is an equivalent dead time. The span, τ_F, establishes the first-order time constant through the tangent slope (aK/τ_F) which is also the initial derivative of the first-order approximation curve.

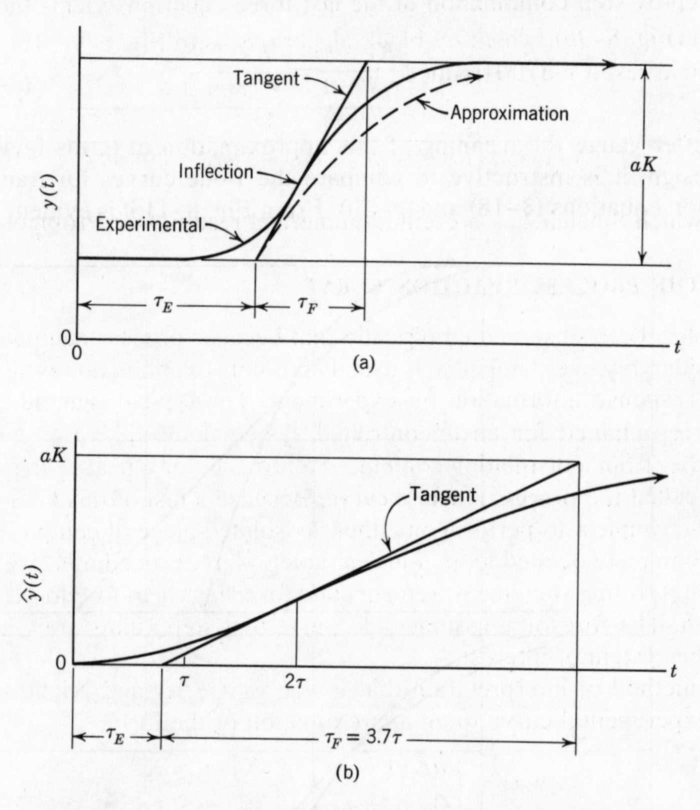

Fig. 8–10. Process-reaction curves. (a) Typical curve and the approximation; (b) response of third-order system.

As an illustration, suppose that the actual dynamic behavior of a system is accurately described by the third-order transfer function:

$$G(s) = K/(\tau s + 1)^3 \tag{8–18}$$

The experimental step response curve would then be

$$\hat{y}(t) = aK\left[1 - e^{-t/\tau}\left(1 + \frac{t}{\tau} + \frac{t^2}{2\tau^2}\right)\right] \tag{8–19}$$

which is shown in Fig. 8–10*b*. A tangent is drawn at the inflection point: it intersects the time axis at $t = \tau_E = 0.80\tau$. From the span of the tangent, $\tau_F = 3.7\tau$, a first-order approximation is made which coincides with the tangent at its intersection with the time axis. The approximation to $\hat{y}(t)$ is then exactly equation (8–17) and

$$G(s)_{\text{Approx}} = \frac{Ke^{-\tau_E s}}{\tau_E s + 1} = \frac{Ke^{-0.8\tau s}}{3.7\tau s + 1} \qquad (8\text{–}20)$$

To better gauge the meaning of this approximation in terms familiar for design, it is instructive to compare the Bode curves for transfer function equations (8–18) and (8–20). From Fig. 8–11 it is evident that

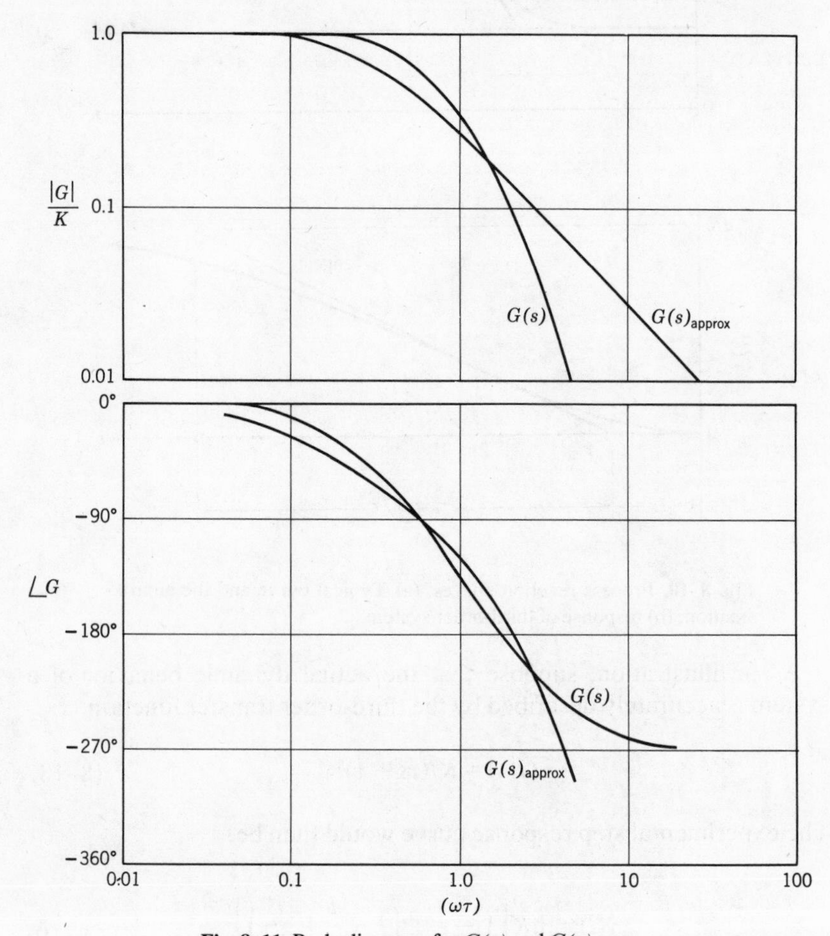

Fig. 8–11. Bode diagrams for $G(s)$ and $G(s)_{Approx}$.

the approximate transfer function will represent the actual dynamics very closely in the range of greatest interest: where $\angle G$ is between $-135°$ and $-180°$.

The desire to better fit the sigmoid reaction curve has stimulated suggestions of second-order approximations. Since second-order responses do not exhibit the discontinuity in slope of equation (8–17), such an approach might be expected to bring considerable improvement. Oldenbourg and Sartorius[10] have shown that the time constants of:

$$G(s) = \frac{Ke^{-\tau_0 s}}{(\tau_1 s + 1)(\tau_2 s + 1)} \qquad \tau_2 < \tau_1 \qquad (8\text{–}21)$$

can be found from the process reaction curve. The dead time can ordinarily be read by inspection; the other two constants are calculated from the simultaneous equations:

$$T_c = \tau_1 + \tau_2 = \tau_1\left(1 + \frac{\tau_2}{\tau_1}\right)$$
$$T_a = \tau_1\left[\frac{\tau_1}{\tau_2}\right]^{\frac{(\tau_2/\tau_1)}{1-(\tau_2/\tau_1)}} \qquad (8\text{–}22)$$

where the experimental T_a and T_c are measured as in Fig. 8–12. Since these equations are not explicit in the desired constants, the solution requires trial or graphical computations.

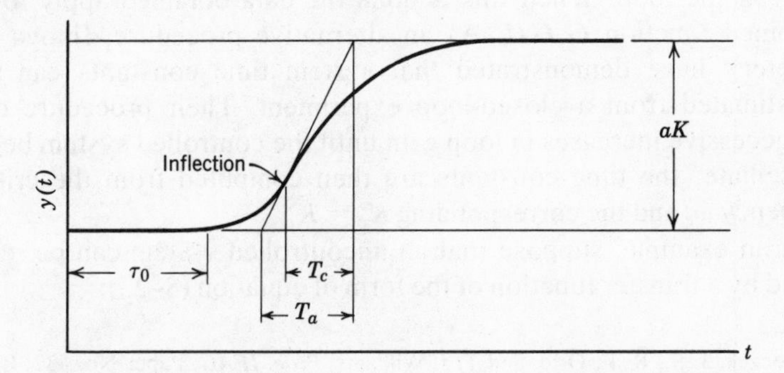

Fig. 8–12. Second-order interpretation of a process-reaction curve.

[10] Oldenbourg, R. C., and H. Sartorius, *The Dynamics of Automatic Controls,* ASME 1948.

It might be thought that first- or second-order approximations are gross oversimplifications for rather complex equipment. They are nevertheless of considerable practical utility, since many of the more complicated multistage and distributed parameter devices can be described by functions such as those in equation (8–4) or (8–21). An extensive computational study by Moczek, Otto, and Williams[11] established, for example, that the composition dynamics of a 50-tray benzene stripping column were reasonably well represented by first- and second-order transfer functions (with dead time) if interest was focused on overhead and bottoms products. Transfer functions of higher order were required for some of the intermediate trays. Hougen and Walsh[12] reached a similar conclusion as a result of their study of commercial heat-exchange equipment. Their measurements suggested second-order behavior with nearly equal time constants:

$$G(s) = \frac{Ke^{-\tau_0 s}}{(\tau s + 1)^2} \tag{8–23}$$

Because these approximations are so often successful, a number of empirical rules have been developed for controller tuning which are associated with Ziegler and Nichols (see fn. 9, p. 136), and Cohen and Coon[13]. Some of these are illustrated in the problems at the end of this chapter.

It should be noted that since the process reaction curve is found experimentally, it can as easily be determined for an entire opened loop as for a single component. It is in fact commonly used to analyze control systems already in existence, by disconnecting the controller to break the loop. When this is done the data obtained apply to the combined function $G_v GH$. As an alternative procedure, Iinoya and Altpeter[14] have demonstrated that system time constants can also be estimated from a closed-loop experiment. Their procedure calls for successive increases in loop gain until the controlled system begins to oscillate; the time constants are then computed from the critical frequency ω_c and the corresponding $K_c = K_c'$.

As an example, suppose that an uncontrolled system can be represented by a transfer function of the form of equation (8–23):

---

[11] Moczek, J. S., R. E. Otto, and T. J. Williams, *Proc. IFAC,* Paper No. 432, Basel, Switzerland, Sept., 1963.

[12] Hougen, J. O., and R. A. Walsh, Paper presented at Annual Am. Inst. Chem. Engnrs. Meeting, 1960, Preprint H.

[13] Cohen, G. H., and G. A. Coon, *Trans. ASME,* **75**, 827 (1953).

[14] Iinoya, K., and R. J. Altpeter, *A.I.Ch.E. Journal,* 7, 478 (1961).

$$G_vGH(s) = \frac{Ke^{-\tau_0 s}}{(\tau s + 1)^2}$$

With proportional control the characteristic equation of the closed loop is

$$\Gamma_n = 1 + L = 1 + \frac{K_c K e^{-\tau_0 s}}{(\tau s + 1)^2} = 0$$

Assume that the system behavior is still linear when the increased K_c first causes the system to **hunt** (oscillate). With $K_c = K_c'$, its critical value:

$$\left|\frac{K_c' K e^{-\tau_0 s}}{(\tau s + 1)^2}\right| = \frac{K_c' K}{\left[\sqrt{1 + (\omega_c \tau)^2}\right]^2} = 1$$

$$\angle L = \angle\left[\frac{K_c' K e^{-\tau_0 s}}{(\tau s + 1)^2}\right] = -\omega_c \tau_0 - 2 \text{ arc tan } \omega_c \tau = \pi - \qquad (8\text{–}24)$$

from which the time constants may be found as

$$\tau = \frac{1}{\omega_c}\sqrt{K_c' K - 1}$$

$$\tau_0 = \frac{1}{\omega_c}(\pi - 2 \text{ arc tan } \omega \tau) \qquad (8\text{–}25)$$

EXERCISES

8–1. Reconsider the data given in Problem 1–5. Can the results be explained by a dead volume in series with a well-mixed region? If so, what percentage of the mixer volume is in this state?

8–2. Use the time-shift theorem to find $X(s)$ for the input signal:

$$x(t) = \begin{cases} 0 & t < 0 \\ at & 0 < t < 1 \\ a & 1 < t < 3 \\ a - a(t-3) & 3 < t < 4 \\ 0 & t > 4 \end{cases}$$

What is the response of a first-order system to this input? Sketch your result. Use the final-value theorem to check the value of $y(\infty)$.

8–3. The following data are frequency response measurements on a mixing vessel, where K and a are the effluent concentration and the feed concentration wave amplitudes respectively. If the data are interpreted as a result of perfect mixing with a distance-velocity lag, find (*a*) the first-order time constant, (*b*) the dead time, (*c*) the gain at zero frequency.

ω, rad/sec	(K/a), dimensionless	Phase Shift, degrees
0.01	0.050	−96
0.02	0.025	−101
0.04	0.012	−112
0.12	0.0042	−157
0.24	0.0021	−223
0.50	0.0010	−367

8–4. In order to reduce undesirable oscillations in the exit concentration from a pipeline, it is suggested that a well-mixed tank be included in the system. Use Sinclair's results below to decide whether an available tank should be put in series (cascade) with the pipe, or arranged in a recycle line, as suggested by Sinclair's model. Consider $\tau/\tau_0 = 1$ and $\tau/\tau_0 = 10$ as two cases.

Attenuation Ratios, dimensionless

$\omega\tau$	$(\tau/\tau_0) = 1$	$(\tau/\tau_0) = 10$
0.01	1.0	0.99
0.02	1.0	0.94
0.04	0.99	0.83
0.06	0.98	0.73
0.1	0.96	0.62
0.2	0.86	0.52
0.4	0.67	0.49
0.6	0.52	0.48
1.0	0.43	0.48
2.0	0.43	0.49
4.0	0.56	0.51
6.0	0.47	0.50
10.0	0.49	0.49

8–5. In oil refineries the major part of the heat needed in the distillation operations is generated in furnaces. These furnaces are usually temperature controlled by automatic manipulation of the pressure to a pneumatic motor valve on the fuel gas line. An experimental frequency-response study on such a furnace was run by Endtz, Janssen, and Vermeulen (*op. cit.*, p. 178). The authors report that their data correspond to a system with two time constants (15 min and 25 sec) and a dead time (20 sec). From their data, the zero frequency gain may be calculated to be 40°C/psi, where the forcing input is the pressure to a motor valve diaphragm and the response is the temperature of the furnace effluent stream.

You are asked to design a control loop for this furnace by connecting a proportional controller and a measuring device with a negligibly small time constant and a gain of 0.2 psi/°C. The controller uses air pressure for input and output signals. What controller setting (proportional gain) would you recommend for:

(*a*) A 45° phase margin.

(*b*) A gain margin of 6 decibels.

The major disturbance variably for the furnace described above is v_i, the temperature of the feed stream. The same investigators report that the open-loop relationship between this variable and the product temperature, v, can be represented by a dead time of 10 min and a single time constant of 1.0 min. The gain of this transfer function is unity.

(*c*) Write the differential equation relating v_1 and v (open-loop) and sketch a curve showing how v would respond to a step increase in v_1 (still open-loop).

(*d*) If the loop is closed and the controller set properly as above, what offset would you predict following a step disturbance in the feed temperature of 20°C?

8–6. Experimental step-response tests on a proposed pressure control system indicate that without a controller the forward path may be represented by the transfer function:

$$G_v GH(s) = \frac{Ke^{-0.5\tau s}}{1+\tau s} \text{ psi/psi}$$

where $\tau = 1$ min, $K = 3$. If a proportional pneumatic controller is added, and the loop is closed, what range of proportional gain settings produce instability? What setting would you suggest? How do your answers compare with values calculated from the rule of Cohen and Coon which for a loop with proportional control only recommends:

$$K_c = \frac{1}{K}\left(1.03\frac{\tau}{\tau_0} + 0.35\right)$$

where K is the zero frequency gain of $G_v GH(s)$. Compare these results with the Ziegler–Nichols rule which calls for:

$$K_c = \frac{1}{K}\frac{\tau}{\tau_0}$$

8–7. For two-mode proportional plus integral control, the Cohen–Coon rule suggests the settings:

$$K_c = \frac{\tau}{K\tau_0}\left(0.9 + \frac{\tau_0}{12\tau}\right)$$

$$\tau_i = \tau_0\left[\frac{30 + (3\tau_0/\tau)}{9 + (20\tau_0/\tau)}\right]$$

for the controller:

$$G_c = K_c\left(1 + \frac{1}{\tau_i s}\right)$$

Referring to the system of the previous problem, what phase margin do these settings correspond to? How do your results compare to the Ziegler–Nichols settings:

$$K_c = \frac{0.9}{K}\frac{\tau}{\tau_0}$$

$$\tau_i = \frac{\tau_0}{0.3}$$

8–8. From experimental frequency and step-response studies Aikman[15] found that the dynamics of a fractionating column could be represented by the block diagram of Fig. 8–13, where $v(t)$ = the overhead vapor temperature (control

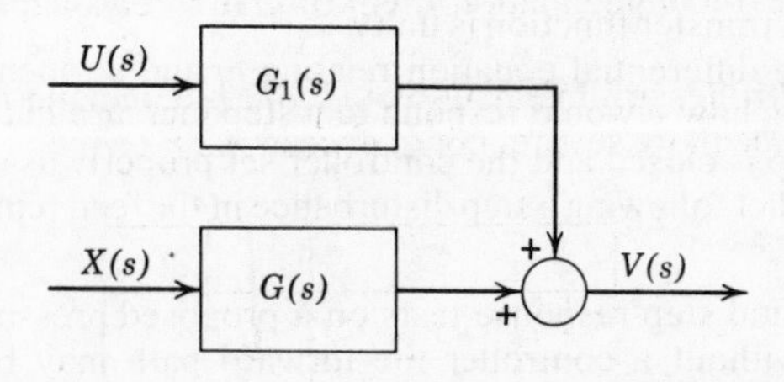

Fig. 8–13. Block diagram for distillation column.

variable), $x(t)$ = the reflux flowrate (manipulating variable), $u(t)$ = the reboiler hot gas flow (disturbance), and

$$G(s) = \frac{Ke^{-\tau_0 s}}{(\tau_1 s + 1)(\tau_2 s + 1)} \text{ °F/\% flow}$$

$$G_1(s) = \frac{K_1 e^{-0.33s}}{(4.2s + 1)\,(0.8s + 1)} \text{ °F/(ft}^3\text{/min)}$$

The constants τ_0, τ_1, and τ_2 were evaluated from the following data as 0.075 min, 0.83 min, and 0.083 min respectively.

ω, cycles/min	|G|, °F/% flow	∠G, degrees
0.244	92.2	− 68
0.416	71.6	− 95
0.565	41.0	−115
0.86	21.6	−131
1.5	10.3	−162
1.85	9.84	−180
2.86	5.13	−205
3.86	3.00	−242
6.5	1.37	−355
7.5	0.770	−407
12.9	0.795	−530

(a) Use a Bode plot to estimate K.

(b) When a typical step disturbance was introduced an offset of 10.5°F was observed for the *uncontrolled* system. What % P.B. would you recommend for a *controlled* offset not to exceed 1.0°F (for the same step disturbance), assuming the following hardware is used to close the loop:

---

[15] Aikman, A. R., *ISA Journal*, **3**, No. 10, 412 (1956).

Transducer: $H(s) = K_T = 0.03$ mv/°F
Valve: $G_v(s) = K_v = 8.33\%$ flow/psi
Controller: Proportional, input span = 500 mv, output span = 12 psi

(c) Does your recommendation (item b) give a reasonable gain margin for stability?

(d) What controller arrangement would you recommend if the offset specification were made more severe: not to exceed 0.2°F?

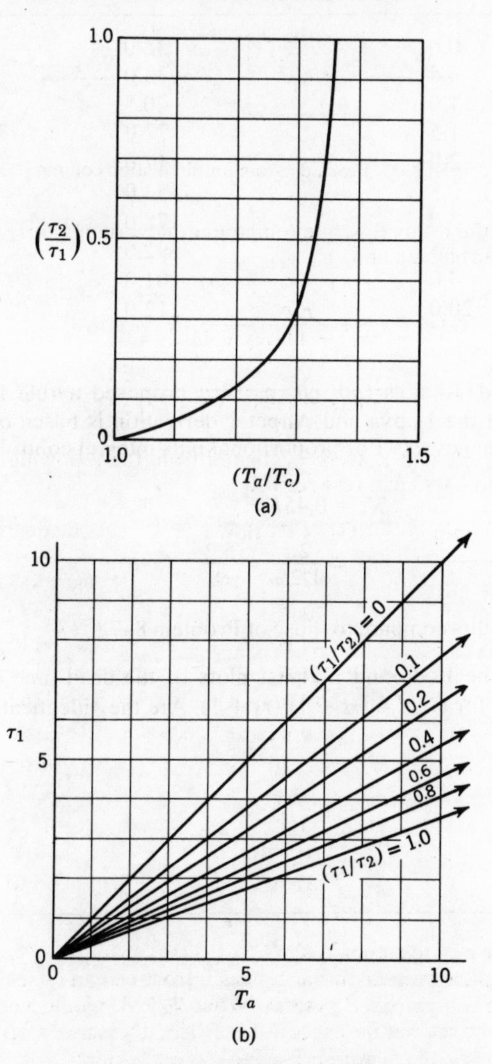

Fig. 8–14. Graphical representation of equations (8–22). Use (a) to find (τ_2/τ_1) from known (T_a/T_c); Use (b) to find τ_1 from known T_a and (τ_2/τ_1).

8–9. The following step-response data were taken in order to characterize a temperature measuring device. Find the time constants by using equations (8–22) (graphed for convenience in Fig. 8–14).

Step-Response Data

Time, min	Temperature Reading, °F
0.0	32.0
0.5	33.0
1.0	40.5
1.5	77.0
2.0	117.0
2.5	153.0
3.0	178.0
3.5	192.0
4.0	201.0
20.0	212.0

8–10. Ziegler and Nichols (*op. cit.* p. 136) proposed a rule for controller tuning which like the Iinoya and Altpeter derivation is based on the closed-loop critical frequency, ω_c. For proportional plus integral control they suggest setting:

$$K_c = 0.45K_c'$$

$$\tau_i = \frac{2\pi}{1.2\omega_c} = \frac{5.2}{\omega_c}$$

How do these results compare to those of Problem 8–7?

8–11. Compare the Bode and Nyquist plots of the dead time element $G(s) = e^{-s\tau}$ with those for $G(s) = (\tau s - 1)/(\tau s + 1)$. Are they identical in any region of frequencies?

9 *Multiloop Systems*

There are several ways in which control systems arise that have more than a single loop. One such situation develops quite naturally when it is necessary to control more than one variable in a plant. In considering a distillation column, for example, even the most superficial analysis suggests several variables as candidates for control: pressure, temperature, flowrates, liquid levels. Other multiloop systems arise not from the plant, but rather from the engineer's desire for closer control. In this chapter we will consider two such schemes and develop arguments to justify feedforward and cascade control. Finally, it will be shown that naturally occurring multivariable systems show behavior that leads to the artificially created multiloop control schemes.

9–1. INTERACTING LOOPS

For the chemical engineer there are probably no applications more important than control of a distillation column. To reduce such a system to a bare minimum of control equipment, we consider here only four control variables: pressure, temperature, bottoms level, and top accumulator level. The reader will note that no explicit mention is made of stream compositions – a surprising omission since production of streams with specified compositions is the purpose of distillation. Although considerable progress has been made recently in developing the necessary transducers for composition measurements, the relative ease of fast and accurate pressure and temperature measurements have favored their substitution. For a binary system, the chemical compositions are in fact fixed once pressure and temperature are set, but in multicomponent distillation some composition variation is allowed by this approach.

Furthermore, our simplified treatment assumes that other variables of evident importance are either controlled independently by loops upstream or are potential disturbances. Included in these categories are feed composition; and the enthalpies and flowrates of coolant, heating medium, and feed. Given the preceding list of qualifications, we are left with the four-loop system shown in Fig. 9–1; it is perhaps

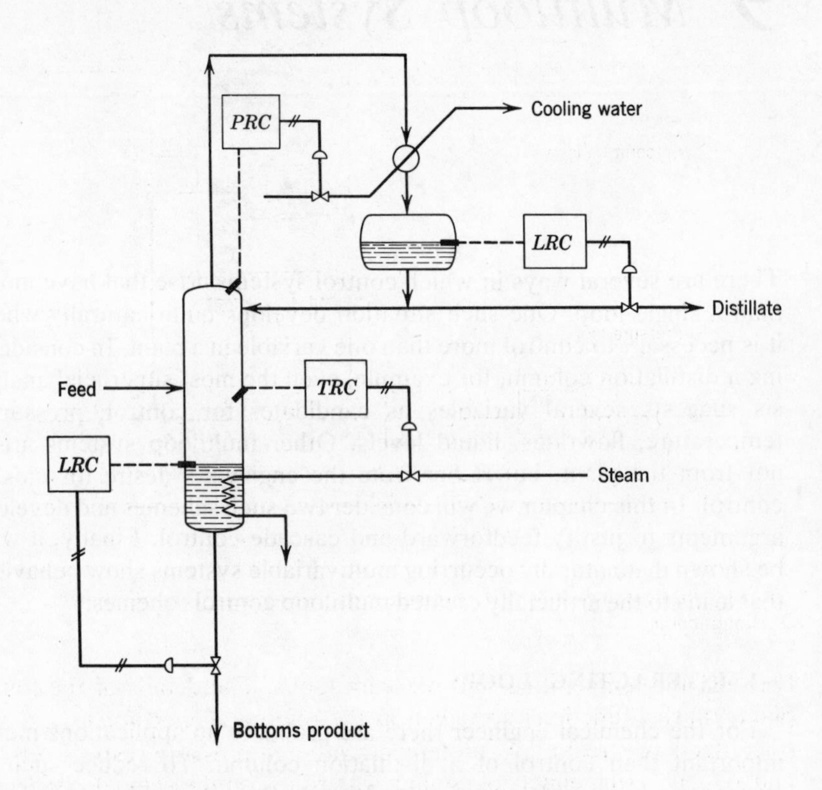

Fig. 9–1. A simple control arrangement for distillation.

the simplest of a great many possible variants. Each loop acts on one of the four control variables: (1) pressure by manipulation of the coolant rate, (2) temperature through the steam rate, (3) bottoms level, and (4) top accumulator level by the bottoms- and the overhead-product rates respectively. It is most important to recognize, moreover, that we are dealing here not with four simple loops, but with an interacting system. A moment's reflection should convince the reader that a change in any one variable will affect all the loops, since all are related through the energy and material balances on the column.

To illustrate this point in a block diagram, the data of Endtz, Janssen and Vermeulen[1] are useful. Restricting our attention to only two of the four loops, Fig. 9–2 shows the interaction that would be expected

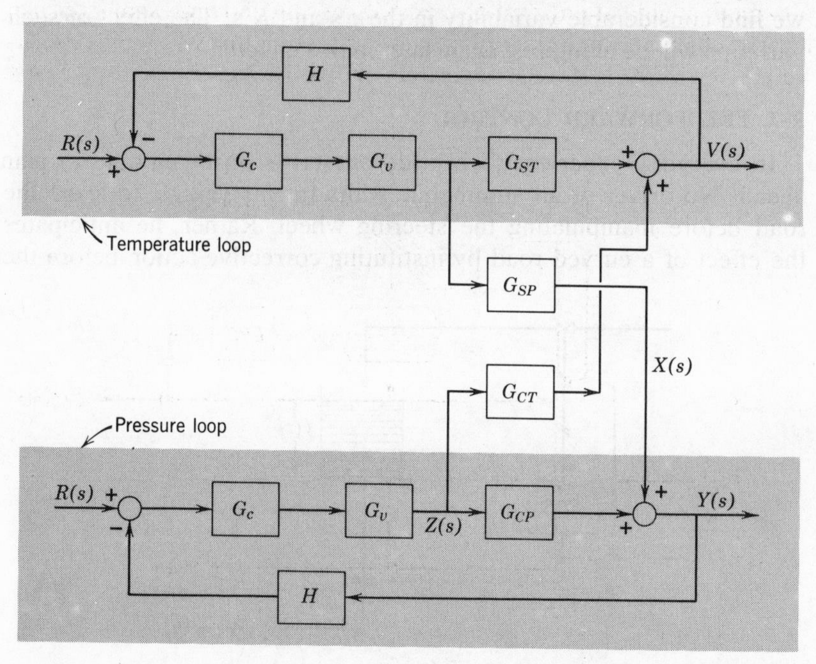

Fig. 9–2. Column loops for pressure and temperature control, showing interaction.

between the temperature and pressure loops. The details of the four plant transfer functions are given in the reference cited for G_{ST}, G_{SP} (the effects of stream flow on temperature and pressure respectively), and G_{CT}, G_{CP} (the effects of cooling water flow on the same dependent variables). By a straightforward though rather tedious analysis this problem can be reduced to a study of a single loop, using the other loop as a parameter. Even more important, however, are the qualitative implications of interaction. Suppose for the moment that the investigators of this system had been so shortsighted as to ignore the pressure-control loop entirely, lumping all plant dynamics into the single transfer function, G_{ST}. It is clear from Fig. 9–2 that any change in the pressure

[1] *Op. cit.*, p. 136

loop would then appear to the investigator as a variation in G_{ST}. Such a situation is not necessarily to be blamed on the naivete of the engineer, for unexpected inputs can disturb even the most carefully and thoroughly laid plans. Thus we should not be surprised if in fitting a simplified $G(s)$ to data from a complex multistage distillation column, we find considerable variability in the τ's and K's. The effect of such variation will be of interest again later in this chapter.

9-2. FEEDFORWARD CONTROL

In everyday experience we pride ourselves on being able to plan ahead. No driver of an automobile waits for his vehicle to leave the road before manipulating the steering wheel. Rather, he anticipates the effect of a curved road by instituting corrective action before the

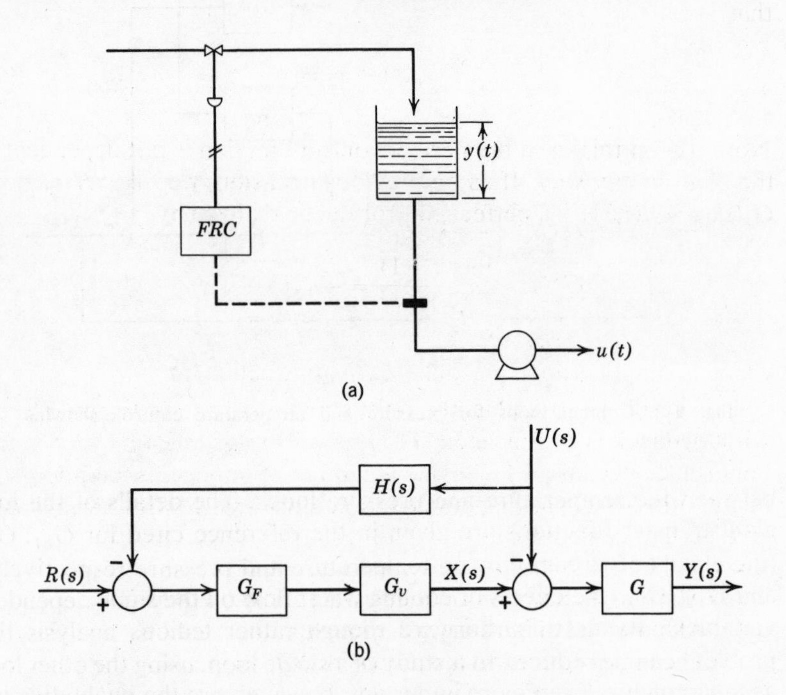

Fig. 9-3. A feedforward loop for level control. (a) pictorial representation; (b) block diagram.

control variable is affected. When this idea is formally applied to a control system, the loop that is generated is called **feedforward**, in recognition of the fact that the manipulating variable is responsive to a disturbance rather than to the control variable.

To illustrate by a specific example, suppose it is desired to control the level in the vessel of Fig. 2–5. As an alternative to feedback it is feasible to correct for variations in $u(t)$ by manipulating $x(t)$ before it has affected $y(t)$. To close the loop a flow-measuring transducer is needed on $u(t)$, and the usual controller and valve complete the loop in the form of Fig. 9–3. The subscript F is used on the controller block to emphasize the feedforward aspect of the loop. By the ordinary block algebra,

$$Y(s) = [-G(s) - HG_F G_v G(s)]U(s) \tag{9–1}$$

Ideally it would be desirable to pick $G_F(s)$ so that the bracket of equation (9–1) would reduce to zero, for then the disturbance would have no effect on the level at all. Such perfect regulator action requires that

$$G_F(s) = \frac{-1}{HG_v} \tag{9–2}$$

Note that in this case the perfect control function is not dependent on the plant in any way. If as on previous occasion, we take: $H(s) = K_T$, $G_v(s) = K_v/(\tau_v s + 1)$, perfect control can be realized by

$$G_F(s) = \frac{-(\tau_v s + 1)}{K_T K_v} = -K_F(1 + \tau_d s)$$

which is simply proportional plus derivative action.

This result is so eminently satisfactory that one is tempted to ask why feedback is ever needed. The answer to this question is of utmost importance because it highlights a number of implicit assumptions that might otherwise pass unnoticed. Feedforward control does indeed give perfect control *if*:

(1) All transfer functions in the system are known exactly.
(2) All potential disturbances are known.
(3) The required control function is realizable.

For the particular level control system used for this discussion, these criteria are almost met exactly; even here, however, some reservations are in order. What if a disturbance were momentarily large enough to **saturate** the valve (move it to the end of its travel)? The level would move from its desired point, never to return. What if a small leak developed in the tank? The level would fall until the tank was empty. In fact, the system is entirely uncontrolled with regard to any disturbance whatever other than the one for which it was designed. Finally, regarding realizability it should be noted that the $G_F(s)$ required has one zero but no pole. Although it is true that such a function cannot be synthesized exactly over the entire frequency range, this is not a practical limitation, since it can be approximated as closely as desired.

Computed control functions can however be unrealizable in still another sense where possible approximations are severely limited in principle. Consider, for example, the column-control problem outlined for Problem 8–8. A feedforward loop is shown in Fig. 9–4, from which

$$V(s) = [G_1 - HG_FG_vG(s)]\ U(s)$$

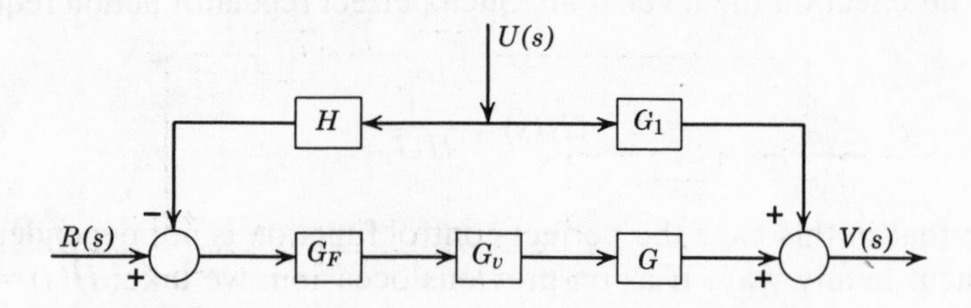

Fig. 9–4. A feedforward loop for distillation temperature control.

The perfect controller is now a function of G and G_1:

$$G_F(s) = \frac{G_1}{HG_vG} \tag{9–3}$$

Assuming the simplest $H(s) = K_T$, $G_v(s) = K_v$, and substituting the experimentally determined functions given in Problem 8–8,

$$G_F(s) = K_F\,\frac{(0.83s+1)(0.083s+1)}{(4.2s+1)(0.8s+1)}\,e^{+0.255s}$$

The point of interest is the positive sign on the exponential. A controller acting according to this function would show negative dead time; that is, its output signal would have to anticipate the input – an obvious impossibility.

In spite of the difficulties that we have emphasized, feedforward control is a very useful device if it is used in conjunction with feedback. In combination the feedback action compensates for the ignorance, variability, or unrealizable character of the feedforward control. A typical combination control is shown in Fig. 9–5.

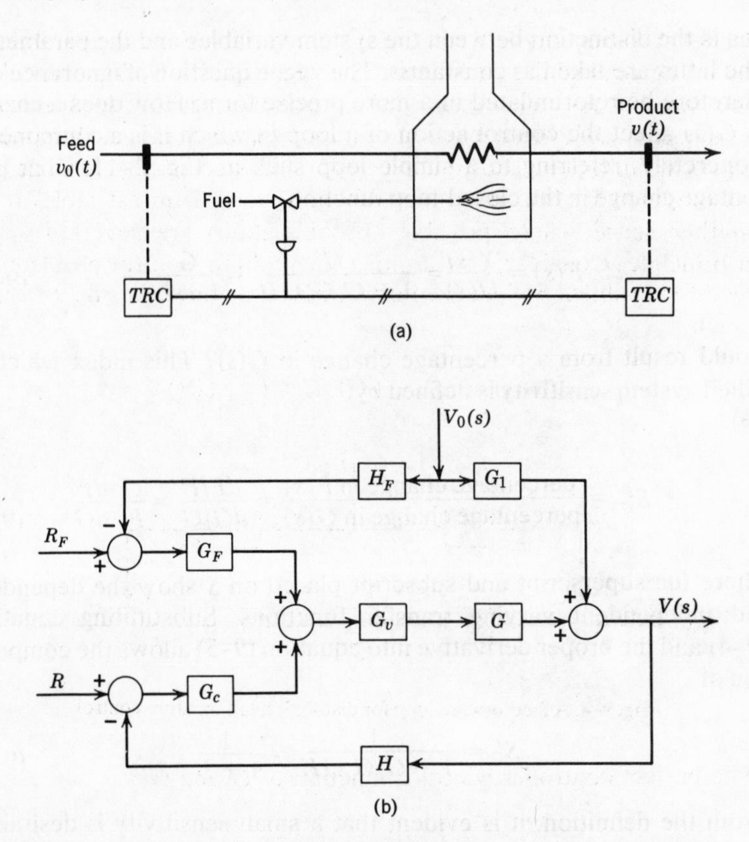

Fig. 9–5. Combination feedback–feedforward control of a furnace. (a) pictorial representation; (b) block diagram.

9–3. THE EFFECT OF IGNORANCE

We have seen that the use of feedback is intimately tied up with the matter of ignorance, in the sense that it is necessary when a variable is either unmeasured or unpredictable. It is true that if all inputs were known for all time and if all pertinent functional relationships were known, there would in principle be no need for feedback. Such an eventuality seems to be quite remote in many areas of knowledge but even if it were to be realized, practical considerations might favor feedback, especially if the complexity of a system required elaborate feedforward hardware. In any event it is productive to ask what effects unexpected changes may have.

In transfer-function notation all the parameters of a system are included in one or more of the gain or time constants in $G(s)$; indeed this is the distinction between the system variables and the parameters (the latter are taken as constants). The vague question of ignorance can therefore be reformulated in a more precise form: How does a change in $G(s)$ affect the control action of a loop in which it is a component? Concretely, referring to a simple loop such as Fig. 2–11, what percentage change in the closed-loop function

$$F(s) = \frac{Y(s)}{U(s)} = \frac{G}{1 + G_c G_v G H} = \frac{G}{1 + L} \tag{9–4}$$

would result from a percentage change in $G(s)$? This index which is called system **sensitivity** is defined by:

$$S_G^F = \frac{\text{percentage change in } F(s)}{\text{percentage change in } G(s)} = \frac{dF/F}{dG/G} = \frac{G}{F}\frac{dF}{dG} \tag{9–5}$$

where the superscript and subscript placed on S show the dependent and independent varying transfer functions. Substituting equation (9–4) and the proper derivative into equation (9–5) allows the computation of

$$S_G^F = \frac{1}{1 + G_c G_v G H} = \frac{1}{1 + L} \tag{9–6}$$

From the definition, it is evident that a small sensitivity is desirable; that is, it would be advantageous to have control which remains at a high level of quality in spite of parameter changes. The form of equation (9–6) is fortunate, for we see by inspection that system sensitivity is lowered by an increase in G_c, precisely the design criterion that improves control quality in any case. It is probably above all this characteristic of feedback loops that has made it possible to control successfully such a wide range of systems as yet inadequately understood in basics.

But this coincidence is not found universally as can be demonstrated by examining the sensitivity with respect to variation in the valve function, G_v:

$$S_{G_v}^F = \frac{-G_c G_v G H}{1 + G_c G_v G H} = \frac{-L}{1 + L} \tag{9–7}$$

In this case, unlike the first, an increase in G_c unfortunately acts to increase the magnitude of sensitivity. This will be the result when the transfer function whose variation is being studied lies in the feedback path. The sign of S is of course immaterial since changes in $G(s)$ can occur so far as we know in either direction. This discussion may be summarized as follows: (1) If parameter variation occurs in forward-path transfer functions, sensitivity problems do not ordinarily arise, because the same design factor that favors good control, reduces sensitivity; (2) If, on the other hand, parameter variation occurs in feedback transfer functions, a simple loop will not be adequate to give good control *and* low sensitivity. What then is to be done for such cases? One answer appears in the next section.

9–4. CASCADE CONTROL

In retrospect, it should not surprise us that a simple loop sometime fails to meet simultaneously conditions on loop gain *and* sensitivity. On the contrary, it is the case where this is true that is unexpected, since such a design requires a single transfer function to perform two jobs. It may be considered a coincidence that this is ever the case. This viewpoint suggests that perhaps a two-controller system would supply the degree of freedom that is lacking in the design of some simple loops.

Let us examine the cascade control system shown in block-diagram form in Fig. 9–6. The two-control and transducer transfer functions

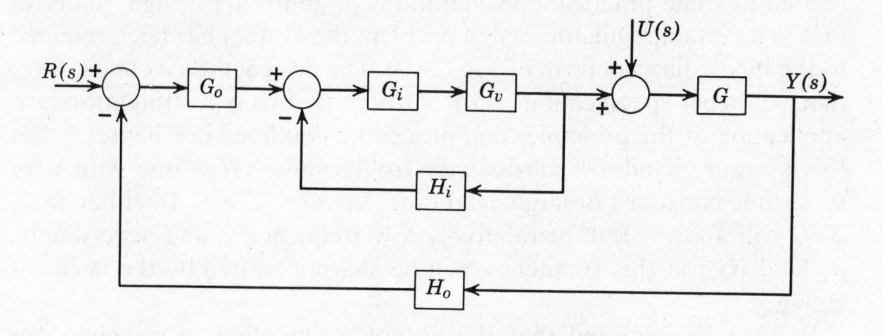

Fig. 9–6. A cascade control system.

are designated by subscripts for i, the inner, and o, the outer loop, respectively. In this arrangement the output signal of controller G_o serves to adjust the setpoint of G_i, the inner-loop controller. To see whether this configuration serves our purposes we must write out the details for $F(s) = Y(s)/U(s)$ and $S^F_{G_v}$. The first of these can be recalled from Problem 2–10, which yielded:

$$F(s) = \frac{G(1 + G_i G_v H_i)}{1 + G_i G_v H_i + G_o G_i G_v G H_o}$$

$$= \frac{G(1 + L_i)}{1 + L_i + L_o} = \frac{G}{1 + [L_o/(1 + L_i)]} \quad (9\text{–}8)$$

The sensitivity must be calculated from its definition. The reader can verify that

$$S^F_{G_v} = \frac{-G_o G_i G_v G H_o}{(1 + G_i G_v H_i)(1 + G_i G_v H_i + G_o G_i G_v G H_o)}$$

$$= \frac{-L_o}{(1 + L_i)(1 + L_i + L_o)} \quad (9\text{–}9)$$

Detailed study of these functions shows that both $F(s)$ and $S^F_{G_v}$ can indeed be made small simultaneously by adjusting the two control functions so that the open-loop transfer functions satisfy: $L_i >> 1$, $L_o >> L_i$.

9–5. A PRACTICAL CONSIDERATION

There is yet another benefit of cascade control that is more closely related to some practical considerations of controller design. Suppose that in a certain regulator design problem the system has been reduced to the block diagram form of Fig. 2–10. The designer must choose a G_c that will meet specifications on F. Ordinarily this is a straightforward application of the principles and procedures outlined in Chapter 7, but this system includes a particularly troublesome $G(s)$, one with very large time constants or large dead time, say $G = G' e^{-\tau s}$. In either case, $\angle L$ will show $-180°$ at relatively low frequencies, and accordingly, $|L|$ and $|G_c|$ at this frequency will be sharply limited by the need for stability.

It must be admitted that this is not a limitation in principle, for there is nothing in all this that would prevent a clever engineer from forming a $G_c(s)$ that has high gain at low frequency and the requisite low gain at the critical frequency. Unfortunately, however, it is not likely that the needed G_c would be associated with commercially packaged hardware. Take, for example, the control function that Smith[2] has

[2] Smith, O. J. M., *ISA Journal*, 6, No. 2, 28 (1959).

suggested for use in regulating a plant of the form: $G = G'e^{-\tau s}$. With reference again to Fig. 2–10, his controller function may be written as:

$$G_c = \frac{G_c'}{1 + G_c'G_vG'H(1 - e^{-\tau s})} = \frac{G_c'}{1 + L'(1 - e^{-\tau s})} \qquad (9\text{–}10)$$

where G_c' is the relatively simple control function that would arise from a design based on G', the plant function with the dead time disregarded. To prove that Smith's controller function will perform as expected it is only necessary to write:

$$F(s) = \frac{G'e^{-\tau s}}{1 + [L'e^{\tau s}/1 + L'(1 - e^{\tau s})]} = \frac{G'e^{-\tau s}[1 + L'(1 - e^{-\tau s})]}{1 + L'} \qquad (9\text{–}11)$$

and note that the characteristic equation (and hence the stability characteristic) of this loop is precisely the one obtained by disregarding the plant dead time. As Smith has pointed out, the hardware needed for the control function (equation 9–10) needs special synthesis.

To return to the mainstream of this argument, there is other relief from the practicality limitation to be found in cascade control. When we compare equations (9–4) with (9–8) it is evident that the identical degree of regulation can be guaranteed if

$$L = \frac{L_0}{1 + L_i} \qquad (9\text{–}12)$$

but whereas L might present the practical difficulties just alluded to, the dual choice of L_o and L_i provides another degree of freedom. Instead of being forced to satisfy

$$|L| < 1 \qquad \text{where} \qquad \angle L = -180°$$

with $|L|$ large at low frequency, the equivalent conditions are

$$\left|\frac{L_o}{1 + L_i}\right| < 1 \qquad \text{where} \qquad \angle L_o - \angle(1 + L_i) = -180°$$

with $|L_o/(1 + L_i)|$ large at low frequency. The latter conditions are so much less stringent that they can often be satisfied by easily available controllers for G_o and G_i. Moreover, the extra freedom of a two-controller design can produce notable improvement in control quality even if the option of a simple-loop design exists.

It is in applications to distillation control that the dual-loop advantages are most apparent, for here one can find superimposed all three characteristics that favor cascade control. Consider that:

(1) Physical complexity, interaction between variables, nonlinearities, and unexpected inputs act to produce on occasion parameter variations in virtually all transfer functions.

(2) Plant transfer functions show relatively large time constants and dead times.

(3) Sizable fluctuations appear in supply or downstream pressures of steam and water lines, which may be interpreted as variations in the valve transfer function, G_v.

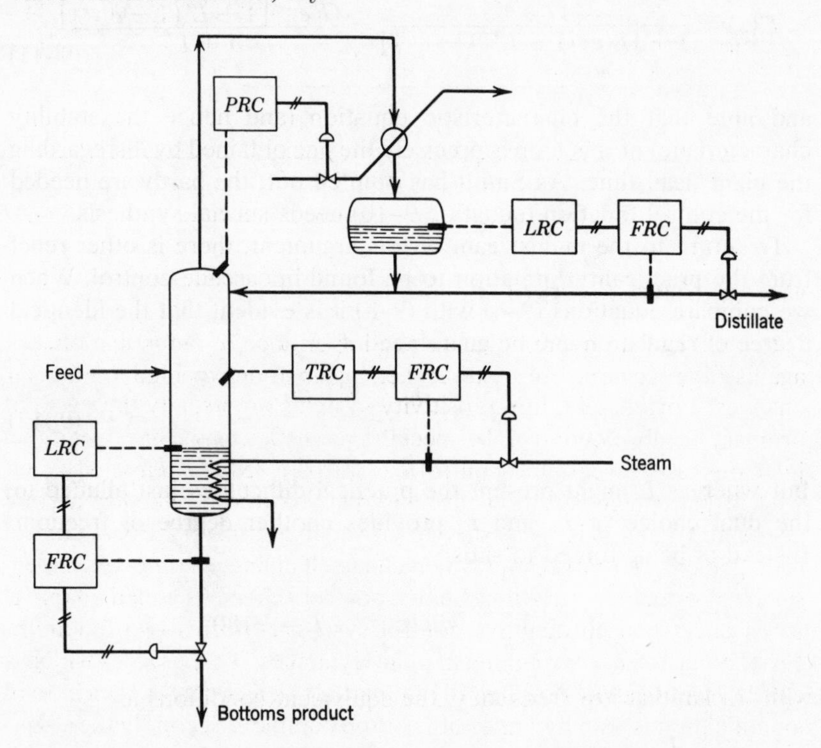

Fig. 9–7. A control arrangement for distillation showing three cascade control loops.

The first point implies a need for especially low sensitivity, the second indicates that specifications on L would not be easily attained, and the last item suggests that a cascade with an inner flow loop could appreciably reduce sensitivity.

In point of fact it is unusual to find a column that does not have several cascade arrangements. In Fig. 9–7, for example, a typical controlled column is shown pictorially. Comparison with the simplified

Fig. 9–1 points up the differences. To show how such a pictorial arrangement may be reduced to a block diagram, consider only the temperature control loop which uses steam flow as the manipulating variable. The cascade control is represented by Fig. 9–8, where $Z(s)$ and $V(s)$ are steam flowrate and column temperature, and $U_1(s)$ and $U_2(s)$ are representative disturbances, say steam pressure and reflux flowrate.

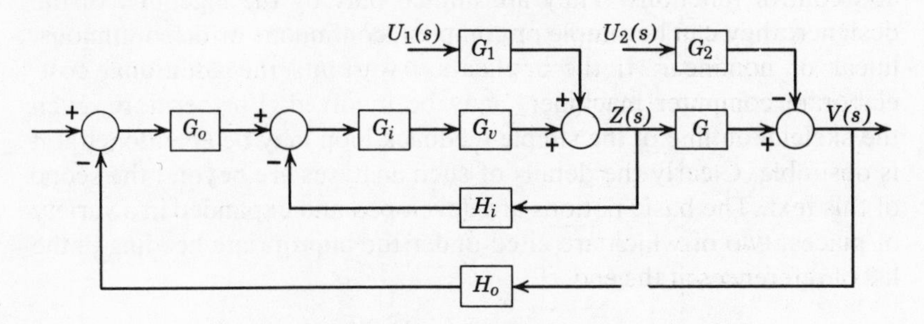

Fig. 9–8. Cascade control of column temperature.

9–6. ADAPTIVE CONTROL

It is difficult to overemphasize the importance of defending oneself against the vagaries of nature; i.e., against unexpected parameter changes. Fortunately, low-sensitivity systems are usually the result of ordinary feedback control. In special circumstances we have seen that judicious use of cascade control can further reduce sensitivity. But what if parameter variations are so great that these remedies are not adequate? Then it is necessary to consider not merely a best control arrangement, but rather one which can itself change in time to compensate for parameter variation. Such a control scheme is called **adaptive**. In essence then an adaptive control system performs two functions. First, it must sense variations in plant dynamics. This process which is called **identification** is generally a partial measurement, since total identification is usually impossible or too complex. Secondly the adaptive device must be able to adjust some controller parameter or function. This step is called **actuation**. Within these broad requirements there are obviously many possible schemes.

For illustration a simple adaptive scheme is shown in Fig. 9–9. In spite of its appearance, this diagram is not a block diagram in the strict sense. Rather, it is a schematic intended to emphasize the identification and actuation functions. To trace the control operation, start by examining the identification part. If the plant model G_m is exactly equal to the actual plant function G, the signals x and y are identical and the generalized error $\epsilon = 0$. Therefore, in the absence of parameter variation in G, the system is a simple feedback loop. When on the other hand, variation does appear in G, the actuator will respond to the ϵ-signal by changing a predetermined part of the control function G_c.

The foregoing description is intentionally vague about the actuation and control functions. They are limited only by the ingenuity of the designer; they can be simple or complex, continuous or discontinuous, linear or nonlinear. If the application warrants the additional cost, elaborate computer machinery may be involved. Furthermore, even the skeletal outline of the simple feedback loop may be abandoned if it is desirable. Clearly the details of such analyses are beyond the scope of this text. The basic notions are developed and expanded in a variety of places, two of which are cited under the appropriate heading in the list of references at the end.

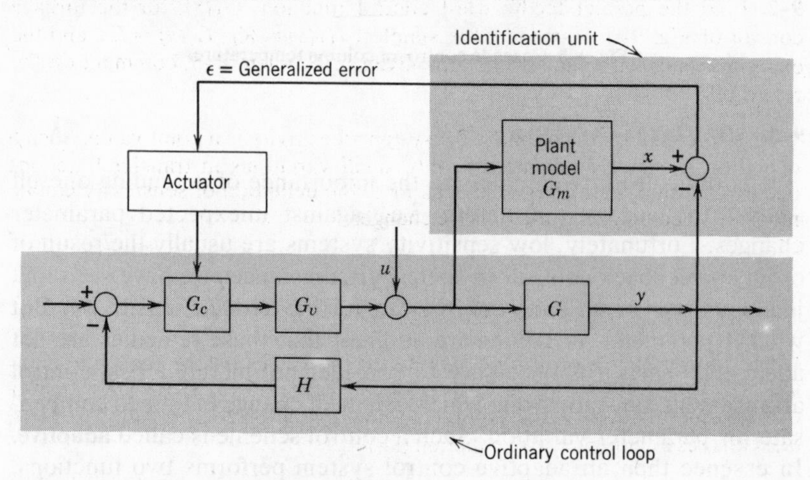

Fig. 9–9. An adaptive control arrangement.

REMARKS

This chapter focuses entirely on the part played by the controller in a loop, and on the relative advantages and limitations associated with various arrangements, the other major topic of this book—that of dynamic problem formulation—having been completed earlier. The appraisals of feedforward control and the effects of ignorance are very much at the heart of the matter, since by contrast they show most clearly what feedback is all about. By the nature of things it is very often the task of an engineer to analyze problems and design solutions at a stage when, scientifically speaking, they are still not well understood. In this light the subject of multiloop arrangements or indeed of control itself can well be looked at as a study of alternatives in order to minimize the penalty paid for remaining ignorance.

EXERCISES

9–1. Endtz, Janssen, and Vermeulen have shown experimentally that the transfer function G_{CP} (see Fig. 9–2) never has an angle shift more negative than –90°. As a consequence they argue that the controller of the pressure control loop can be set for very high gain, leading to the relationship

$$\frac{Z(s)}{X(s)} = -\frac{1}{G_{CP}}$$

By block algebra show that this does indeed follow from their premise, and use this equation to reduce the problem to a single simple loop. What is the equivalent plant function in your simple loop?

9–2. Find the perfect feedforward control function, $G_F(s)$, for the furnace control of Fig. 9–5. Assuming the simplest $H_F(s) = K_F$, $G_v(s) = K_v$, and the experimentally determined functions given in Problem 8–5, comment on the realizability of your G_F.

9–3. As defined by equation (9–5), system sensitivity is a point value. Such a definition is entirely adequate if only small variations in transfer functions occur. For analysis of large changes in G the definition of sensitivity can be modified to contain the ratio of finite changes

$$S_G^F = \frac{\Delta F/F_o}{\Delta G/G_o} = \frac{G_o(\Delta F)}{F_o(\Delta G)} = \frac{G_o(F - F_o)}{F_o(G - G_o)}$$

where the subscripts on F_o and G_o refer to the values before change in parameters. Apply this definition to the system of Fig. 2–11. Does your answer differ from equation (9–6)? Apply the new definition to compute $S_{G_v}^F$. How does this result compare with equation (9–7)?

9–4. Draw a detailed block diagram for the cascade control shown in Fig. 9–10. Compare the sensitivity functions of the simple and cascade loops. The significant disturbance is feed temperature. The parameter variations effect the transfer function between the jacket temperature and the fluid temperature v.

9–5. Explore the effect of cascade control on the jacketed vessel described by the block diagram of Fig. 9–11, where

$U_i(s)$ = steam supply pressure, psi
$U_0(s)$ = feed flowrate, (gal/min)
$X(s)$ = steam flowrate, (ft³/min)
$P(s)$ = controller output, psi
$G_v(s)$ = steam-valve transfer function, (ft³/min)/psi

$$G_1(s) = \frac{K_1}{(3s+1)(0.5s+1)} \quad \text{°F/(ft}^3\text{/min)}$$

$$G_2(s) = \frac{K_2}{(10s + 1)(0.67s + 1)} \quad \text{°F/°F}$$

with all time constants in minutes.

$V_j(s)$ = jacket temperature, °F

$V(s)$ = product temperature, °F

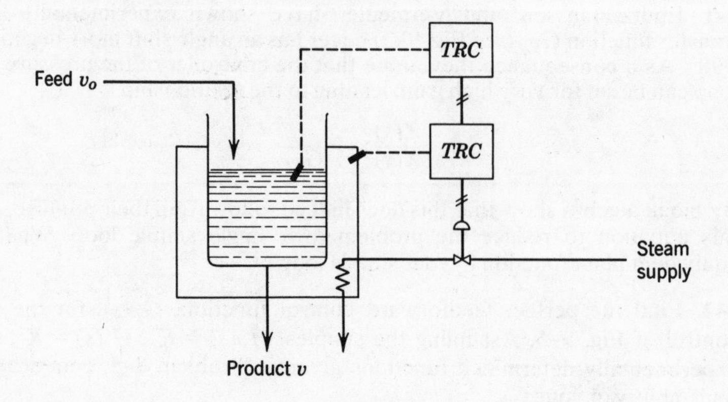

Fig. 9–10. Cascade control of a jacketed vessel.

For simplicity assume that all control, valve, and transducer functions are constants, and compare simple-loop and cascade designs as regards controller gain and offset. Where possible base your design on a 45° phase margin. (For safety, the inner loop is usually designed to be stable by itself.) Which disturbance is more successfully attenuated? How does this compare with the prior findings on sensitivity?

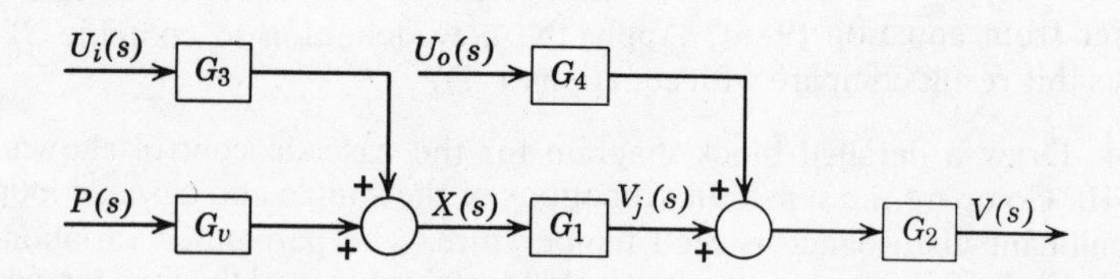

Fig. 9–11. Block diagram for a jacketed vessel.

9–6. Show that Smith's control function can be extended to plants of the form shown in Fig. 9–12 by using

$$G_c = \frac{G_c'}{1 + G_c'G_vG_1'G_2'H(1 - e^{-(\tau_1 + \tau_2)s})} = \frac{G_c'}{1 + L'(1 - e^{-(\tau_1 + \tau_2)s})}$$

9–7. Sometimes it is simpler to base an adaptive system on an input measurement than on a variable within the loop. Considering Fig. 9–13 from this point of view, what function would you suggest for the model?

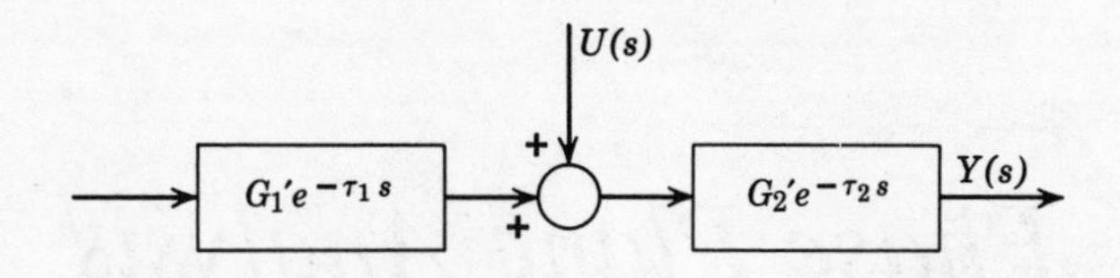

Fig. 9–12. A general plant function for Smith's method.

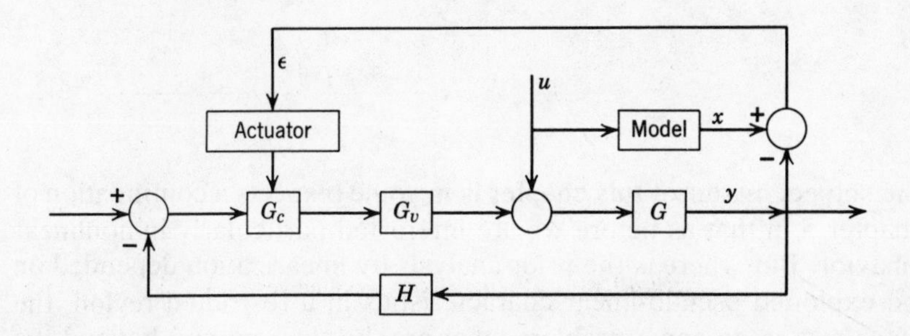

Fig. 9–13. An adaptive system using an input for identification.

10 *Phase Plane Analysis*

The subject matter of this chapter is in some respects a continuation of Chapter 5 in that as before we are interested particularly in nonlinear behavior. But whereas the prior analysis by linearization depended on and exploited pseudo-linear characteristics in a restricted region, the focus here is on some problems that are, by their nature, beyond the reach of linear approximation. To do this we are called upon to make a great sacrifice, to abandon entirely the apparatus of operational calculus and the many associated conveniences. Our sacrifice will be rewarded, however, by finding behaviors that would have been entirely unexplainable by linear analysis, and we will treat in detail systems that simply have no satisfactory linear counterpart.

10–1. ON-OFF CONTROL

To this point there has been no mention of the most common of all control functions, a simple two-position switch, because the discontinuity at the all-important time of switching is nonlinearizable. To study a system controlled by such a device, it is convenient to return to a consideration of the electrically heated batch-storage vessel first described in Section 1–5. The essential difference in our present analysis will be the closed loop shown in Fig. 10–1. It is desired to maintain the water temperature v close to 170° F in spite of convective heat loss to the surroundings.

A simple energy balance gives

$$\rho V C_p \frac{dv}{dt} = Q - UA(v - v_A) \tag{10–1}$$

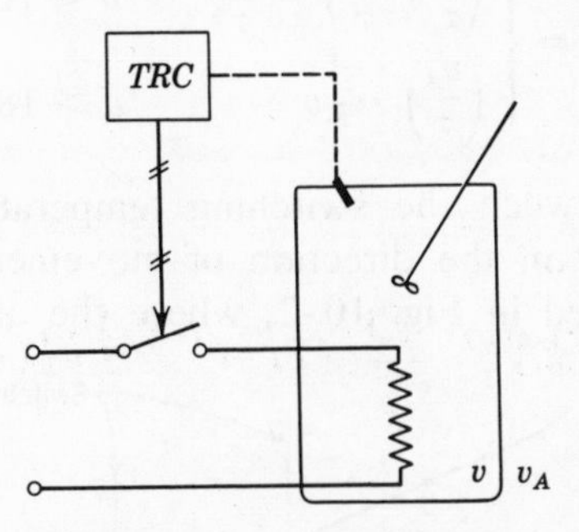

Fig. 10–1. An electrically heated vessel on closed-loop On-Off control.

where the various parameters are as before assumed to be constant, and Q is the energy added in the form of electrical power when the switch is closed. To prevent excessive wear caused by too frequent switching action, it is usual to cause the switching to occur not exactly at the desired temperature, but rather at either end of a small **differential gap**. Thus, say

$$Q = 0, \quad v > 180°\text{F (switch off)}$$
$$Q = Q, \quad v < 160°\text{F (switch on)}$$

and for all temperatures between these limits, the switch maintains whatever position it took at the last switching.

To introduce the graphical viewpoint of this chapter we first adopt the notation $\dot{v} = (dv/dt)$ and rewrite equation (10–1) as

$$\dot{v} = \left(\frac{Q}{\rho V C_p} + \frac{U A v_A}{\rho V C_p}\right) - \left(\frac{UA}{\rho V C_p}\right) v \qquad (10\text{–}2)$$

or, using the lumped constants defined as equations (1–13) and (1–14):

$$\dot{v} = \left(\frac{a}{\tau} + \frac{v_A}{\tau}\right) - \frac{1}{\tau} v$$

This is the equation of a straight line in the $\dot{v}$ versus v coordinate plane. More precisely, since Q can take on two different values, we are dealing with two lines having the same negative slope:

$$\dot{v} = \begin{cases} \left(\frac{a}{\tau} + \frac{v_A}{\tau}\right) - \frac{1}{\tau}v & v < 160°\text{F} \\ \left(\frac{v_A}{\tau}\right) - \frac{1}{\tau}v & v > 180°\text{F} \end{cases} \tag{10–3}$$

In the region between the switching temperatures, the applicable equation depends on the direction of movement. These characteristics are illustrated in Fig. 10–2, where the arrows are reminders

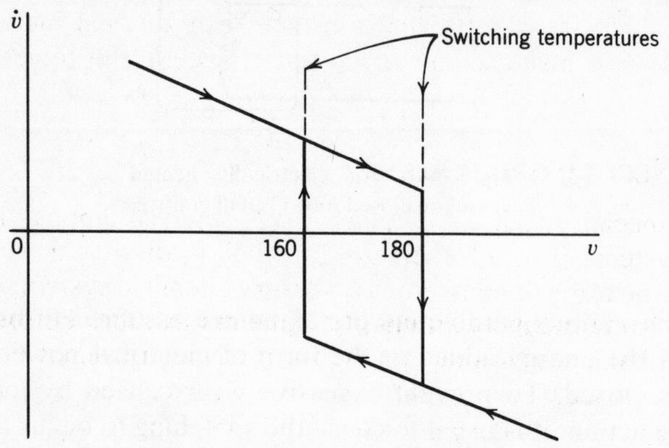

Fig. 10–2. Phase-plane portrait for an On–Off control system.

that the temperature rises from below and falls from above the switching temperatures. The graphical representations of these lines are called **trajectories.** The same lines are also the loci of all possible conditions of the system since any v chosen will dictate a $\dot{v}$ by one or the other of equations (10–3) and thereby locate a point on one of the lines.

In this analysis $\dot{v}$ and v are called **state variables** because their specification is sufficient to entirely fix the dynamic state of the system. A graph of trajectories in the plane of the state variables such as Fig. 10–2 is called a **phase-plane portrait.** Ordinarily, the number of state variables does not exceed the order of the system, and indeed only the temperature variable would be needed in this problem if it were not for the On-Off control switch. The presence of this device makes it necessary, however, to add an additional item of information in order to determine which of the two equations (10–3) is governing if the temperature is in the range between the switching points. In other cases the number of state variables may exceed the order for a multivariable system.

That the choice of $\dot{v}$ as a state variable is satisfactory in this case can be seen in Fig. 10–2. As a trajectory crosses an applicable switching line, the value of Q changes and the state of the system abruptly changes to one described by the other trajectory. On the diagram the two trajectories may be connected by verticals to establish a **limit cycle,** a closed trajectory. Of particular interest here is the observation that the same limit cycle will be developed in this system regardless of the initial condition.

Admittedly, this heater problem is highly idealized. It may be argued with some justification that no real device could reverse the sign of the temperature derivative instantaneously. With this in mind Problem 10–2 includes a more realistic heater with thermal inertia, but this generalization produces a second-order system, the topic of the next section.

10–2. A SECOND-ORDER SYSTEM

The special strengths of phase-plane analysis appear for second-order systems. For a framework in which to discuss these points, we examine next the dynamics of a reversible chemical system. Under well-stirred, isothermal conditions the system is described by respective material balances on reactant (subscript 1) and product (subscript 2):

$$V\frac{dy_1}{dt} = qx_1 - qy_1 - Vr$$

$$V\frac{dy_2}{dt} = qx_2 - qy_2 + \gamma Vr \qquad (10\text{–}4)$$

where r is in general a function of the concentrations of both reactant and product, and γ is the number of moles of product formed for each mole of reactant used: the ratio of stoichiometric numbers for the reaction. These equations provide a complete description of the dynamics if only a single reactant and single product are involved, or if all reactants are present in stoichiometric ratio. We will not treat more complex arrangements here, except to note that for such cases each additional component calls for another differential equation.

To translate equation (10–4) into a phase-plane diagram requires first of all a choice of state variables. Although several combinations of concentrations and their derivatives are possibilities, the straightforward pair to use for this problem is (y_1, y_2). It is generally simpler to work with whatever dependent variables appear when the system is written as a set of first-order equations. The key point is to recast the relationships in a form that retains the state variables, but eliminates time as an explicit variable. When this is done to equations (10–4), we obtain

$$\frac{dy_2}{dy_1} = \frac{qx_2 - qy_2 + \gamma Vr}{qx_1 - qy_1 - Vr}$$

which for constant total flowrate may be written

$$\frac{dy_2}{dy_1} = \frac{x_2 - y_2 + \gamma\tau r}{x_1 - y_1 - \tau r} \tag{10–5}$$

a first-order differential equation which is in general not simply solved in closed form because of the nonlinear chemical rate $r(y_1, y_2)$. The feed concentrations x_1 and x_2 are taken as constant. The problem is then to find the trajectories in the (y_1, y_2) plane from various initial conditions.

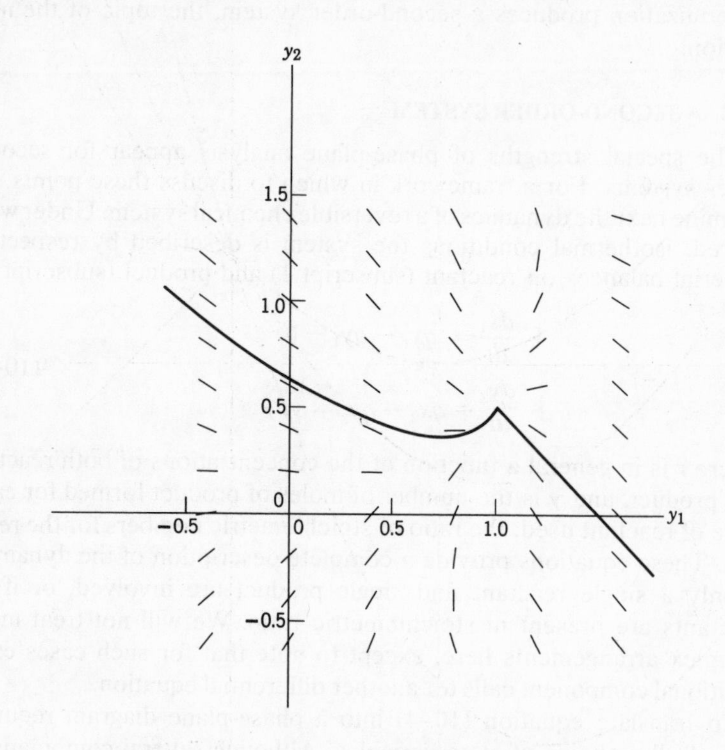

Fig. 10–3. Trajectory tangents with two interpolated paths.

Consider the following numerical procedure for graphically estimating a trajectory. At a particular point in the (y_1, y_2) plane, evaluate r from the known kinetics and the derivative (dy_2/dy_1) from equation (10–5). This derivative is the slope of the trajectory at the point studied. Repeat this computation at a sufficient number of points to prepare a diagram such as Fig. 10–3, on which the short line segments are tangent to the trajectories. Sketch paths in the plane from any initial conditions of interest to the steady state by interpolating between the directional lines.

There is an alternative to the foregoing which can shorten considerably the numerical work required. Rather than compute the slope at selected points, a locus is found algebraically along which all trajectories

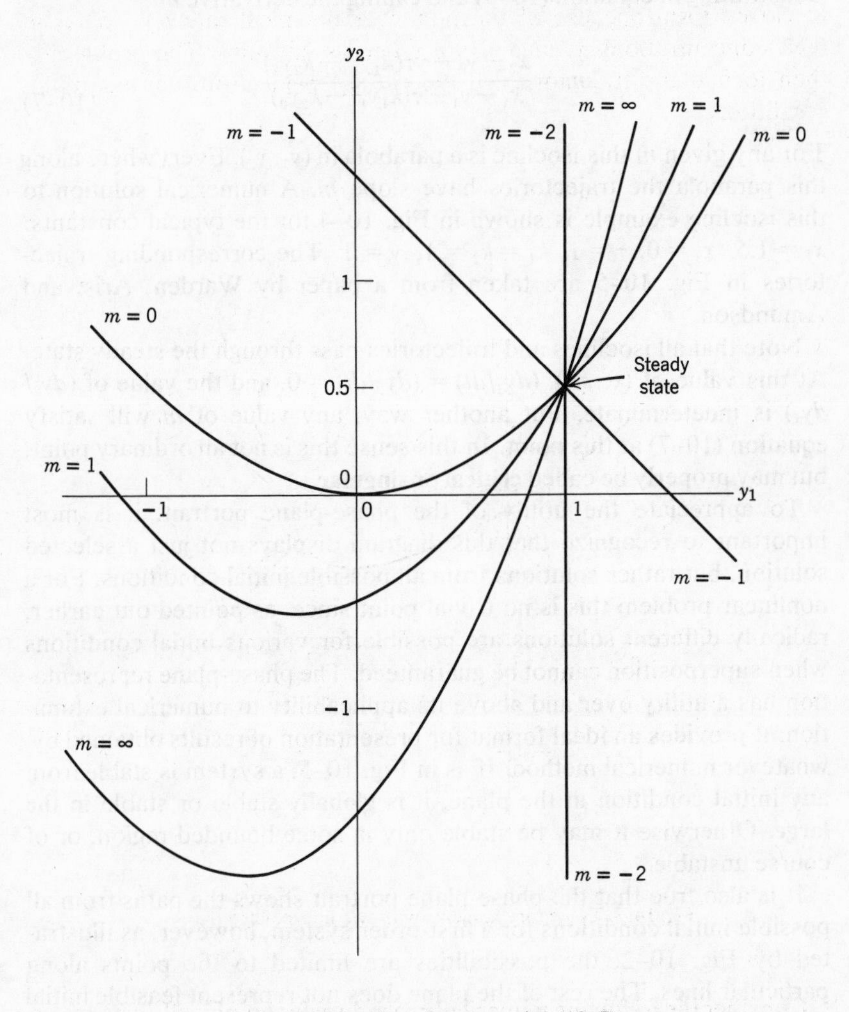

Fig. 10–4. Isoclines from equation (10–7).

have the same slope. Such a locus is called an **isocline.** The remaining steps are as before: a series of tangents are drawn and the trajectory paths sketched.

As an example, let the kinetics be second-order forward and first-order reverse:

$$r = k_1 y_1^2 - k_2 y_2 \tag{10-6}$$

Substituting in equation (10–5) and calling the derivative m:

$$m = \frac{x_2 - y_2 + \gamma\tau(k_1 y_1^2 - k_2 y_2)}{x_1 - y_1 - \tau(k_1 y_1^2 - k_2 y_2)} \tag{10-7}$$

For any given m this isocline is a parabola in (y_1, y_2). Everywhere along this parabola the trajectories have slope m. A numerical solution to this isocline example is shown in Fig. 10–4 for the typical constants: $x_1 = 1.5$, $x_2 = 0$, $\tau = 1$, $k_1 = k_2 = 1$, $\gamma = 1$. The corresponding trajectories in Fig. 10–5 are taken from a paper by Warden, Aris, and Amundson.[1]

Note that all isoclines and trajectories pass through the steady state. At this value of (y_1, y_2), $(dy_1/dt) = (dy_2/dt) = 0$, and the value of (dy_2/dy_1) is indeterminate. Put another way, any value of m will satisfy equation (10–7) at this point. In this sense this is not an ordinary point, but may properly be called **critical** or **singular**.

To appreciate the utility of the phase-plane portrait, it is most important to recognize that this diagram displays not just a selected solution, but rather solutions from all possible initial conditions. For a nonlinear problem this is no trivial point since, as pointed out earlier, radically different solutions are possible for various initial conditions when superposition cannot be guaranteed. The phase-plane representation has a utility over and above its applicability to numerical estimation: it provides an ideal format for presentation of results obtained by whatever numerical method. If as in Fig. 10–5, a system is stable from any initial condition in the plane, it is **globally** stable or stable **in the large.** Otherwise it may be stable only in some bounded region, or of course unstable.

It is also true that the phase-plane portrait shows the paths from all possible initial conditions for a first-order system, however, as illustrated by Fig. 10–2, the possibilities are limited to the points along particular lines. The rest of the plane does not represent feasible initial conditions. In the second-order case, the possible trajectories fill the plane entirely. From this it may be correctly inferred that systems of third order and higher would require higher dimensional *phase space* for representation of trajectories. The obvious complications in

---

[1]Warden, R. B., R. Aris, and N. R. Amundson, *Chem. Eng. Sci.*, **19,** 149 (1964).

visualizing lines and surfaces in higher dimensions are a serious limitation on such analyses, as might be expected.

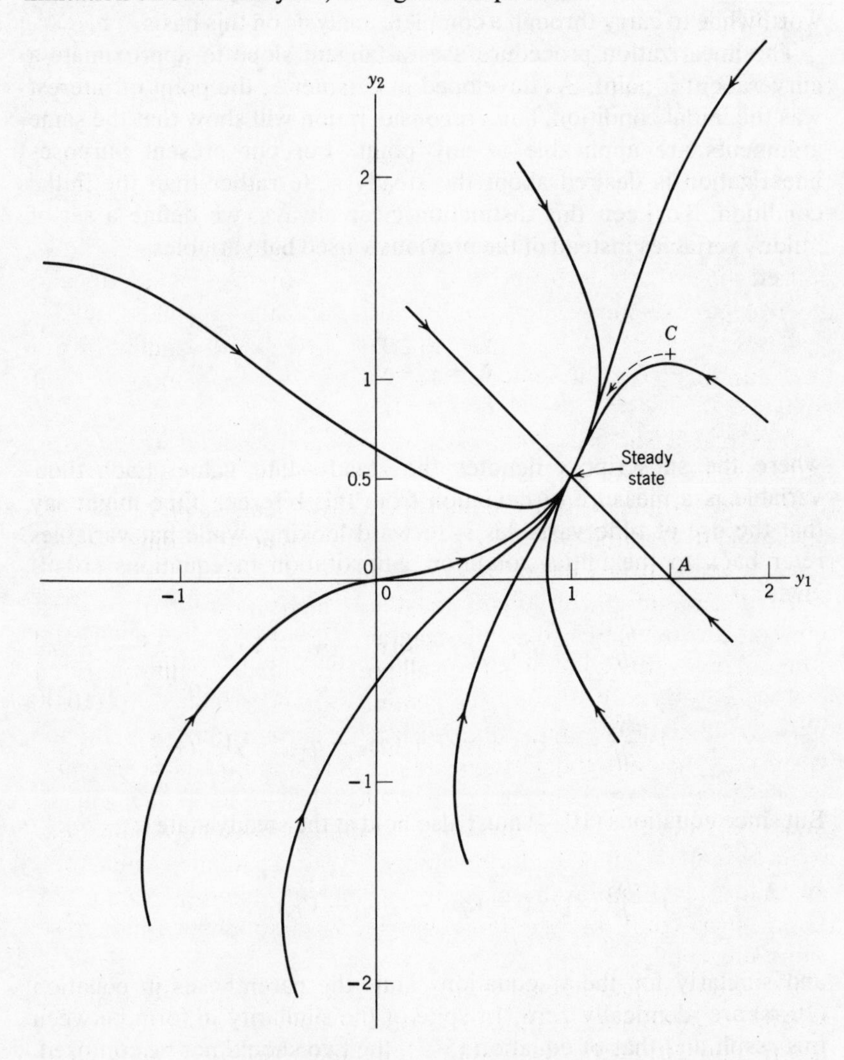

Fig. 10–5. Trajectories for equation (10–7). (After Warden, Aris, and Amundson.)

10–3. THE FUNDAMENTAL THEOREM OF STABILITY

The phase-plane results of the last section offer an opportunity for an evaluation of the linearization approximation, because the phase-plane portrait is a complete and precise display of all solutions. What differences in results would have arisen had the system equations been linearized? Because the comparison is remarkably instructive, it is worthwhile to carry through a complete analysis on this basis.

The linearization procedure uses a tangent slope to approximate a curve about a point. As developed in Chapter 5, the point of interest was the initial condition, but a reconsideration will show that the same arguments are applicable at any point. For our present purposes linearization is desired about the steady state rather than the initial condition. To keep this distinction clear always, we define a set of "tilde" variables instead of the previously used hat variables.

Let:

$$\tilde{y}_1 = y_1 - y_{1s}$$
$$\tilde{y}_2 = y_2 - y_{2s}$$
$$\tilde{r} = r - r_s$$

where the subscript s denotes the steady-state value. Each tilde variable is a measure of deviation from this referent. One might say that the use of tilde variables is forward looking, while hat variables refer back to the initial condition. Substitution in equations (10–4) gives

$$V\frac{d\tilde{y}_1}{dt} = -q\tilde{y}_1 - V\tilde{r} + (qx_1 - qy_{1s} - Vr_s)$$

$$V\frac{d\tilde{y}_2}{dt} = -q\tilde{y}_2 + \gamma V\tilde{r} + (qx_2 - qy_{2s} + \gamma Vr_s) \tag{10–8}$$

But since equations (10–4) must also hold at the steady state ($t \to \infty$):

$$V\frac{dy_1}{dt}(\infty) = 0 = (qx_1 - qy_{1s} - Vr_s)$$

and similarly for the y_2 equation. Thus the parentheses in equation (10–8) are identically zero. In spite of the similarity in form between this result and that of equation (5–7), the two should not be confused. In effect the use of tilde variables shifts the origin to the steady-state position and consequently locates the initial condition away from the origin. Because the tilde variables do not have zero initial values, they could not be used to derive transfer functions. On the other hand, the previously used hat variables cannot be used for our present purposes, since in that coordinate system the origin was moved to the initial condition.

To continue, we use the linearization:

$$\tilde{r} = \left(\frac{\partial r}{\partial y_1}\right)_s \tilde{y}_1 + \left(\frac{\partial r}{\partial y_2}\right)_s \tilde{y}_2$$

which for the rate equation (10–6) reduces to

$$\tilde{r} = 2k_1 y_{1s}\tilde{y}_1 - k_2\tilde{y}_2 \qquad (10\text{–}9)$$

Substitution in equations (10–8) gives the linear equations

$$V\frac{d\tilde{y}_1}{dt} = -q\tilde{y}_1 - 2k_1 y_{1s}V\tilde{y}_1 + k_2 V\tilde{y}_2$$

$$V\frac{d\tilde{y}_2}{dt} = -q\tilde{y}_2 + 2\gamma k_1 y_{1s}V\tilde{y}_1 - \gamma k_2 V\tilde{y}_2 \qquad (10\text{–}10)$$

and

$$\frac{d\tilde{y}_2}{d\tilde{y}_1} = \frac{(2\gamma k_1 y_{1s}\tau)\tilde{y}_1 - (1 + \gamma k_2\tau)\tilde{y}_2}{-(1 + 2k_1 y_{1s}\tau)\tilde{y}_1 + (k_2\tau)\tilde{y}_2}$$

With the same numerical values as before:

$$\frac{d\tilde{y}_2}{d\tilde{y}_1} = \frac{2\tilde{y}_1 - 2\tilde{y}_2}{-3\tilde{y}_1 + \tilde{y}_2} = m \qquad (10\text{–}11)$$

From this, the isoclines may be determined; they are the straight lines:

$$\tilde{y}_2 = \frac{3m + 2}{m + 2}\tilde{y}_1 \qquad (10\text{–}12)$$

which all pass through the steady state $\tilde{y}_1 = \tilde{y}_2 = 0$. These isoclines as well as resultant trajectories are shown as Fig. 10–6.

We are now in a position to make the essential observation of this section. Comparing the "correct" phase-plane portrait of Fig. 10–5 with the linearized trajectories of Fig. 10–6, it is apparent that they are practically identical in the region of the steady state. This intuitive result is the essence of a most important theorem proved rigorously by Liapunov before the turn of the century. Stated more formally it is called the **fundamental stability theorem** or sometimes the theorem of Liapunov[2]: in the neighborhood of a steady state of a nonlinear system, the stability characteristics of the solution are the same as for the linearized system. (Exceptions can arise if the nonlinear equations cannot be expanded to include linear terms. This is not a restriction

---

[2]Davis, H. T., *Introduction to Nonlinear Differential and Integral Equations,* U.S. Atomic Energy Commission, Washington, D. C. (1960); p. 318.

of much practical importance to engineers.) The proof of this theorem does not require that the boundaries of a stability region be established

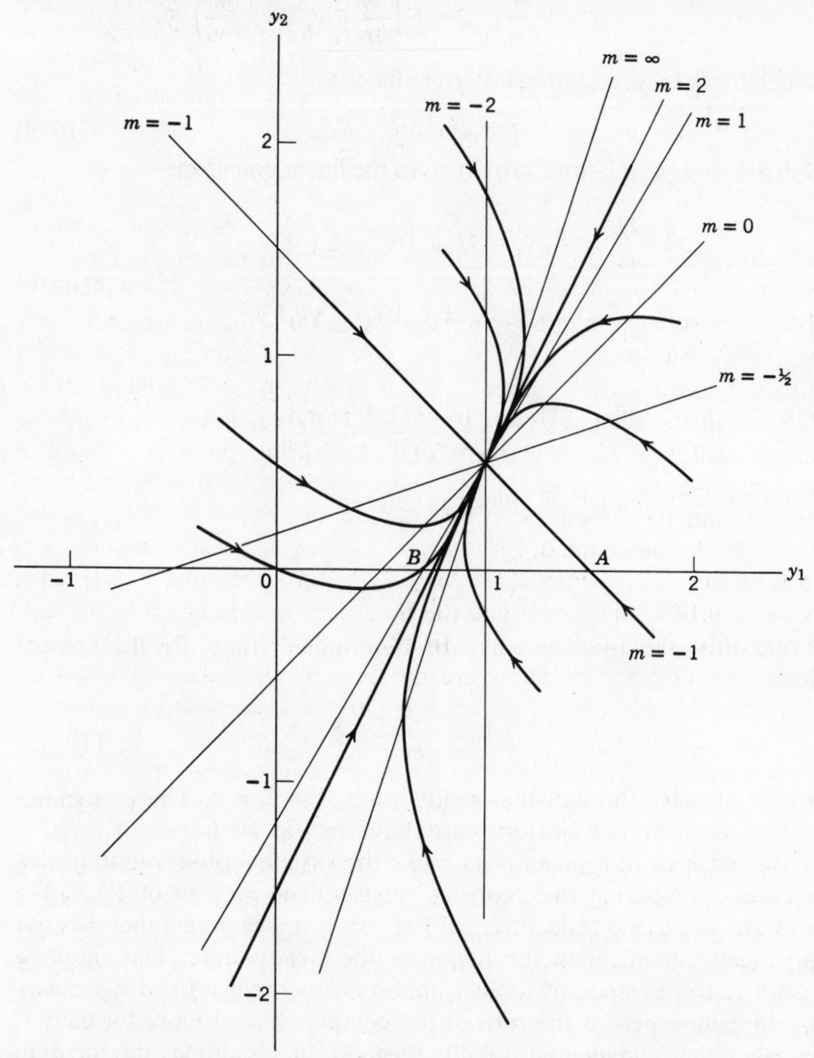

Fig. 10–6. Isoclines and trajectories for equation (10–11).

numerically, although this can also be done for any specific problem of interest.[3] If a region is not computed explicitly, we can speak only of **local stability.**

[3]Gura, I. A., and D. D. Perlmutter, *A.I.Ch.E. Journal*, **11**, 474 (1965).

The point that concerns us at this juncture is that it is a relatively simple matter to establish the local stability (or instability) of the steady state for any nonlinear system by systematic linearization. This is often adequate for a qualitative phase-plane analysis, especially if as is the case here, large regions of the phase space have no physical significance. Obviously, only the positive concentrations of the first quadrant are of interest in this example.

10–4. STARTUP

To illustrate some strengths and weaknesses of phase-plane analysis and linearization, suppose that it is desired to startup an isothermal reactor—specifically the one whose trajectories are shown in Fig. 10–5. Presumably there is initially no product in the reactor; i.e., $y_2(0) = 0$. Any trajectory must start from the y_1 axis, but we are still free to choose $y_1(0)$, the initial reactant concentration. If the reactor is filled with the feed before the reaction is initiated (say thermally, or catalytically), then $y_1(0) = x_1$. Such a starting point is labeled A in Fig. 10–5; the reactor state (y_1, y_2) will follow the straight line up to the left until it settles at the steady state.

If, on the other hand, the reactor is brought to reaction conditions before any of y_1 is introduced (say by heating the solvent) the initial state will be at the origin and the trajectory will move up to the right toward the same steady state. In either case, the transient is smooth and overdamped, and there are no apparent difficulties to be anticipated. In a later section we will find that for a temperature-dependent reactor such a carefree conclusion is not always justified.

But what of the linearization? Could the nonlinear analysis have been avoided by using instead the approximate solutions of Fig. 10–6? As the trajectories of this diagram show, a linearization of this problem would have led to an unnecessarily restrictive recommendation, for it appears from Fig. 10–6 that realizable paths are only possible if $y_1(0)$ is greater than some minimum value (point B). As might perhaps be expected, linearization must be used with some caution; nevertheless, to balance the picture, it may be noted that the trajectories from point A are identical on the two figures.

The foregoing discussion is useful, too, to show a major limitation on the phase-plane method. Because it was assumed in the derivation of the trajectory equation (10–5) that the forcing functions x_1 and x_2 are constant, only simple system inputs are acceptable. Step inputs are treated by letting $x = x(0^+)$, using the value of $x(0^-)$ to determine only the initial conditions. In effect the initial condition represents the steady state that existed before $t = 0$ when $x = x(0^-)$. In the framework of the startup problem for example, where $x_2 = 0$, the initial condition at the origin corresponds to $x_1(0^-) = 0$, whereas an initial state at the point marked C on Fig. 10–5 would result from $x_1(0^-) = 2.62$. Therefore, a step drop in feed concentration from 2.62 to 1.50 would cause the reactor state to follow the trajectory path from C to the final steady state shown in the figure.

A similar line of reasoning will allow the treatment of impulse disturbances, in this case by thinking of the initial condition as the result of an instantaneous jump away from the steady state at $t = 0$. For all $t \neq 0$ the forcing variable x is constant at the value that existed before and after the impulse. Finally to complete the catalog of possibilities, it should be mentioned that under some circumstances, this argument can be extended to include ramp inputs, but there it stops. In general, this approach is useful for simple transients only.

10–5. THE EFFECTS OF FEEDBACK

In this section the isothermal reactor is put on closed-loop control by manipulating a forcing variable as a function of the feedback from one of the responses. Specifically, from among the several combinations possible, we choose the feed concentration x_1 to be manipulated by the product concentration y_2; i.e., $x_1 = f(y_2)$. Substitution in equation (10–5) produces

$$\frac{dy_2}{dy_1} = \frac{x_2 - y_2 + \gamma\tau r}{f(y_2) - y_1 - \tau r}$$

a relationship between y_1 and y_2 which although perhaps a bit more complicated algebraically, can be analyzed on the phase plane as before once the details of f are known. Rather than continue with an arbitrary choice of nonlinearity among the endless number possible, it is more rewarding for our purposes to go on with the linearized kinetics of equation (10–9) and the simple proportional control mode:

$$\tilde{x}_1 = K_0\tilde{y}_2 = (x_1 - x_{1s}) = K_0(y_2 - y_{2s}) \qquad (10\text{–}13)$$

The reader ought to take note of two assumptions implied by equation (10–13). First, the single proportionality constant K_0 is the product for the cascade of components in the feedback loop. It includes a transducer, a controller, and a final-control element, presumably all simple proportional devices. Secondly, this control function is such that it will correct toward the steady state, not toward the initial condition as would be the case if $\hat{x}_1 = K_0\hat{y}_2$. This last item is again tied to the matter of the reference values used in defining the deviation variables.

Besides its obvious arithmetic advantages, the choice of equation (10–13) will allow a study of the complete range of behaviors that one can practically find in the neighborhood of a simple critical point. Recalling the fundamental theorem, this list will also encompass all possible varieties of trajectory patterns about a nonlinear steady state.

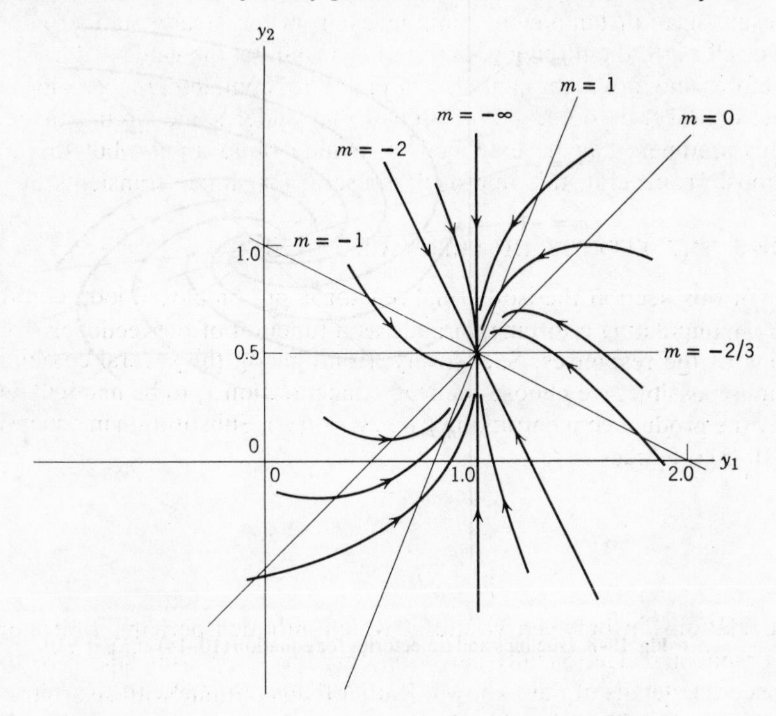

Fig. 10–7. Isoclines and trajectories for equation (10–14) at $K_0 = -1$.

Substitution of equations (10–9) and (10–13) in equations (10–8) yields, after simplification

$$\frac{d\tilde{y}_2}{d\tilde{y}_1} = \frac{2\tilde{y}_1 - 2\tilde{y}_2}{-3\tilde{y}_1 + (K_0 + 1)\tilde{y}_2} = m \qquad (10\text{–}14)$$

The isoclines are then

$$\tilde{y}_2 = \frac{3m + 2}{(K_0 + 1)m + 2}\tilde{y}_1 \qquad (10\text{–}15)$$

It remains now only to choose a range of values of K_0, the control gain. A choice of $K_0 = 0$ (no control) reduces equation (10–15) to equation (10–12) as of course it should. The effects of other values are illustrated on the phase plane in Figs. 10–7, 10–8, and 10–9. These shapes are called **node**, **focus**, and **saddle** respectively. They comprise

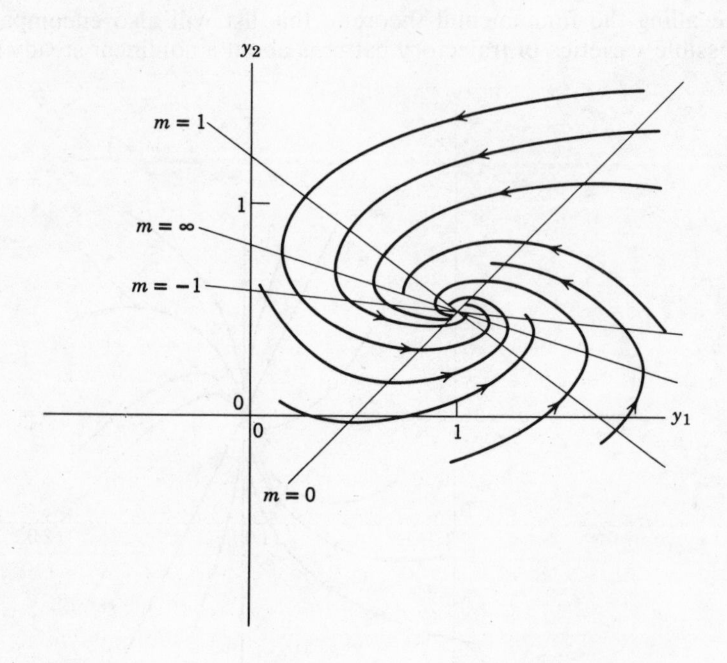

Fig. 10–8. Isoclines and trajectories for equation (10–14) at $K_0 = -10$.

the entire field of possible shapes, except for some degenerate straight lines and ellipses of interest only as limiting cases. These pathological cases are demonstrated in Problems 10–5 and 10–11, but need not distract us at this point. The node and focus can be stable or unstable, depending on the direction of the trajectory. This piece of information cannot be found from the isocline equation, since the separate signs of (dy_1/dt) and (dy_2/dt) have been lost by division. The individual signs can be established readily though by returning to a form such as equations (10–10) or the original equations (10–4). The saddle is always unstable, since all trajectories either avoid the steady state or pass right through it without termination. To summarize this linearized control analysis, Table 10–1 shows the effect of variation in K_0.

TABLE 10–1

Stability Results For Various Control Settings (Equation 10–14)

Range of K_0	*Trajectory Shape*	*Stability*
$< -1\frac{1}{8}$	Focus	Stable
$-1\frac{1}{8}$ to $+2$	Node	Stable
> 2	Saddle	Unstable

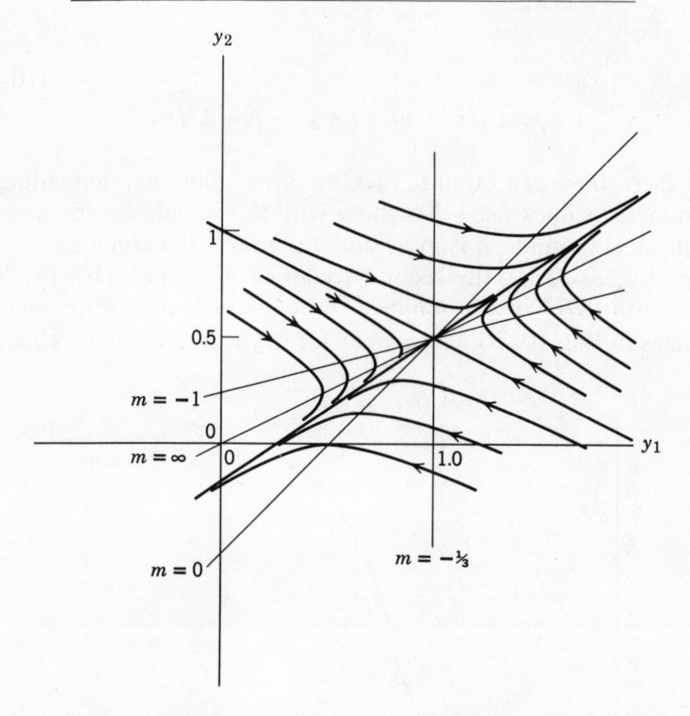

Fig. 10–9. Isoclines and trajectories for equation (10–14) at $K_0 = +5$.

10–6. MULTIPLE STEADY STATES

In the foregoing, no special attention was paid to the matter of computing steady states. It was rather taken for granted that this point could always be found by solving simultaneously the algebraic equations that were produced by setting all time derivatives equal to zero. For the system of equations (10–4) for example, the steady state was the solution of

$$0 = qx_1 - qy_{1s} - Vr(y_{1s}, y_{2s})$$
$$0 = qx_2 - qy_{2s} + \gamma Vr(y_{1s}, y_{2s})$$

For linear systems there is indeed no further complication, since two equations in two unknowns produce a unique solution. However, our emphasis here is on nonlinear behavior where any number of solutions can result from n equations in n variables.

A most important chemical engineering example may be drawn from Chapter 5, where mass and energy balances on a temperature-dependent system were written as equations (5–13). Here a steady-state solution must satisfy

$$\begin{aligned} 0 &= qx - qy - Vr \\ 0 &= \rho q C_p(v_i - v) + hA(v_A - v) + \Delta H V r \end{aligned} \tag{10–16}$$

and, in fact, there can be one, two, or three solutions, depending on the parameter values used. To show why this should be the case on more physical grounds, it is most direct to follow the argument of Van Heerden.[4] Considering the second equation of the pair (10–16), note that the term (ΔHVr) is a nonlinear function of temperature, sigmoid in shape as in Fig. 10–10. It accounts for the heat released by chemical

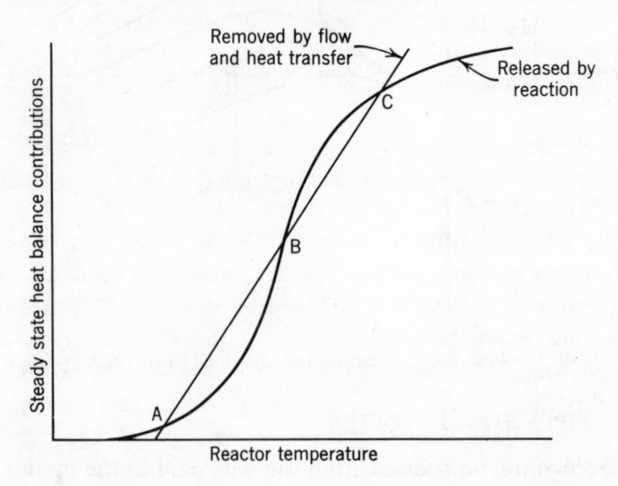

Fig. 10–10. Comparison of heat balance terms. (After Van Heerden).

reaction. The other two terms of the same equation are linear in v, accounting for the net heat removed from the reactor by flow and heat transfer. As is shown by Fig. 10–10, there are potentially three points of intersection at which the reactor is in the thermal balance.

[4] Van Heerden, C., *Ind. Eng. Chem.*, **45**, 1242 (1953).

Detailed solution of equation (10–5) confirms this reasoning. The matter of local stability thus turns out to hinge on not one, but three questions applied in turn to each of the steady states. The answers may be found by the linearization procedure already described in detail, since as noted above, the linear approximation may be applied at any point.

A most thorough computational and analytic study of the system (equations 5–13) was carried out by Aris and Amundson[5] for kinetics of the form of equation (5–1), with $n = 1$. They showed by linearization that while the two steady states A and C (Fig. 10–10) are

TABLE 10–2

Parameter Values For Phase-Plane Figs. 10–11, 10–12, 10–13

$(\Delta H/\rho C_p) = 200°K/(\text{g-mole/1})$
$(hA/\rho V C_p) = 1\ \text{min}^{-1}$
$(q/V) = 1\ \text{min}^{-1}$
$x = 1$ g-mole/1
$v_A = v_i = 350°K$
$Q = 10{,}000$ cal/g-mole
$k_0 = e^{25}\ \text{min}^{-1}$

stable, the intermediate state B is unstable. The same result can also be established from the Van Heerden diagram directly by noting that stability requires the slope of the heat removal curve to exceed that of the heat generation curve (and vice versa), but the linearization shows in addition whether a node, focus, or saddle characterizes the local behavior. Using the concentration and temperature as state variables, and the parameter values listed in Table 10–2, Aris and Amundson found a stable node at $v_s = 354°K$, $y_s = 0.964$ g-mole/liter; an unstable saddle at $v_s = 400$, $y_s = 0.5$; and a stable focus at $v_s = 441$, $y_s = 0.0885$. These are shown in Fig. 10–11, together with the phase-plane trajectories given in the same reference. Such a diagram can yield benefits that could never have been found by linear analysis alone. Consider for example, as do the authors of the reference, that the entire plane can be divided along line GBF such that all transients from initial conditions to the right end at steady state C, whereas all trajectories that start on the left go ultimately to A. Furthermore, observe the potential danger of attempting a startup with the reactor

[5]Aris, Rutherford, and N. R. Amundson, *Chem. Eng. Sci.*, 7, 121, 132 (1958).

initially containing reactant at the feed concentration. The trajectories from such initial conditions would move far out to the right to possibly excessive temperatures before returning to stèady state *C*.

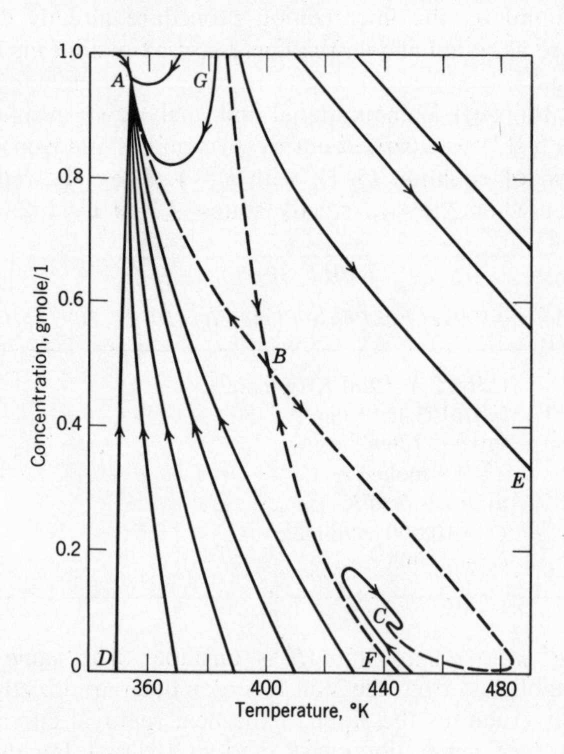

Fig. 10–11. Trajectories for uncontrolled reactor. (Ref. 5.)

Finally, there is the matter of feedback control. In general, how does control action alter the phase-plane portrait? In particular, is it possible to modify system behavior to make the steady state at *B* a stable operating point? The subject is taken up in the next section, but it would be well, before leaving the matter of multiple steady states, to refer to the linearized study of Hoftyzer and Zwietering[6] on the polymerization of ethylene. These authors were able to show that the use of kinetics half-order in catalyst concentration leads for some parameter values to a system with five steady states. Moreover, of perhaps more immediate practical significance is their conclusion that the steady state of usual industrial interest is unstable when the reactor

[6] Hoftyzer, P. J. and T. N. Zwietering, *Chem. Eng. Sci.*, **14**, 241 (1961).

is uncontrolled. It is clear that for a nonlinear reactor system the number of steady states and their stability can be quite sensitive to changes in kinetics.

10-7. CONTROL OF REACTOR TEMPERATURE

In practice, temperature is one of the simplest variables to measure, and flowrate is perhaps the easiest to manipulate. Certainly with the hardware currently available both of these are far more convenient to work with than chemical compositions. It seems most reasonable therefore to propose a closed loop for reactor control that operates by manipulating the coolant flow rate q_c in response to deviations in the reactor temperature υ. The fact that the variable q_c does not appear explicitly in equations (5–13) is not a serious difficulty, if we recall that both the heat-transfer coefficient h, and the average coolant temperature υ_A are functions of q_c. It was possible to treat them as constants up to now only because it was implied that the coolant rate did not change.

In the present circumstance the function h versus q_c can be obtained from standard dimensionless-group correlations:

$$\frac{h}{h_s} = \left(\frac{q_c}{q_{cs}}\right)^{0.8} \tag{10–17}$$

The average coolant temperature is determined from the heat balance that equates the loss from the reactor to the gain of the coolant:

$$hA(\upsilon_A - \upsilon) = 2p_c q_c C_{pc}(\upsilon_A - \upsilon_c)$$

where υ_c is the coolant inlet temperature and the c subscripts on the density and heat-capacity parameters stand for the coolant properties, assumed constant. The factor 2 arises from the use of an average coolant temperature which is halfway between the inlet and outlet extremes. Accordingly, $2(\upsilon_A - \upsilon_c)$ is equal to the total increase in coolant temperature. Rearranging:

$$\upsilon_A = \frac{hA\upsilon - 2\rho_c q_c C_{pc}\upsilon_c}{hA - 2\rho_c q_c C_{pc}} \tag{10–18}$$

a function of q_c and h, which is in turn a function of q_c through equation (10–17). By algebraic substitution of equations (10–17) and (10–18) into the system equations (5–13) it is now possible to write the latter as explicitly dependent on q_c. The reader should note, however, that such a result is most difficult to use for computations because of the horrendous arithmetic required.

To reduce the equations to more manageable proportions, Aris and Amundson have demonstrated that the total effect of coolant flow on the entire heat-transfer term can very satisfactorily be approximated by writing

$$hA(v_A - v) = (h_s A + \alpha \tilde{q}_c)(v - v_c) \qquad (10\text{–}19)$$

where α is a constant evaluated in the reference but of no immediate interest to this discussion, and $\tilde{q}_c$ is the deviation of the manipulated variable from its steady-state value. For simple proportional control:

$$\tilde{q}_c = K_0 \tilde{v} = (q_c - q_{cs}) = K_0(v - v_s)$$

and

$$hA(v - v_A) = [h_s A + \alpha K_0(v - v_s)](v - v_c)$$

This relatively simpler expression, quadratic in v, can be substituted in equations (5–13) to give:

$$V\frac{dy}{dt} = qx - qy - Vr$$

$$\rho V C_p \frac{dv}{dt} = \rho q C_p(v_i - v) - [h_s A + \alpha K_0(v - v_s)](v - v_c) + \Delta H V r$$

For the numerical values given in Table 10–2, these may be reduced to the state-variable form:

$$\frac{dy}{dt} = x - y - r$$

$$\frac{dv}{dt} = (v_0 - v) - [1 + (k/200)(v - v_s)](v - v_c) + 200r$$

where $k = (200\alpha K_0/\rho q C_p)$, a control parameter proportional to the feedback gain. Including the selected numerical values for v_0, v_s, and v_c the trajectory equation is finally:

$$\frac{dy}{dv} = \frac{x - y - r}{-2(v - 350) - (k/200)(v - 400)(v - 350) + 200r} \qquad (10\text{–}20)$$

which may be evaluated for various control settings k. The stability results are summarized by Table 10–3 and selected trajectories are

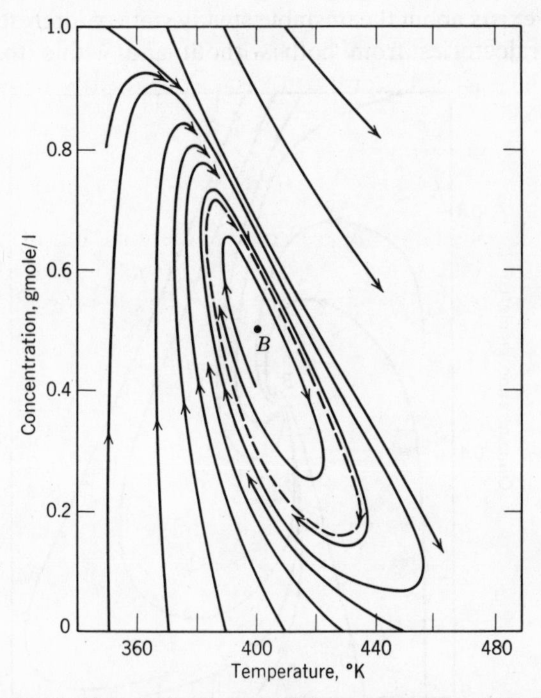

Fig. 10–12. Trajectories for controlled reactor with $k = 8$. (Ref. 5.)

TABLE 10–3

Stability Results For Various Control Settings (Ref. 5)

Range of k	*Local Trajectory Shape*	*Stability*
0.0 to 4.5	Saddle	Unstable
4.5 to 5.0	Node	Unstable
5.0 to 9.0	Focus	Unstable
9.0 to 45.0	Focus	Stable
> 45.0	Node	Stable

shown in Figs. 10–12 and 10–13. The figures provide the answers to the question concerning the usefulness of feedback. As shown in Fig. 10–13, an adequate feedback gain constant will indeed stabilize the intermediate steady state; it will in fact alter the system such that this point becomes the only steady state.

It is equally interesting to find that for somewhat smaller $k = 8$ a limit cycle exists about the unstable steady state of interest (Fig. 10–12). Because trajectories from both without and within the limit cycle

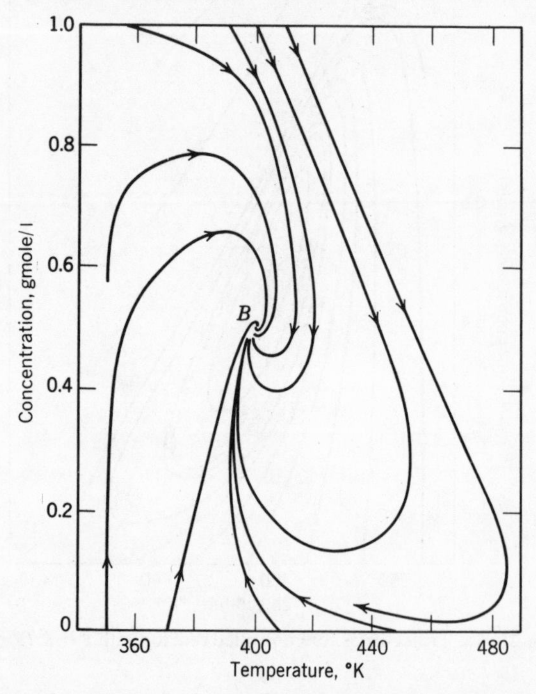

Fig. 10–13. Trajectories for controlled reactor with $k = 30$. (Ref. 5.)

converge on this closed contour, it is called *stable from both sides.* Limit cycles are also known that show only stability from within, or without, or that are unstable from both sides, but these have not been found in chemical reactor studies. Evidence that the existence of a limit cycle is not unique to the particular kinetics of this example may be found in several other studies. Gurel and Lapidus[7] extended the problem to second-order kinetics of the form

$$r = k_0 y^2 e^{-Q/v}$$

They adopted the same control equations and parameter values, but had to double ΔH and reduce x by 25% in order to get the same

[7]Gurel, C., and Leon Lapidus, Paper presented at Annual A.I.Ch.E. Meeting, 1962, Preprint 149.

unstable steady state with the new kinetics. Their limit cycle is shown in Fig. 10–14 for $k = 8$, superimposed for comparison on the limit cycle for first-order kinetics.[8]

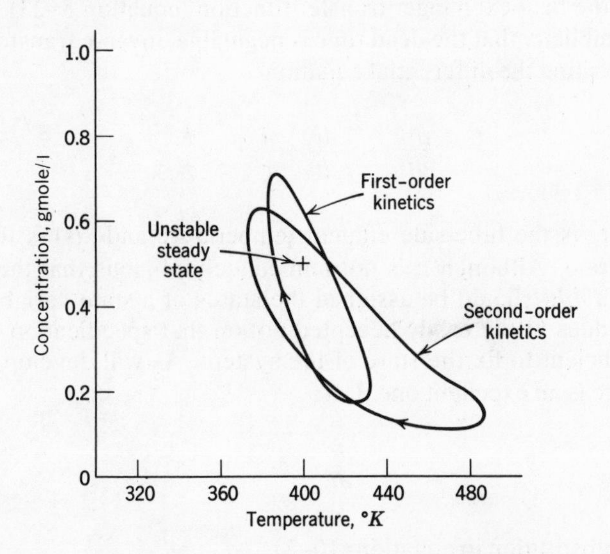

Fig. 10–14. Limit cycles for chemical reactors. (After Gurel and Lapidus.)

The occurrence of limit cycles may have far-reaching implications in certain hard-to-control reactors where either peculiar kinetics or physical limitations on feedback make it impractical to pass over the unstable region entirely. It is not hard to conceive of circumstances where it might be better to operate an oscillating system than one that is stable at an undesirable steady state. Volter[9] has suggested that unforced cycling may indeed be ordinary behavior for the polymerization reactors that he has investigated analytically and experimentally.

10–8. OTHER STATE VARIABLES

On occasion, a problem presents itself in the form of a single, second-order differential equation. In mechanics such relationships arise quite naturally from the acceleration term in Newton's second law. In chemical engineering analysis, it is more common to deal with

---

[8]In reference 7 the symbol β_1 is used for a parameter scale half as large, defined in a slightly different manner. For this reason, the limit cycle is there given for $\beta_1 = 16$.

[9]Volter, B. V., *Proc. IFAC*, Paper no. 507, Basel, Switzerland (Sept., 1963).

a set of equations derived from the first-order energy and mass balances; however, this is not always the case. Consider as an illustration the second-order dependence of temperature on flowrate that is implied by the heat exchanger transfer function (equation 8–23). Assuming for simplicity that the dead time is negligible, inverse transformation permits writing the differential equation

$$\frac{d^2\hat{v}}{dt^2} + \frac{2}{\tau}\frac{d\hat{v}}{dt} + \frac{1}{\tau^2}\hat{v} = \frac{K}{\tau^2}\hat{x} \qquad (10\text{–}21)$$

where $v(t)$ is the tube-side effluent temperature and $x(t)$ is the shell-side flowrate. Although it is not immediately obvious that the derivative $\dot{v} = (d\hat{v}/dt)$ should be assigned the status of a state variable, such a choice does fit the easily accepted notion that specification of $\hat{v}$ and $\dot{v}$ are sufficient to fix the state of the system. As will develop shortly, this choice is an excellent one. Let

$$\frac{d\hat{v}}{dt} = \dot{v} \qquad (10\text{–}22)$$

then by substitution in equation (10–21)

$$\frac{d\dot{v}}{dt} = \frac{K}{\tau^2}\hat{x} - \frac{2}{\tau}\dot{v} - \frac{1}{\tau^2}\hat{v} \qquad (10\text{–}23)$$

In this way the second-order equation (10–21) is reduced to the set of two first-order equations (10–22) and (10–23). From the latter:

$$\frac{d\dot{v}}{d\hat{v}} = \frac{(K/\tau^2)\hat{x} - (2/\tau)\dot{v} - (1/\tau^2)\hat{v}}{\dot{v}} \qquad (10\text{–}24)$$

which defines the trajectories in the $(\dot{v}, \hat{v})$ phase plane once x is specified.

To uncover some other interesting points, a nonlinear feedback-control function may be included in the analysis: $x = f(v)$. Suppose that it is desirable to use mild corrective action for small deviations from the set point, but relatively more severe feedback for large deviations. The function

$$\hat{x} = \begin{cases} -K_0\hat{v}^2 & \hat{v} \geq 0 \\ +K_0\hat{v}^2 & \hat{v} < 0 \end{cases} \qquad (10\text{–}25)$$

might be satisfactory for this application. The sign change in this function is needed in order to maintain the proper direction of response, for the term $\hat{v}^2$ is positive, regardless of the direction of deviation. Eliminating $\hat{x}$ from equation (10–24) produces the trajectory equation:

$$\frac{d\dot{v}}{d\hat{v}} = \frac{\mp(KK_0/\tau^2)\hat{v}^2 - (2/\tau)\dot{v} - (1/\tau^2)\hat{v}}{\dot{v}} = m \qquad (10\text{–}26)$$

and the isoclines:

$$\dot{v} = \frac{1}{\tau(m\tau + 2)}[\mp KK_0\hat{v}^2 - \hat{v}]$$

For numerical solution, let $KK_0 = 1$, $\tau = 1$. The families of isoclines and trajectories are shown in Fig. 10–15; the steady state of the proposed control system is evidentally a stable focus for at least a moderate range of disturbances.

Because alternatives are sometimes available in choosing state variables, it is appropriate to comment on a circumstance that sometimes favors the use of a derivative. While the explicit details of time dependence are intentionally disguised in defining the state variables (in order to ease the graphical developments) there sometimes arises a need for explicit time information. Such information may be recovered by making use of the identity:

$$t = \int_0^{\hat{v}} \frac{d\hat{v}}{d\hat{v}/dt} = \int_0^{\hat{v}} \frac{d\hat{v}}{\dot{v}}$$

In most problems, the integration will entail some numerical approximation. If a graphical integration is to be performed, the state variables of Fig. 10–15 are especially well suited for obtaining an auxiliary plot of $\hat{v}$ versus $1/\dot{v}$; otherwise, information may still be obtained from the trajectory, but supplementary calculations will also be needed. For either of the reactor systems equations (10–4) or (5–13), for example:

$$\frac{t}{\tau} = \int_{y_1(0)}^{y_1} \frac{dy_1}{dy_1/dt} = \int_{y_1(0)}^{y_1} \frac{dy_1}{x_1 - y_1 - r}$$

but r must be computed from the appropriate kinetics. In any event whether simple numerically or more involved, it is possible to calculate values of t along the path of any trajectory. When advantageous for some reason, these results can be shown as a parameter on the phase plane.

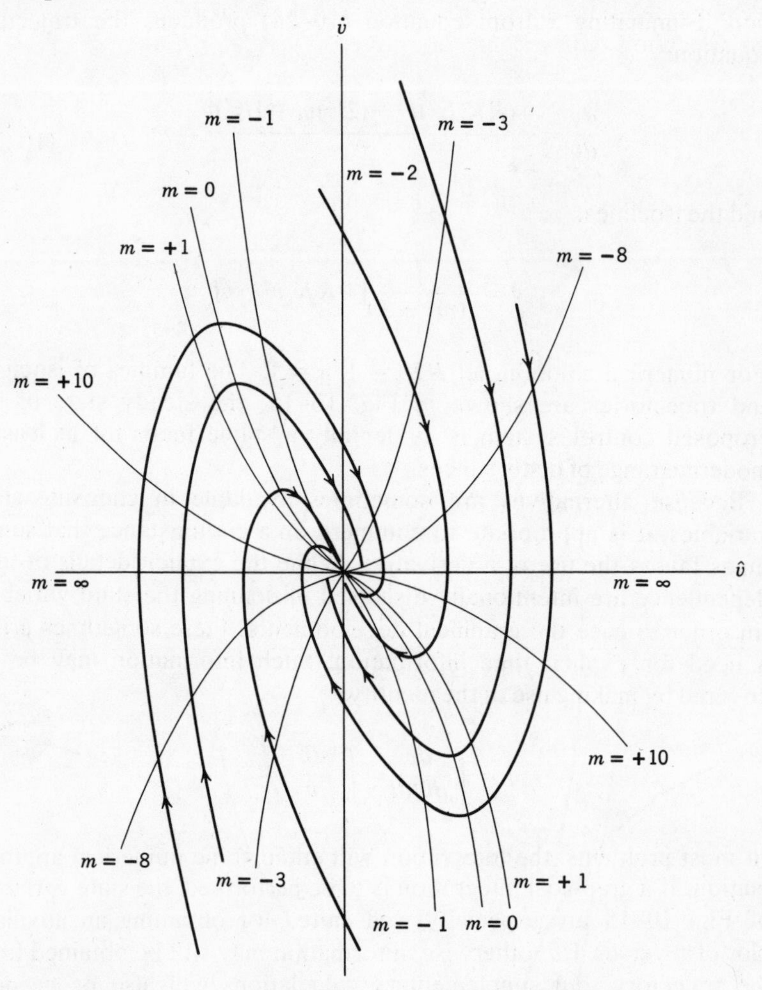

Fig. 10–15. Isoclines and trajectories for equation (10–26) for $KK_0 = 1, \tau = 1$.

10–9. SATURATION

If a system component operates at its physical limit it is said to be saturated. Since all real devices have some finite range, any component can saturate, whether it is electrical, mechanical, hydraulic, thermal, or biological (the list can be extended); in fact, it only makes sense to ignore this possibility if one is safely between the practical limits. Viewed in this way, there are no truly linear systems because linearity extends to infinite positive and negative values. More practically speaking, the vital question is not whether or not linear systems exist, but rather how wide a range they cover.

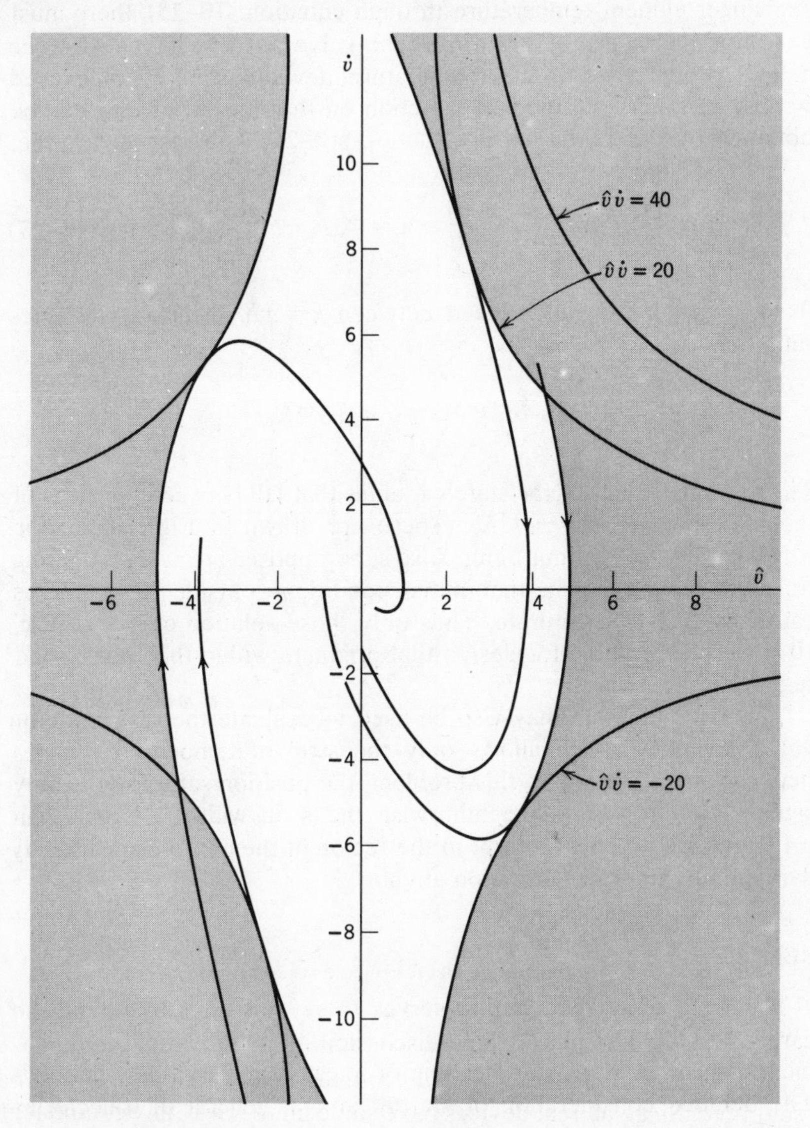

Fig. 10–16. Saturation limitations in the phase-plane.

To bring the matter down to cases, we may examine the effect of valve saturation on the analysis of the last section. A "linear" control valve may saturate in two ways: (1) Its range of opening is of necessity limited between zero and some maximum flow; and (2), its speed of motion is limited. Correspondingly, since the flow is linked to the exchanger effluent temperature through equation (10–25), there must exist limiting values of $\hat{v}$ and $\dot{v}$. If the valve position limits are to be held between $\hat{x} = \pm a$, the temperature deviations may not exceed $\hat{v} = \pm\sqrt{A/K_0}$. An additional restriction on the rates of change can be obtained by differentiation of equation (10–25) with respect to time:

$$\frac{d\hat{x}}{dt} = \dot{x} = \mp 2K_0 \hat{v}\,\dot{v} \qquad (10\text{–}27)$$

To now hold the valve speed between $\dot{x} = \pm b$, the state variables must satisfy

$$-b/2K_0 \leqslant \hat{v}\,\dot{v} \leqslant +b/2K_0$$

This permits values of the state variables that fall between the arms of the hyperbolae: $\hat{v}\,\dot{v} = \pm b/2K_0$. These are drawn in Fig. 10–16, for $K_0 = 0.5$, $b = 20$ (gal/min)/min. Also superimposed are several limiting trajectories—limiting in that initial conditions outside these curves cause the valve to saturate. Thus only those solution curves of Fig. 10–15 are acceptable for design that originate within the undarkened region of the plane.

The same diagram may also be used to evaluate the restriction on valve position, which allows only the strip of temperature values between $\hat{v} = \pm\sqrt{a/K_0}$. In this problem, the position saturation is only significant if $a < 12$, since otherwise the strip width is larger than ± 4.9 and has no effect except in the region of the phase-plane already darkened by the rate saturation anyhow.

REMARKS

The material of this chapter serves in several ways to extend the earlier results. The phase-plane discussion of stability and the fundamental theorem show the meaning of linearization in a new context. The detailed consideration of startup and in general of trajectories relatively far removed from steady-state may properly be thought of as problems in servo control, complementing the linearization of Chapter 5 for regulator loops. The study of feedback through a two-position switch connects logically with the elementary examples in Chapter 1. In another sense this chapter offers a striking contrast by solving problems without any reference to *s*-domain analysis. This gives an important perspective, providing a last reminder that as powerful as it is, the transform approach should not be mistaken for the field of dynamic analysis in its entirety.

EXERCISES

10–1. The heater problem formulated as equation (10–3) is **piecewise-linear**; that is, the system behaves linearly except at the switching instant. For such problems the phase-plane analysis is convenient, but not necessary. Solve the problem to obtain the limit cycle in the time domain and compare your result with Fig. 10–2. Are they essentially equivalent in the information they convey?

10–2. In Section 10–1 it was suggested that the water-heater problem could be brought a step closer to reality by including the thermal inertia of the resistance heater.

(a) Show that simultaneous energy balances on the water and the heater, respectively, produce:

$$\rho V C_p \frac{dv_1}{dt} = h_2A_2(v_2 - v_1) - h_1A_1(v_1 - v_A)$$

$$MC\frac{dv_2}{dt} = Q - h_2A_2(v_2 - v_1)$$

(b) Use the method of isoclines to sketch the limit cycle in the (v_1, v_2) phase plane, assuming the same On-Off feedback control as before. For numerical results, let

$$h_2A_2/\rho V C_p = 1\ \text{hr}^{-1}$$

$$h_1A_1/\rho V C_p = 1\ \text{hr}^{-1}$$

$$h_2A_2/MC = 100\ \text{hr}^{-1}$$

$$Q/MC = 10{,}000^\circ\text{F/hr}$$

$$v_A = 70^\circ\text{F}.$$

(c) It has been suggested that a change in the power supplied might reduce the magnitude of temperature oscillations in this system. Investigate this proposal by phase-plane comparisons at different values of Q.

10–3. How many differential equations are needed to describe the dynamics of the isothermal well-stirred reaction:

$$A + 2B \rightleftharpoons AB_2$$

assuming that the reactants are not fed in stoichiometric proportion? How may the system be simplified if the feed is in the ratio two moles B for each mole A?

10–4. Show that for the linear kinetics:

$$r = k_1 y_1 - k_2 y_2$$

the system of equations (10–4) has characteristic roots $-1/\tau$ and $-k_1 - k_2 - 1/\tau$. What can you conclude regarding stability and oscillatory behavior in the uncontrolled reactor?

Consider for numerical study the case: $\tau = 1$ hr, $k_1 = 2$ hr^{-1}, $k_2 = 1$ hr^{-1}. In ordinary steady-state operation the feed contains reactant at a concentration of 0.50 moles/ft^3, and the product stream contains reactant and product in concentrations of 0.25 moles/ft^3 each. A momentary (impulse) disturbance has shifted the reactor away from its steady-state to the state:

$$y_1(0) = 0.10 \text{ moles/ft}^3$$
$$y_2(0) = 0.20 \text{ moles/ft}^3$$

Use the method of isoclines to sketch the trajectory in the y_1 versus y_2 phase plane. Does your result conform to the previous generalizations?

10–5. Sketch the phase-plane portrait for the feedback-control system of equation (10–14) for $K_0 = 2$. Note that this is one of the limiting cases referred to in Section 10–5. Is the steady state stable? Sketch a root-locus diagram for this system. For what value of K_0 does the steady state become unstable?

10–6. Explain why the curve ΔHVr versus v of Fig. 10–10 should be sigmoidal in shape. Note that it is not a locus at constant y, but along changing values of y_s.

10–7. If the kinetics of equation (5–13) are assumed to be first-order and independent of temperature, $r = ky$ and the system reduces to an elementary linear problem.

(a) Sketch the temperature-concentration phase-plane portrait for this case using the parameter values given in Table 10–2, except that $k = 1$ hr^{-1} and the activation energy is zero.

(b) Rearrange the simplified system into the form of a single, second-order differential equation in temperature. Sketch the $\dot{v}$ versus v phase-plane trajectories.

10–8. Use linearization to confirm the following conclusion of Reference 5: the unstable steady state of the reactor system represented by equations (10–19) and (5–13) cannot be stabilized by the control action $\tilde{q}_c = K_0 \tilde{y}$, regardless of K_0.

10–9. In the study cited as Reference 5, Aris and Amundson used as state variables the reduced concentration $\xi = (y/x)$, and the reduced temperature $\eta = (\rho C_p v/\Delta H x)$. Sketch the Figs. 10–12 and 10–13 on the (ξ, η) phase plane. What is the advantage in such coordinates? Compare these reduced variables to those used by Gurel and Lapidus: $(y - y_s)/y_s$ and $(v - v_s)/v_s$. Sketch Fig. 10–14 in these coordinates.

10–10. Show by linearization that for $k = 16$ the steady state is unstable in the second-order chemical system studied by Gurel and Lapidus. Is it locally a saddle, an unstable node, or an unstable focus? At what k is stability first achieved?

10–11. Consider feedback control of the heat exchanger described in Section 10–8 according to the proportional plus derivative action:

$$\hat{x} = K_0\hat{v} + K_D\dot{v}$$

Sketch the phase plane for the settings $KK_0 = -1$, $KK_D = 2\tau$. Note that in this case the trajectory equation may be integrated directly, and approximation by the isocline method is not necessary. This is another of the limiting cases mentioned in Section 10–5. It is called a **vortex**. How does it differ from a limit cycle?

10–12. If the signs of the control function equation (10–25) were reversed, would the control improve or deteriorate? Support your answer with a phase-plane sketch corresponding to Fig. 10–15.

Postscript

It seems appropriate in an introductory text to end with some remarks directing the reader to the next step. In Chapters 8 and 9 we have barely scratched the surface on the process dynamics of complex systems having multiple interacting stages or distributed parameters. Although there has been considerable work done in this area, control schemes for such systems are still active research problems. Within the limited scope of this book several topics of great importance did not get more than brief mention: adaptive control, multivariable systems, stochastic inputs.

Other subjects, though certainly not less important, did not find a place in context. The analog computer is very well suited to many phase-plane studies of the sort described in Chapter 10, especially for design work where parameter variation is of primary interest. Sampled-data systems need to be explored when intermittent measurements (as from a chromatograph) are to be used for control.

Perhaps the most active research field in control today is optimization. The methods of dynamic programming, Pontryagin's maximum principle, and the classical calculus of variations for dynamic systems, as well as direct search procedures and linear programming for static systems are usually included under this title. When appropriate, these techniques can provide a rigorous answer to the sort of design questions raised in Section 4–5, but answered there only qualitatively. They yield a best control policy for maximizing (or minimizing) an arbitrary criterion, requiring, however, prior agreement on a suitable measure of control quality. The numerical details of such a solution frequently demand the assistance of a digital computer.

For those who wish to go on to some of the topics mentioned here or elsewhere in the book, a selected list of references is appended.

Selected References, by Subject

GENERAL AND SUPPLEMENTARY

Chestnut, H., and R. W. Mayer, *Servomechanisms and Regulating System Design,* John Wiley, New York, 1951.

Truxal, J. G., *Automatic Feedback Control System Synthesis,* McGraw-Hill, New York, 1955.

MODELING AND DIFFERENTIAL EQUATIONS

Marshall, W. R., Jr., and R. L. Pigford, *The Application of Differential Equations to Chemical Engineering Problems,* Univ. of Delaware, Newark, 1947.

Mickley, H. S., T. K. Sherwood, and C. E. Reed, *Applied Mathematics in Chemical Engineering,* McGraw-Hill, New York, 1957.

PROCESS DYNAMICS

Buckley, P. S., *Techniques of Process Control,* John Wiley, New York, 1964.

Campbell, D. P., *Process Dynamics,* John Wiley, New York, 1958.

LAPLACE TRANSFORM

Churchill, R. V., *Modern Operational Mathematics in Engineering,* McGraw-Hill, New York, 1944.

CONTROL HARDWARE

Considine, D. M., *Process Instruments and Controls Handbook,* McGraw-Hill, New York, 1957.

Eckman, D.P., *Automatic Process Control,* John Wiley, New York, 1958.

Holzbock, W. G., *Instruments for Measurement and Control,* 2nd Ed., Reinhold, New York, 1962.

NYQUIST CRITERION AND CATALOG OF TYPICAL DIAGRAMS

Grabbe, E. M., S. Ramo, and D. E. Wooldridge, *Handbook of Automation, Computation and Control,* **1**, John Wiley, New York, 1958.

Kuo, B. C., *Automatic Control Systems,* Prentice-Hall, Englewood Cliffs, N. J., 1962.

MIKHAILOV CRITERION

Popov, E. P., *The Dynamics of Automatic Control Systems,* Addison-Wesley, Reading, Mass., 1962.

MULTILOOP SYSTEMS

Horowitz, I. M., *Synthesis of Feedback Systems,* Academic Press, New York, 1963.

Mamzic, C. L., "Basic Multiloop Control Systems," *ISA Journal,* **7**, No. 6, 63 (1960).

Wills, D. M., "Simple Multiloop Control Systems," *Instrumentation* (Minneapolis-Honeywell Co.), **15**, No. 3, 10 (1962).

ADAPTIVE CONTROL

Bellman, R., *Adaptive Control Processes; A Guided Tour,* Princeton Univ. Press, Princeton, N. J., 1960.

Mishkin, E., and L. Braun, Jr., *Adaptive Control Systems,* McGraw-Hill, New York, 1961.

NONLINEAR SYSTEMS

Cunningham, W. J., *Introduction to Nonlinear Analysis,* McGraw-Hill, New York, 1958.

Gibson, J. E., *Nonlinear Automatic Control,* McGraw-Hill, New York, 1963.

MULTIVARIABLE SYSTEMS

Kavanagh, R. J., "The Application of Matrix Methods to Multivariable Control Systems," *J. Franklin Inst.*, **262**, 349 (1956).
Mesarovic, M., *Control of Multivariable Systems,* John Wiley, New York, 1960.

STOCHASTIC PROCESSES

Davenport, W. B., Jr., and W. L. Root, *Introduction to Random Signals and Noise,* McGraw-Hill, New York, 1958.
Laning, J. H., Jr., and R. H. Battin, *Random Processes in Automatic Control,* McGraw-Hill, New York, 1956.
Solodovnikov, V. V., *Introduction to the Statistical Dynamics of Automatic Control,* Dover Publ., New York, 1960.

ANALOG COMPUTER

Johnson, C. L., *Analog Computer Techniques,* McGraw-Hill, New York, 1956.
Lamb, D. E., R. L. Pigford, and D. W. T. Rippin, "Dynamic Characteristics and Analog Simulation of Distillation Columns," *Chem. Eng. Prog. Symp, Ser.* 36, **57,** 132 (1961).

SAMPLED-DATA SYSTEMS

Jury, E. I., *Sampled-Data Control Systems,* John Wiley, New York, 1958.
Ragazzini, J. R., and G. F. Franklin, *Sampled-Data Control Systems,* McGraw-Hill, New York, 1958.

STATIC OPTIMIZATION

Fan, L., and Wang, C., *The Discrete Maximum Principle, A Study of Multistage Systems Optimization,* John Wiley, New York, 1964.
Llewellyn, R. W., *Linear Programming*, Holt, Rinehart, and Winston, New York, 1964.
Wilde, D. J., *Optimum Seeking Methods,* Prentice-Hall, Englewood Cliffs, N. J., 1964.

DYNAMIC PROGRAMMING

Aris, R., *The Optimal Design of Chemical Reactors, A Study in Dynamic Programming,* Academic Press, New York, 1961.

Bellman, R., and S. Dreyfus, *Applied Dynamic Programming*, Princeton Univ. Press, Princeton, N. J., 1962.

Roberts, S. M., *Dynamic Programming in Chemical Engineering and Process Control*, Academic Press, New York, 1964.

OPTIMAL CONTROL

Chang, S. S. L., *Synthesis of Optimal Control Systems*, McGraw-Hill, New York, 1961.

Leitmann, G., *Optimization Techniques With Applications to Aerospace Systems*, Academic Press, New York, 1962.

Merriam, C. W., *Optimization Techniques and the Design of Feedback Control Systems*, McGraw-Hill, New York, 1964.

Index

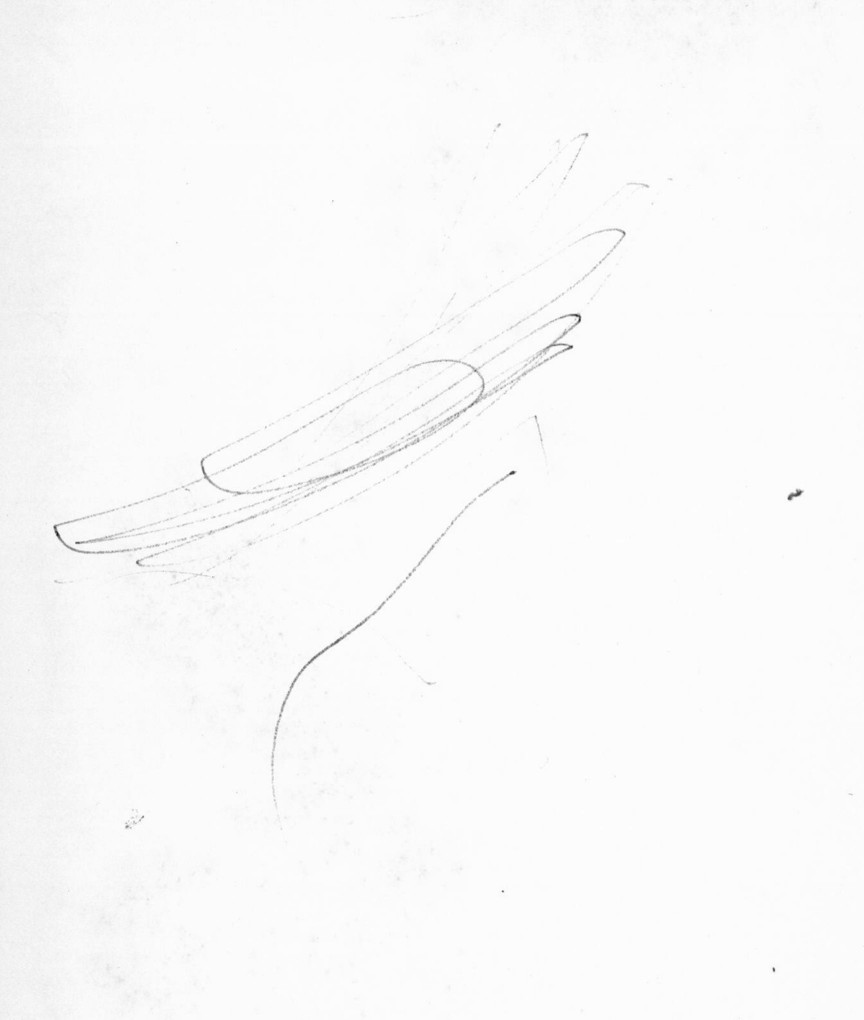